The Ecology *of* Fishes

The Ecology *of* Fishes

G. V. NIKOLSKY

Department of Ichthyology, Biology-soil Faculty
Moscow State University

Translated from the Russian by

L. BIRKETT

1963

ACADEMIC PRESS
London and New York

ACADEMIC PRESS INC. (LONDON) LTD.
Berkeley Square House
Berkeley Square, London, W.1

U.S. edition published by

ACADEMIC PRESS INC.
111 Fifth Avenue,
New York, New York 10003

Library of Congress Catalog Card Number: 62–18582
SBN: 12-519750-0

REPRODUCED PHOTOLITHO IN GREAT BRITAIN BY
J. W. ARROWSMITH LTD., BRISTOL 3

AUTHOR'S PREFACE

This book represents a brief essay on the ecology of fishes.

The present edition is based on my book "The Biology of Fishes," published in 1944, though this has been radically revised. Chapters on the role of fishes in the life of mankind, and on the biological bases of a rational fishery have been added. All the remaining chapters have been virtually rewritten.

The book differs in structure from others. Following a short introduction, in which the basic theoretical concepts of modern fish ecology are examined, conclusions are drawn concerning the interrelations between the fish and its organic and inorganic environment. In the second part of the book the fundamental links in the life-histories of fishes are examined. In selecting the examples, I used where possible data concerning species of commercial importance. Primarily, I examine those aspects of the ecology of fishes which are important for the construction of a rational fishery. Since the ecology of separate species of fishes has been dealt with in detail by E. K. Suvorov in his "Bases of Ichthyology" (1948) and in my "Special Ichthyology" (1950, 1954), I thought it advisable to omit the section dealing with special ichthyology from this edition.

In writing this book I have had considerable assistance from my colleagues in the Department of Ichthyology in Moscow University, and in the Ichthyology Laboratory of the A. N. Severtsov Institute of Animal Morphology, Soviet Academy of Sciences. The artist N. N. Kondakov has made a number of original drawings for this book. Professor P. G. Borisov undertook the reading of the manuscripts and made a number of valuable critical remarks. I am extremely grateful to all those who helped me in the writing of this book.

Naturally, I should like to think that this book would facilitate the working out of the biological bases of a rational fishery and would to some extent be of assistance in the training of ichthyological specialists.

Undoubtedly, however, the book contains many defects. I shall be grateful for any remarks from readers.

G. V. NIKOLSKY

Department of Ichthyology,
Biology-soil Faculty, Moscow State University
September 1962

CONTENTS

Part III

INTRODUCTION

THE common science of biology falls into a number of isolated disciplines, of which morphology is the study of the structure of organisms, systematics their natural system, physiology the function of organs and of the whole organism, and ecology the mode of life.

The ecology of fishes is the section of ichthyology in which the mode of life of fishes is investigated, namely: the dynamics of fish populations, intraspecific (shoals, colonies) and interspecific groupings, distribution, migrations, the diurnal and seasonal rhythms of life, the character of feeding inter-relationships, reproduction, and so on. Naturally, the mode of life of any organism (including fishes) is inseparably connected with its structure and the function of its organs.

Since the form, function, and mode of life of an organism are inseparably related, the study of the mode of life of the organism is only possible if it is based upon a knowledge of its structure and the function of its organs.

The unity of the organism (or species) and its environment is a basic theoretical principle of modern ecology, including that of fishes. The organism cannot exist without the environment. Any organism, population, or species lives at the expense of its environment; without this interaction it ceases to exist. A property of life is its adaptive interaction with the environment, which ensures its development and existence.

The system of adaptive relationships of the animal with its environment is composed of inter-relationships with the abiotic (soil, water and the oxygen and salts dissolved in it, suspended mineral particles, etc.) and the biotic environment. In turn, the biotic inter-relationships are divided into interspecific—relationships with food organisms, predators, parasites, and so on, and intraspecific—inter-relationships between the parents and the offspring, males and females, individuals of various age groups, and so on.

Relationships of the organism to the separate elements of the abiotic and biotic environment cannot be isolated; they form a united, inseparable system of relationships. For instance, the feeding conditions of the roach in the North Caspian depend both on the quantity, quality and behaviour of the food organisms, and also on those of other species of fish and predatory invertebrates which feed on these organisms (interspecific relationships), and on the number and condition of the feeding individuals of the given species (intraspecific relationships), on the character of the ground, which to a significant extent determines the availability of the food organisms, on the turbidity of the water, waves, and so on (abiotic relationships).

Thus, in nature the connection between an organism and any particular element of its environment is not isolated from other connections, but is inseparably interdependent upon them. This interdependence must be borne in mind in experimental investigations in which some particular system of connections is isolated.

The alteration in nature of any fundamental biotic or abiotic connection inevitably evokes a reconstruction of the entire system of relationships between the organism and its environment.

The character of the interdependence of the organism and its natural environment is specific not only for the various species, but also for different individuals of the same species.

For different species the same natural body may serve different purposes. Thus for the roach [*Rutilus rutilus caspicus* (Jak.)] or the black chinese roach [*Mylopharyngodon piceus* (Rich.)], molluscs are food, while the bitterling [*Rhodeus sericeus* (Pall.)] uses the mollusc as a site for oviposition (spawning substrate). The same natural body may be used differently by various stages of development of an organism. Thus, the copepod *Cyclops* is a predator on the eggs and newly hatched free pro-larvae of the carps, using them as food. As they grow, the fish larvae become unavailable for the *Cyclops*, which ceases to be a predator on them, changing from an element of the environment to an indifferent element of the external world. However, as they grow still more the fish larvae in their turn begin to feed upon the *Cyclops*, and these crustaceans again become an element of their environment, but a different one—their food. Feeding on *Cyclops* continues until such time as the fish reaches a size at which the expenditure of energy for the capture of *Cyclops* is no longer fully compensated for by the calorific value of the *Cyclops* as food. The fish then ceases to feed upon *Cyclops*, and the crustaceans once again become an indifferent element of the fishes' external world.

We adopt the following definitions of the basic general concepts used in ecology.

External world—nature, mankind, and human activities. Objectively existing reality.

Habitat (biotope)—the element of the landscape inhabited by the organism, population, species. Sometimes called the environmental habitat by certain authors.

Environment—natural bodies and phenomena with which the organism, population, species is connected by direct adaptive relationships. Some authors call this the environment of existence.

Conditions of life—the separate elements of the environment, which determine the separate relationships of the organism, population, species with the environment. (Separate conditions, as stated, are not isolated from each other, but are interconnected.)

The interaction of the organism and the environment bears an adaptive character. Every adaptation is specific, there are no general adaptations, but there is adaptation to a particular element of the environment. The pharyngeal teeth of the wrasses (Labridae) or of the roach [*Rutilus frisii* (Nordm.)] are adaptations to feeding upon molluscs with hard shells, but not for seizing live fishes; the teeth of the herring shark (*Lamna cornubica* Gmel.) or of the common pike (*Esox lucius* L.) are adaptations for seizing and holding active prey, but not for crushing the shells of molluscs. Adaptation is a property directed towards securing the preservation and flourishing of the species under the conditions under which it lives and to which it adapted itself in the process of its evolution. In certain cases the preservation of the population may be attained through the premature death of some of the individuals. Thus, in many lakes the larger individuals of the common perch (*Perca fluviatilis* L.) feed almost entirely on its own young, obtaining in this way the zooplankton, on which it is not adapted to feeding directly. This enables the perch to live in water-masses in which, due to the absence of suitable foods, it could not otherwise exist.

The system of specific relationships of the organism of a species with the environment is called a *niche*, or a *general niche* (Elton, 1934; Vasnetsov, 1938, 1953).

Particular niche—this is the combination of the relationships of an animal (fish) to the components of the environment in connection with any one of its life functions: feeding, reproduction, etc. For instance, we may speak of the niche of a zooplanktophage, i.e. the relationships of a fish in respect of its feeding upon plankton, or the niche of an ostracophile, i.e. the relationships between a fish and the bivalve molluscs which serve as its spawning substrate.

Ecology is the study of the mode of life of species of animals and plants. The species is an objective reality. It exists in nature, and not as a conditional concept, invented by scientists for the convenience of their investigations.

The species is a freely interbreeding association of organisms, which is continually being renewed as a result of the mortality of the older individuals and the birth of young. The species is characterized by a relative morpho-physiologo-ecological stability, which is the result of adaptation to a particular environment under the conditions of which the species was formed and with which the species is in unity. The features of the species reflect its adaptation to particular conditions of existence. The individuals of any species do not reflect all of its properties. The species is a continually changing plurality, and the very character of this change, i.e. the type of its population dynamics (time of spawning, life-span and so on), are specific features. The variability of the specific features does not go beyond the limits of the species characteristics. This variability is the greater in species adapted to the more variable conditions. Populations of species which live under less stable conditions possess a greater amplitude of variation in those features which are adaptations to the varying factors of the environment. Populations of species which live under more stable conditions possess less variability. The amplitude of variability is also an adaptive property which ensures more favourable conditions of life for the population. For example, when the feeding conditions are unfavourable, the short-barbelled form feeds on one species of food, the long-barbelled on another, and the food supply for the whole population is thereby increased.

The amplitude of variation of the features and properties of species with a restricted distribution is usually less than that of species with a wide distribution. Within the limits of distribution of the species, the amplitude of variation, like other species properties, ensures the unity of the species with the environment. The species reacts to changes in its conditions of life by changes in the amplitude of variation.

The species has a definite area of distribution, within the limits of which the conditions correspond to its morpho-physiologo-ecological specificity. The morphological, physiological, and ecological properties of the species are relatively stable in time.

Thus, for example, the bream (*Abramis brama* L.), occurring in the Likhvinsk interglacial deposits, separated from us in time by half a million years, is completely indistinguishable in its external characters from the modern bream; the same is also true of the perch and other species of fishes found in these deposits (Fig. 1). This stability of modern species of fishes has been preserved over a very long period. For many species it is possible to follow their unchanging specific properties as far back as the middle of

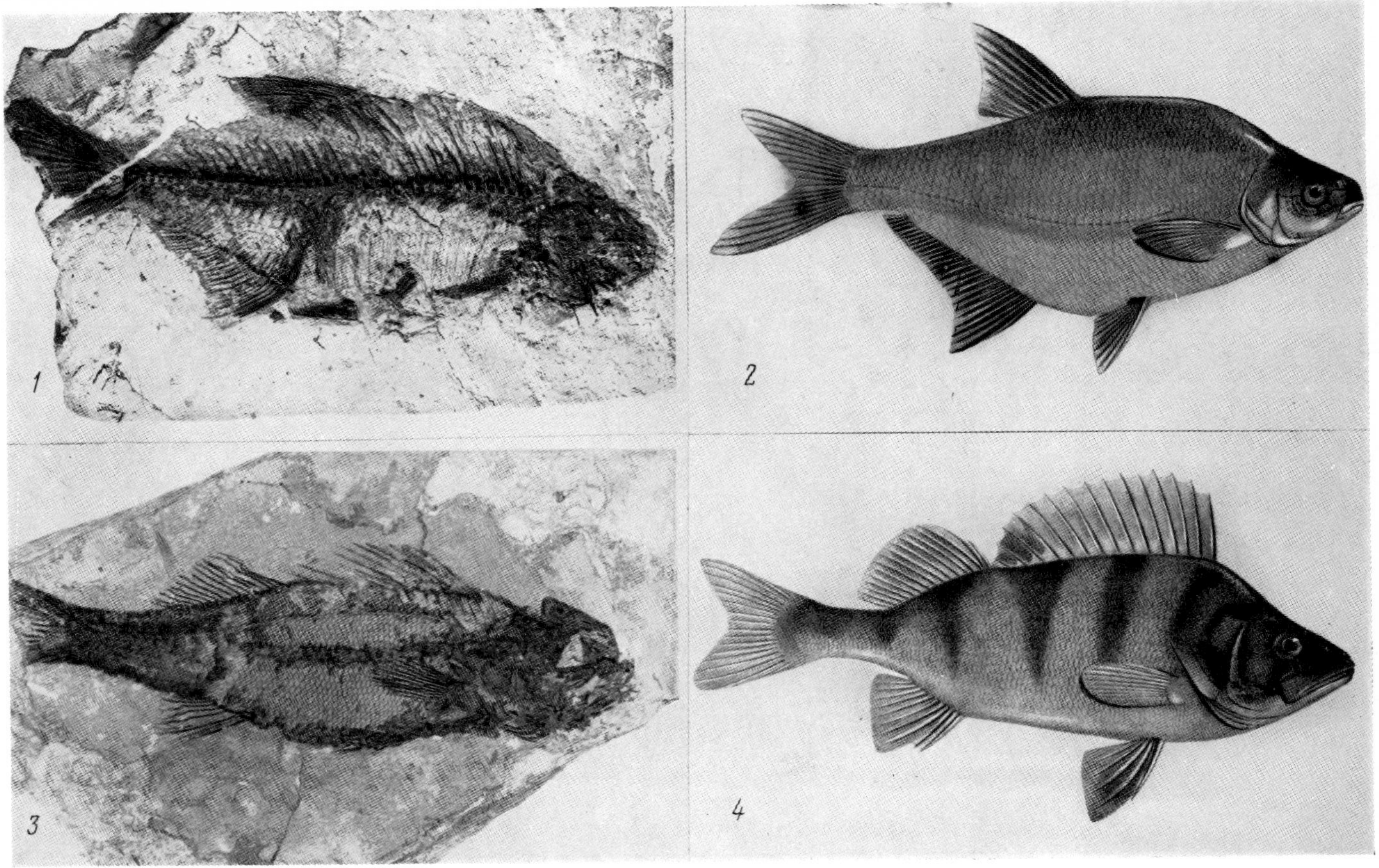

FIG. 1. The relative stability of fish species in time. 1, A bream from the Likhvinsk interglacial strata; 2, a modern bream; 3, a common perch from the Likhvinsk strata; 4, a modern perch.

the Tertiary period, and it is even possible that the entire modern fresh-water ichthyofauna of the northern hemisphere had its origins in the middle of the Tertiary period.

The historical development of living nature proceeds by means of relatively rapid changes in species, followed by periods of relative stability. The process of species evolution is the result of the reconstruction of the system of inter-relationships between the individuals which comprise the species, and their environment, i.e. the result of changes in the conditions of existence and in the associated morpho-physiological-ecological properties of the in-dividuals of the population. In the process of evolution of a species there is an adaptation to both the abiotic and the biotic conditions. Because of this, the evolution of species is usually a group process, frequently involving a significant part of the interdependent species of the fauna, ensuring their mutual adaptation.

Changes within the species, apart from those connected with age and sex, bear a local character, i.e., they are adapted to a particular habitat (station) or to a definite geographical part of the range of distribution. This group variability is a species adaptation, which ensures either that a greater variety of habitats are occupied (for example, the occurrence in many species of fish of both an elongated, river form and a high-bodied, lake form), or else a wider geographical distribution.

Group variability, naturally, occurs through variations in the individuals comprising a population, and because of this the so-called individuality of separate members of a population, if it is not pathological in its character, is also a population adaptation.

Fishes, like other animals, occupy definite, characteristic habitats. A specific animal and plant population is largely related to a specific habitat.

As a result of the adaptation of fishes to definite habitats, it is customary to subdivide them into ecological groups of marine, freshwater, migratory, and brackish-water fishes.

I. *Marine fishes*, which live in sea-water, are further subdivided into *pelagic* fishes, inhabiting the water column, such as, the anchovy (*Engraulis*), mackerel (*Scomber scombrus* L.), tunny, moon-fish (*Mola mola* L.), and *demersal* fishes, which live on the bottom. This group includes for example, the skates, flatfishes, cottids, and others.

Marine fishes are also subdivided into *oceanic* species, which live in the surface zone of open seas (many flying fishes, mackerel-pike, tunnies, etc.), *neritic* species, which inhabit the coastal marine waters (majority of Sparidae, gobies, flatfish, etc.), and *deep-water* or *abyssal* species. The latter are in turn divided into *bathypelagic* (luminescent Myctophidae, and Ceratioidei) and *demersal* (*Pseudoliparis amblystomopsis* Andriashev and others).

II. *Freshwater fishes* always inhabit fresh water and do not usually occur in brackish water. Freshwater fishes are subdivided into *rheophilic* species, adapted to living in a current [trout, many species of *Schizothorax*, minnows (*Nemachilus*), etc.], and *limnophilic* species, adapted to living in still water (bream, carp, loach, Misgurnus, etc.).

The fishes of running waters (rheophilic) and still waters (limnophilic) are subdivided into pelagic (inhabiting the water column), subdemersal, and demersal species.

The two following groups occupy an intermediate position between the marine and freshwater fishes, and they undoubtedly evolved partly from one or the other of them.

III. *Migratory fishes* move for reproductive purposes either from the sea to fresh water (salmon, shad, sturgeon) or else from fresh water to the sea (eel, *Galaxias attenuatus* Jenyns; and certain others). According to where the feeding grounds of the adult migratory fishes occur, they are subdivided into *trophic marine* (salmon, shad) and *trophic freshwater* (eel).

IV. *Brackish-water fishes* inhabit the less saline regions of the sea, estuaries, and inland seas with reduced salinities. They are subdivided into *semi-migratory* species, which enter the lower reaches of rivers to spawn, and feed in brackish water, such as many whitefish (*Coregonus*), the roach (*Rutilus rutilus caspicus* Jak.), and *truly brackish-water* species, which live constantly in the brackish parts of the sea (gobies, flounder, marine stickleback).

The ecology of fishes, like any other scientific discipline, can only develop successfully if there is a close relationship of science with life, from the industrial aspect.

The fishing industry is constantly presenting problems in the ecology of fishes, and in ichthyology as a whole, on the solution of which its own successful development depends. The basic problems which at present confront fishery ecologists are those of the dynamics of populations and biomass of fish stocks, and those of migration and group behaviour. These problems are of considerable theoretical significance. The first is related to the solution of such problems as the principles which govern the individual development of fishes, their growth, the principles of intraspecific and interspecific relationships. This problem is also related to that of the species. The solution of the problem of population dynamics of fishes is of enormous commercial significance; on the one hand, for the improvement of methods of making forecasts of the possible catches of commercial fishes and for the facilitation of more successful planning of fisheries, and on the other, for the purpose of working out methods of controlling the dynamics of commercial species in order to improve their productivity and to raise the value of the fish products.

The second basic problem of modern fish ecology is that of migrations and group behaviour. It is related to the solution of such theoretical problems as the protective, searching, and migratory significance of the shoal, the biological significance of the noises emitted by fishes, the role of various sense organs and of the behaviour of fishes, and so on. The solution of this problem is of importance to the consideration of such practical matters as the improvement of the methods of searching for fish, raising the effectiveness of fishing gear, and development of new means of capture.

PART I

INTER-RELATIONSHIPS BETWEEN FISHES AND THEIR ABIOTIC AND BIOTIC ENVIRONMENT

Part I

INTER-RELATIONSHIPS BETWEEN FISHES AND THEIR ABIOTIC AND BIOTIC ENVIRONMENT

OF THE earth's total surface, which comprises approximately 510 million sq. km, about 361 million, or 71 %, is occupied by the surfaces of oceans and seas. In addition, up to 2·5 million sq. km., or about ½ % of the earth's surface, is occupied by inland water-bodies. The greatest known oceanic depth is about 11,000 m. The area of the oceans with depths greater than 3000 m occupies 51–58 % of the total sea surface, according to various authors. Such are the dimensions of the habitat in which fishes are distributed.

It is quite natural that the water-bodies, which are distributed from the poles to the equator and which occur between the limits of altitude of more than 6000 m and of oceanic depths greater than 10,000 m should vary enormously in respect of living conditions for fishes. The fishes, being dependent throughout their lives upon the water, are likewise distributed from highland lakes to oceanic depths and occur both in polar waters and under the tropics. Naturally, in order to live under such varied conditions, they have had to acquire extremely varied adaptations, which have enabled them to exist both in mountain currents moving at a velocity of two or more metres per second, and in static waters at enormous depths greater than 10,000 m where the pressure reaches 1000 atmospheres, as well as at the surface. The adaptations to temperature have equally great amplitudes. Fishes live at temperatures close to that of freezing salt water (-2, $-3°C$) and at $+50°C$. The amplitude of fluctuations in salinity which fishes can tolerate is equally great.

The biotic conditions under which fishes live—they are attacked by the most varied predators, from plants, coelenterates, and molluscs to birds and mammals—are no less variable. Just as varied is the food of fishes, comprising plants, invertebrates, and also fishes. There are many other types of relationships between fishes and their biotic environment.

It is natural that the adaptation to the corresponding biotic and abiotic

3

conditions should be related to morpho-physiological changes. The variety of conditions under which fishes live determines the diversity of the fishes themselves.

This explains the fact that, among vertebrates, fishes are the richest group in species, comprising as they do over 20,000 living representatives. However, it is natural that, together with such a great diversity of structure and mode of life of fishes, they should possess a number of common features, which are determined by their common origin and adaptation to the aquatic life. Foremost among these common features are the gills, which serve for the respiration of dissolved oxygen; limbs in the form of fins, which facilitate movement through the water; the tail, which eliminates the turbulence and counter-currents set up by movement through the water, and also serves as a rudder in turning; the skin, rich in glands which secrete slime, so reducing the resistance of the fish when moving through the water. It is true that in an insignificant number of species the last three properties may be slightly nonspecific, but the factors mentioned above are most characteristic for the group of fishes as a whole.

As has already been noted, the interrelationships between the fish and the elements of its abiotic and biotic environment are not isolated; they are interdependent, and any changes in one system of relationships inevitably produce changes in the other. Because of this, although for the purpose of analysis we shall separate the interrelationships of the fish with the various elements of its environment, it must be borne in mind that such separation is subjective, because in nature all the interrelationships of the organism with its environment are interconnected. It must also be emphasized that the character of the interaction of the fish with any particular elements of its environment depends to a significant extent upon the condition of the fish itself: its state of nourishment, fat content, the state of maturity of its gonads, and so on. A fish can react differently to the same stimulus, according to its biological condition. For example, the autumn drop in temperature causes well-nourished bream in the Aral Sea to cease feeding and commence the winter migration, whereas undernourished individuals of the same species remain on the feeding grounds and continue to feed intensively. Well-nourished carp are less prone to disease during the overwintering period than are undernourished ones.

All these factors must be taken into account in studying the interactions of the fish with any particular element of its abiotic or biotic environment.

Adaptations of Fishes to Abiotic Environmental Factors

The role of physical factors in the life of the fish is enormous. The conditions for the movement of the fish through the water depend largely upon the density of the water. The optical properties of the water and its content of suspended particles affect both the conditions of hunting for food, in fish which orientate themselves by means of the visual organs, and the conditions for protection from predators.

The water temperature determines the rate of metabolic processes in fish to a significant extent. Changes in the temperature often act as natural stimuli, determining the onset of spawning, migrations, and so on. Other physical and chemical properties of the water, such as its salinity, saturation with oxygen, viscosity, are also of enormous importance.

DENSITY AND PRESSURE OF THE WATER

The density of the water depends primarily upon its salt content and temperature. The density increases as the amount of dissolved salts increases, On the other hand, as the temperature rises (above $+4°C$) the density falls.

Living matter is usually heavier than water. Its specific gravity is 1·02–1·06. The specific gravity of different species of fishes varies, according to data given by Andriashev (1944) for Black Sea species, from 1·01 to 1·09. Consequently, in order to remain in the water column, the fish must possess some special adaptations, which, as we shall see, can be somewhat varied.

The primary organ which enables the fish to regulate its specific gravity, and thus to adapt itself to a particular water depth, is the swim-bladder. Only a few of the species which inhabit the water column lack swim-bladders. These include sharks and certain scombroids. These fish can only regulate their position in respect of depth by movements of the fins.

The specific gravity of fishes which possess the swim-bladder, such as the horse-mackerel *Trachurus*, the labrids *Crenilabrus* and *Ctenolabrus*, the southern haddock *Odontogadus merlangus euxinus* Nordm., etc., is 1·012–1·021, slightly lower than that of fishes which lack the swim-bladder. The specific gravity of fishes which lack the swim-bladder [*Scorpaena porcus* L., *Uranoscopus scaber* L., the gobies *Neogobius melanostomus* (Pall.) and *N. fluviatilis* (Pall.), etc.] varies from 1·06 to 1·09.

It is of interest to note the interrelation between the specific gravity of a fish and its mobility. Among those fish which lack the swim-bladder, the most active species have the lowest specific gravities, such as the mullet *Mullus barbatus* (L.) (averaging 1·061), and demersal burrowing species have the highest, that of *Uranoscopus*, for example, averaging 1·085. The same principle also holds for fishes with swim-bladders. Naturally, the specific gravity of a fish depends not only upon its possession or otherwise of a swim-bladder, but also on the fat content of the fish, the development of bony formations (presence of armour), and so on.

The specific gravity changes as the fish grows, and also seasonally in relation to changes in its nourishment and fat content. Thus in the herring *Clupea harengus pallasi* Val., the specific gravity changes from 1·045 in November to 1·053 in February (Tester, 1944).

In the majority of the more ancient groups of fishes (among bony fish, nearly all the clupeiform and cypriniform species, and also in lungfishes, and bony and cartilaginous ganoids) the swim-bladder is connected to the intestine by a special duct, the *ductus pneumaticus*. In the remaining fishes, percomorphs, gadiforms, and other bony fishes, there is no such connection in the adult state.

In certain clupeoids and anchovies, such as the oceanic herring *Clupea harengus* L., the sprat *Sprattus sprattus* (L.), and the anchovy *Engraulis encrasicholus* (L.), the swim-bladder has two apertures. Besides the *ductus pneumaticus* there is another external aperture at the posterior end of the swim-bladder, which opens immediately behind the anus (Svetovidov, 1950). This aperture enables the fish, when it either sinks rapidly or rises from a depth to the surface in a short time, to extrude excess gas from its swim-bladder. When the fish sinks, extra gas appears in the bladder under the influence of the pressure, which increases with the depth. When the fish rises, following the sudden decrease in the external pressure, the gas in the bladder tries to occupy the largest possible volume, so that the fish is frequently forced to extrude gas. A shoal of herring which is rising to the surface may often be located by the stream of bubbles rising from the depths. In the lantern fishery for sardines on the Albanian coast of the Adriatic Sea, the Albanian fishermen unfailingly forecast the early rise of this fish from the depths by the appearance of the gas bubbles extruded by it. The fishermen say: "The foam has appeared, the sardines will also shortly appear" (communication from G. D. Poliakov).

In fishes with open bladders, and apparently in the majority with closed bladders, the bladder is not filled with gas immediately on hatching from the egg. While the hatched free embryo is in the passive state, attached to the stems of plants or else lying at the bottom, there is no gas in the swim-bladder. It is filled by gas being swallowed from outside. In many species the channel which connects the bladder with the intestine is absent in the adult state, but present in the larvae, and it is through this channel that the bladder becomes filled with gas. This observation is confirmed by the following experiment. Perch larvae were hatched out in a vessel in which the water surface was separated from the bottom by a fine net, which the larvae could not penetrate. Under natural conditions the bladder of perciform fish is filled with gas on the second to third day after hatching. The experimental fish were kept in this way for 5–8 days, after which the barrier separating them from the water surface was removed. However, by this time the connection between the bladder and the intestine was disrupted, and the bladder remained unfilled by gas. Thus, the initial filling of the bladder with gas takes place in a similar way in fishes with closed and open bladders.

In the pike-perch the gas appears in the swim-bladder when the fish reaches a length of about 7·5 mm. If the swim-bladder should remain free of gas at this time, the larva, with an already closing bladder, even if it is given the opportunity to swallow a bubble of gas, fills the intestine with it, but the gas cannot enter the bladder and goes out through the anal aperture (Kryzhanovsky, Dissler, and Smirnova, 1953).

For some reason, the secretion of gas into the swim-bladder from the blood vessels cannot take place until a small amount of gas has entered from without.

The method whereby the amount and composition of the gas in the swim-bladder is regulated varies according to the species of fish. In fishes which possess a connection between the swim-bladder and the intestine, the gas enters or leaves the bladder mainly via the *ductus pneumaticus*. In fishes with closed bladders, after the initial filling with gas from the exterior, further changes in the amount and composition of the gas are brought about by its secretion and absorption by the blood. Such fish have, on the internal wall of the bladder, the *red body*, an organ which is extremely densely permeated with blood capillaries. In the two red bodies in the swim-bladder of the eel, there are 88,000 venous and 116,000 arterial capillaries with a total length of 352 and 464 m. Yet the volume of all these capillaries is only 64 cubic mm, i.e. not more than a medium-sized drop. The red body varies from species to species from a small patch to a powerful gas-secreting gland, consisting of a cylindrical glandular epithelium. Sometimes the red body occurs in fishes which possess a *ductus pneumaticus*, but it is then usually less well developed than in fishes with closed bladders.

The composition of the gas in the swim-bladder varies not only according to the species, but also between individuals of the same species. The tench usually has about 8 % of oxygen, the perch 19–25 %, the pike about 19 %, the roach 5–6 %. Since the blood system can supply mainly oxygen and carbon dioxide, the swim-bladder contains mostly these two gases; nitrogen comprises a very small percentage. On the other hand, when gas is removed from the swim-bladder by the circulatory system, the percentage of nitrogen in the bladder increases sharply. Marine fishes usually have a higher proportion of oxygen in the swim-bladder than freshwater fishes. This is apparently connected with the predominance among marine fishes of species with closed bladders. The oxygen content is particularly high in the swim-bladders of secondarily deep-water species.

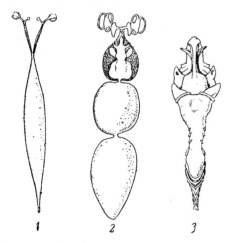

FIG. 2. Scheme of the connections between the swim-bladder and the auditory organ in fishes (from Kyle and Ehrenbaum, 1926; Wünder, 1937 and Svetovidov, 1937). 1, In the oceanic herring *Clupea harengus* L. (Clupeiformes); 2, in the carp *Cyprinus carpio* L. (Cypriniformes); 3, in *Physiculus japonicus* Hilg. (Gadiformes).

The gas pressure in the swim-bladder of fishes is usually transmitted by some means to the auditory labyrinth (Fig. 2). In clupeoids, gadoids, and certain other fishes, the fore part of the swim-bladder has paired outgrowths which reach as far as the stretched membranes of the apertures in the auditory capsules (in gadoids), or even enter them (clupeoids). In cyprinoids the pressure is transmitted from the swim-bladder to the labyrinth by means of the Weberian apparatus, a series of ossicles joining the swim-bladder to the labyrinth.

The swim-bladder not only serves to alter the specific gravity of the fish, it also detects changes in the external pressure. In a number of fishes, for example in the majority of loaches (Cobitidae) which lead a demersal life, the swim-bladder is greatly reduced, and its main function is that of an organ for sensing changes in the pressure. Fishes are able to sense insignificant changes in pressure; their behaviour varies with the pressure, for example before thunder. In Japan certain fishes are kept specially for this purpose in aquaria, and imminent changes in the weather are forecast according to changes in their behaviour.

With the exception of certain clupeoids, fishes which possess a swim-bladder cannot sink rapidly from the surface to the depths or vice versa. In the majority of species which can move vertically rapidly (tunnies, mackerel, sharks), the swim-bladder is either completely lacking or else reduced, and these fishes maintain their position in depth mainly by muscular movements.

The swim-bladder is also reduced in many bottom species, for example, in many gobies (Gobiidae), blennies (Blenniidae), loaches (Cobitidae), and certain others. Reduction of the bladder in bottom fishes is naturally related to the need to have a greater specific gravity. In certain closely related species of fish the bladder may be developed to varying degrees. For example, among the gobies, certain species which are pelagic (*Aphya*) possesses a bladder; in others, such as *Gobius niger* Nordm., it is present only in the pelagic larvae; in those species which have demersal larvae, such as *Neogobius melanostomus* (Pall.), the swim-bladder is reduced in the larva as well as in the adult.

In deep-water fishes, in relation to life at great depths, the swim-bladder often loses its connection with the intestine, because under great pressures the gas would be squeezed out of the bladder. This is a property of even such clupeoid groups as *Opistoproctus* and *Argentina*, some species of which live near the surface and possess the *ductus pneumaticus*. In other deep-water fishes the swim-bladder may be completely reduced, as for example in certain Stomiatoidei.

The adaptation to living at great depths causes other serious changes in fishes which are not directly the effects of pressure. These peculiar adaptations are connected with the absence of natural light in deep water (see page 48), feeding peculiarities (see page 266), reproduction (see page 93), etc.

Deep-water fishes are not all of common origin; they belong to various suborders, often far removed from each other. The time at which they entered into the deep-water mode of life varies considerably among these groups. We can divide all the deep-water fishes into two groups: the ancient, or true, and the secondarily deep-water fishes. The first group contains whole families, and occasionally orders and suborders, all the representatives of which are adapted to living in deep water. The adaptation to deep-water life in these fishes is very significant. Owing to the fact that the conditions of life in deep water are practically uniform throughout the world ocean, fishes belonging to the ancient deep-water group are very widely distributed (Andriashev, 1953). This group includes the angler, suborder *Ceratioidei*, the luminescent anchovies, *fam. Scopeliformes*, the *Saccopharyngiformes*, etc. (Fig. 3).

The second group, the secondarily deep-water fishes, includes those species whose deep-water habit is historically more recent. Usually the families to which the species of this group belong include mainly species which occur within the limits of the continental shelf, or in the pelagial. The adaptation to deep-water life in secondarily deep species is less specific than in representatives of the first group, while their area of distribution is considerably smaller; the group includes no cosmopolitans. Secondarily deep-water fishes usually belong to the historically more recent groups, mainly the Perciformes. We find them among the families Cottidae, Liparidae, Zoarcidae, Blenniidae, etc.

While in the adult fish a reduction in the specific gravity is brought about by means of the swim-bladder, in fish eggs and larvae, it is attained by other means (Fig. 4). In pelagic eggs which develop in the water column the specific gravity is reduced by the presence of one or more oil globules (mainly flatfish), or by dilution of the yolk (the mullet, *Mullus*), or by filling the large perivitelline space with water [Chinese grass-carp, *Ctenopharyngodon idella* (Val.)], or by swelling of the egg-membrane [*Gobiobotia pappenheimi* (Kroy.)].

The percentage water content is much larger in pelagic eggs than in demersal ones. In the pelagic egg of *Mullus*, water comprises 94·7 % of the live weight, in the demersal eggs of *Atherina hepsetus* L., water comprises 72·7 %, and in the goby *Neogobius melanostomus* (L.) only 62·5 %.

Distinctive adaptations also occur among the larvae of fishes which lead a pelagic life. It is well known that the greater the surface area of any body

---

FIG. 3. Deep-water fishes. 1, *Cryptosaurus couesii* (Gill.) (Ceratioidae); 2, *Nemichthys avocetta* Jord. et Gilb. (Anguilliformes); 3, *Chauliodus sloani* Bloch et Schn. (Clupeiformes); 4, *Ipnops murrayi* Günth. (Scopeliformes); 5, *Gastrostomus bairdii* Gill. Ryder (Anguilliformes); 6, *Argyropelecus olfersii* (Cuv.) (Scopeliformes); 7, *Neoliparis mucosus* (Ayres) (Perciformes); 8, *Coelorhynchus carminatus* (Good) (Macruriformes); 9, *Ceratoscopelus maderensis* (Lowe) (Scopeliformes).

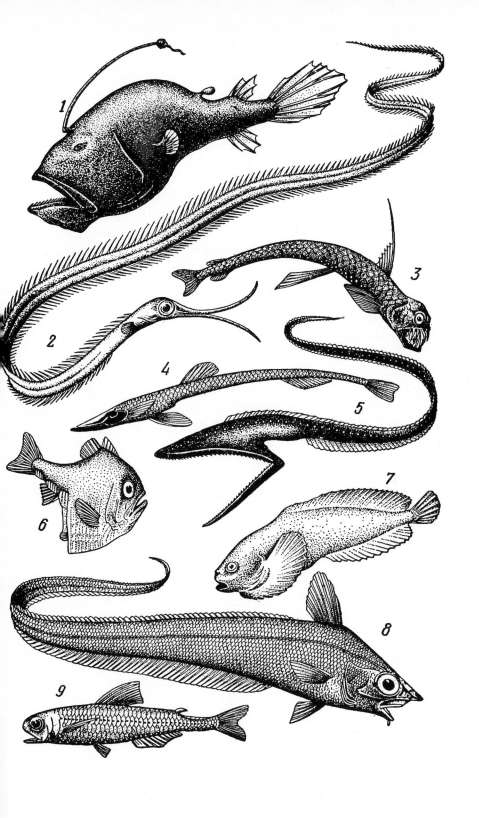

relative to its volume and weight, the greater is its resistance to sinking and the easier for it to maintain a particular level in the water. One type of adaptation, in the form of various spines and outgrowths, which increase the surface area of the body and facilitate the maintenance of its position in the water column, occurs in many pelagic animals including fish larvae (Fig. 5).

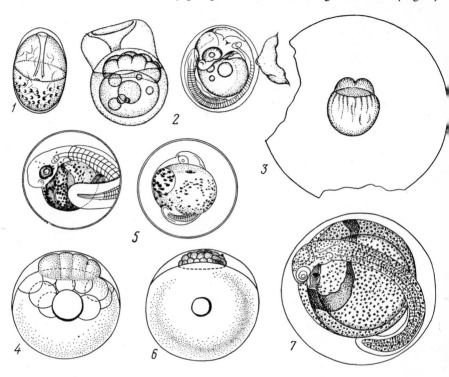

Fig. 4. Pelagic eggs of fishes (not to scale). 1, The anchovy *Engraulis encrasicholus* L.; 2, pond smelt *Hypomesus olidus* (Pall.) (Clupeiformes); 3, *Erythroculter erythropterus* (Bas.) (Cypriniformes); 4, red mullet *Mullus barbatus ponticus* Essipov; 5, Chinese perch *Siniperca chuatsi* Bas. (Perciformes); 6, turbot *Bothus* (*Rhombus*) *maeoticus* (Pall.); (Pleuronectiformes); 7, the snakehead *Ophicephalus argus warpachowskii* Berg (Ophicephaliformes).

Thus, the pelagic larva of the demersal fish the angler, *Lophius piscatorius* L., has long outgrowths of the dorsal and ventral fins, which help it to soar in the water; there are similar changes in the fins of the larva of *Trachypterus*. The larval moonfish, *Mola mola* L. has enormous spines on the body and is somewhat reminiscent of an enlargement of the planktonic diatom *Ceratium*.

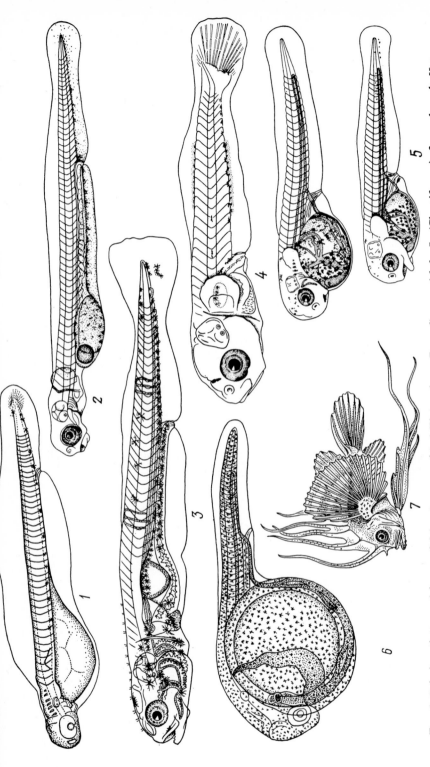

Fig. 5. Pelagic embryos and larvae of fishes (not to scale). 1, The anchovy *Engraulis encrasicholus* L. (Clupeiformes); 2, pond smelt *Hypomesus olidus* (Pall.) (Clupeiformes); 3, *Erythroculter erythropterus* (Bas.) (Cypriniformes); 4, red mullet *Mullus barbatus* L. (Perciformes); 5, Chinese perch *Siniperca chuatsi* Bas. (Perciformes); 6, the snakehead *Ophicephalus argus warpachowskii* Berg (Ophicephalidae); 7, the angler-fish *Lophius piscatorius* L. (Lophiidae).

In certain pelagic fish larvae the surface area is increased by means of a flattening of the body, for example the river eel larva, the body of which is considerably higher and flatter than that of its adult.

In the larvae of certain fish, such as the mullet, even after the embryo has hatched from the egg, the well-developed oil globule retains the function of a hydrostatic organ for a long time.

In other pelagic larvae the role of a hydrostatic organ is fulfilled by a fold of the dorsal fin, which becomes enlarged into an enormous inflated cavity filled with fluid. This occurs, for example, in the larvae of the marine crucian *Diplodus* (*Sargus*) *annularis* (L.).

SALINITY OF THE WATER

The more or less complete constancy of the internal environment is an extremely important factor which enables fishes to adapt themselves to living in waters of various salinities. This constancy is attained by the development of various osmoregulatory adaptations, which enable the fish to regulate the osmotic pressure of its body fluids. The more perfect the osmoregulatory adaptations, the greater the difference between the compositions and pressures of the internal fluids of the organism and its external environment.

In cyclostomes and fishes, excluding myxinoids, in contrast to the majority of marine invertebrates, there is a difference between the osmotic pressure of the body fluids and of the environment. Cyclostomes and fishes are divided into four groups, according to the character of the osmotic pressure of their internal environment:

1. Myxinoids—body fluids isotonic with the surrounding environment.

2. Cartilaginous fishes—internal pressure greater than that of the external water, mainly because of uric salts.

3. Marine bony fishes—osmotic pressure less than that of the surrounding water.

4. Freshwater bony fishes—osmotic pressure of body fluids greater than that of the surrounding water, because of their mineral salt content.

The composition of the substances contained within the internal fluids of fishes also varies. In sharks, besides sodium chloride which comprises 1·42 to 1·77 % of the fluid by weight, urea plays a significant role, forming 2 to 2·6 % in the blood of sharks and 1·42 to 2 % in skates. In sharks and skates which live in fresh water, urea is also present in large quantities in the coelomic fluids, the osmotic pressure being lower in these fishes than in freshwater bony fishes.

Marine bony fishes have a lower salt content in the body fluids than do cartilaginous ones, but because their internal osmotic pressure is lower than their external, they still have almost sufficient salts. The role of such organic compounds as the shark's urea is very small in bony fishes. In marine bony fishes the organic compounds exert only 7–8 % of the osmotic pressure.

In freshwater fishes the quantity of organic matter in the blood is approximately the same as in marine fishes, but the mineral salt content is considerably lower.

The cyclostomes are a heterogeneous group in respect of the salt content of the coelomic fluids. The hagfish *Myxine glutinosa* L. approaches the cartilaginous fishes in the urea content of its coelomic fluid, while in *Polystotrema stouti* (Lock.) the osmotic pressure is exerted mainly by the salts.

The majority of fishes are adapted to living in solutions of more or less definite osmotic pressure, and when transferred to water of different osmotic pressure they die fairly rapidly. Thus, cartilaginous fishes, which have evolved a mechanism that enables them to accumulate a quantity of urea sufficient to maintain the hypertonicity of the coelomic fluids (relative to sea-water), very rapidly reduce their osmotic pressure and die when transferred to fresh water. Those few cartilaginous fishes which are adapted to living in fresh water have the ability to increase the excretion of urine in order to preserve the high osmotic pressure of the body fluids. In so doing they excrete an enormous amount of water. The kidneys retain the urea; its main excretion (up to 70 %) by bony fishes occurs through the gills, while in cartilaginous fishes the gills are only slightly permeable to urea, which also accumulates in the coelomic fluids of these fishes (Korzhuev, 1938).

Amount of Urine Excreted by Cartilaginous Fishes
(per 1 kg Weight per day)

Marine	
Scyllium stellaris (L.)	5·3 cm³
Scyllium canicula (L.)	2–4·0 cm³
Acanthias acanthias (L.)	4·7–12·2 cm³
Freshwater	
Pristis microdon Latham	250·0 cm³

A significant proportion of marine bony fishes are adapted to life at a definite salinity, and die fairly rapidly if transferred to fresh water.

The osmotic pressure of the internal fluids of fishes changes very little in response to significant changes in the salinity. Thus, in the cod when the freezing point of the water changes from 1.09 to $1.89°$ the blood $\varDelta$ changes only from 0.73 to $0.76°$ (i.e. when the external medium changes by 74% the blood $\varDelta$ changes by 4%). In marine bony fishes, because their internal environment is hypotonic to the external, it is essential to retain the water within the organism. Consequently, marine bony fishes must obtain water from their surrounding hypertonic external medium. This necessity is increased still further by the fact that the urine of bony fishes is either hypotonic, or at least isotonic to sea-water. The organism is replenished with water in marine bony fishes through the intestine. All marine fishes "drink" water, and, as experiments on *Myoxocephalus* have established, fishes swallow from 50 to 200 cc of water per 1 kilo weight per day. Cessation of the access of water to the intestine leads to considerable emaciation of the fish and its death on the third or fourth day. The salts are removed from the blood of bony fishes in two ways: through the kidneys (mainly bivalent ions) or else through the gills (monovalent ions). Some part of the salts are also removed through the intestine. The internal fluids of freshwater fishes, as noted above, are hypertonic to the external medium. Rapid transference of freshwater fishes to sea-water also causes their death. However, if accustomed to sea-water slowly, the fish may survive; toward the end of the experiment the internal medium becomes completely isotonic to the external. In contrast to marine forms, in freshwater bony fishes the main osmoregulatory function of the organism leads not to the retention, but to the excretion of surplus quantities of water which has entered osmotically. For this reason, freshwater bony fishes, like cartilaginous ones, usually excrete urine more copiously than marine species.

In migratory fishes, which travel to spawn from rivers to the sea, or vice versa, the osmotic pressure undergoes insignificant changes. On entering fresh water from the sea, the access of water to the organism through the intestine ceases almost completely as a result of the degeneration of its mucous membrane (see the chapter on migrations).

In the river lamprey *Lampetra fluviatilis* (L.), during its migration from the sea to fresh water, owing to the large access of water to the organism through the skin, the excretion of urine rapidly increases, reaching 45% of the body weight per day (Brown, 1957).

TEMPERATURE OF THE WATER

The temperature of the water is of enormous significance in the life of a fish.

Like other poikilotherms, i.e. animals with a variable body temperature, fishes are more dependent on the temperature of the surrounding water than homoithermal animals. The basic difference between them in this respect is in the quantitative aspect of the heat production process. In cold-blooded animals this process is considerably slower than in warm-blooded ones, which have a constant body temperature. Thus a carp weighing 105 g produces 10·2 kcal of heat per kilogram weight daily, while a starling weighing 74 g produces 270 kcal.

In the majority of fishes the body temperature differs from that of the surrounding water by only 0·5–1°C, and only in the tunnies can this difference exceed 10°C.

Changes in the metabolic rate are most closely connected with changes in the temperature of the surrounding water. In many cases changes in the temperature function as a signalling factor, a natural stimulus which determines the start of some process—spawning, migration, and so on.

The rate of development of fishes is also related to a significant extent to changes in the temperature. Within the limits of a certain amplitude of temperature there frequently occurs a direct relation between the rate of development and the change in temperature.

Fishes can live at very different temperatures. The highest temperature, over +52°C, is tolerated by a fish of the family Cyprinodontidae, *Cyprinodon macularius* Baird et Gir., which lives in the small hot springs of California. At the opposite extreme, the crucian *Carassius carassius* (L.), and even more so *Dallia pectoralis* Bean, can survive freezing, though only if the body fluids remain unfrozen. *Boreogadus saida* (Lep.) leads an active life at a temperature of −2°C.

Besides the adaptation of a fish to a particular temperature (high or low), the amplitude of fluctuation of the temperature at which fishes of the same species can live are extremely important. This amplitude of temperature varies considerably from one species to another. Some species can withstand a fluctuation of several tens of degrees (for example, the crucian and tench), others are adapted to an amplitude of no more than 5–7°. Usually tropical and subtropical fishes are more stenothermal than those of boreal and higher latitudes. Marine forms are also more stenothermal than freshwater ones.

If the total amplitude of the temperature at which a species of fish can live is very great, it is significantly less for each stage of development.

Fishes also react differently to temperature fluctuations, according to their biological condition. Thus, the spawn of the salmon can develop at temperatures of from 0 to +12°C, while adult individuals easily tolerate fluctuations of from negative temperatures to +18 or 20°C, possibly even higher.

The sazan (a carp) successfully survives the winter at a temperature fluctuation of from negative to +20°C, but it can feed only at temperatures not less than +8 or 10°C, and usually reproduces at a temperature not less than 15°C.

It is usual to subdivide fishes into stenothermal, i.e. those which are adapted to a narrow amplitude of temperature fluctuations, and eurythermal, those which can live within the limits of a considerable temperature range.

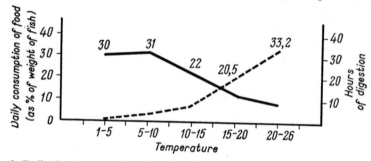

FIG. 6. Daily food consumption (broken line) and rate of digestion of food (solid line) by the Caspian roach *Rutilus rutilus caspicus* Jak. at various temperatures (from Bokova, 1940).

The optimal temperature to which a fish is adapted is also a species characteristic. Fishes of high latitudes have evolved a metabolic type which enables them to feed successfully at very low temperatures. But the activity and feeding rate of cold-water fishes (burbot, taimen [*Hucho taimen* (Pall.)], whitefishes), decrease at high temperatures. Conversely, in fishes of lower latitudes intensive metabolism occurs only at high temperatures.

Within the limits of the optimal temperature for a given species a rise in temperature usually leads to an increase in the rate of digestion. Thus, in the Caspian roach, as can be seen from the graph in Fig. 6, the digestive rate at 15–20°C is three times higher than that at 1–5°C. In connection with the increase in the digestive rate the rate of consumption of food also rises.

The digestion of the food also rises with the temperature. Thus, in the roach at 16°C the digestion of dry matter is 73·9 %; at 22°C it is 81·8 %.

It is interesting that, while in the roach within the limits of these temperatures the digestion of combined nitrogen scarcely varies (Karzinkin, 1952), in the carp, a more carnivorous species than the roach, the digestion of both total food and combined nitrogen increases with rising temperature.

It is natural that the gaseous metabolism of fishes also changes considerably as the temperature varies. There is also frequently a simultaneous change in the minimal oxygen concentration at which the fish can live. Thus, for the carp at a temperature of 1°C the minimal oxygen concentration is 0·8 mg/1, while at 30°C it is 1·3 mg/1 (Fig. 7). Naturally, the amount of oxygen required by the fish at different temperatures is also related to the state of the fish itself.

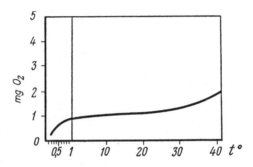

FIG. 7. Variation in the lethal oxygen concentration for the carp with temperature (from Ivlev, 1938).

Changes in the temperature, which affect changes in the metabolic rate, also cause changes in the toxic action of various substances upon the fish. Thus, at 1°C the lethal concentration of CO_2 for the carp is 120 mg/1, while at 30°C it falls to 55–60 mg/1 (Fig. 8).

When the temperature drops significantly the fish may fall into a state which is close to anabiosis, and they may remain for a variable long time in a supercooled state, even when frozen into ice, as for example the crucian, and *Dallia pectoralis* Bean. Experiments have shown that when the body of a fish is frozen in ice its internal fluids often remain unfrozen and have a temperature of about −0·2 or −0·3°C. Further cooling, when the fish freezes up in water, leads to a smooth reduction in the body temperature of the fish, freezing of the coelomic fluids, and death. If the fish is frozen out of water, the freezing is usually accompanied by preliminary supercooling, the body temperature falling for a short time even to −4·8°C, after which freezing of the coelomic fluids commences and there is a rise in temperature due to the release of the latent heat of freezing. If the internal organs and gills freeze, death is inevitable.

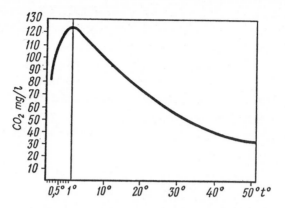

Fig. 8. Variation in the lethal concentration of carbon dioxide for the carp with temperature (from Ivlev, 1938).

The adaptability of fishes to living in a particular, often very narrow amplitude of temperatures is related to the establishment in them of a rather fine reaction to a temperature gradient.

Minimal Temperature Gradient to Which Fishes React
(from Bull, 1936)

Pholis gunnelus (L.)	0·03°
Zoarces viviparus (L.)	0·03°
Myoxocephalus scorpius (L.)	0·05°
Gadus morhua (L.)	0·05°
Odontogadus merlangus (L.)	0·03°
Pollachius virens (L.)	0·06°
Pleuronectes flesus (L.)	0·05°
Pleuronectes platessa (L.)	0·06°
Spinachia spinachia (L.)	0·05°
Nerophis lumbriciformes Penn.	0·07°

Since the fish is adapted to life at a particular temperature, it is natural that its distribution in the water should be related to that of the temperature. As the temperature changes both seasonally and secularly the distribution of the fish also changes.

One may judge the adaptation of separate species of fishes to particular temperatures visually, from the curves showing the frequency of occurrence of each species in relation to the distribution of temperatures (Fig. 9). As examples we have taken representatives of the families Agonidae—*Ulcina olriki* (Lütken) and Stichaeidae—*Eumesogrammus praecisus* (Kröyer). As Fig. 9 shows, both these species are adapted in their distribution to quite definite different temperatures: *Ulcina* has its maximum occurrence at −1·0 to−1·5°C, *Eumesogrammus* at +1 to +2°C. Knowing the adaptations of fishes to particular temperatures it is frequently possible to search for their commercial concentrations by orientating to the distribution of water temperatures.

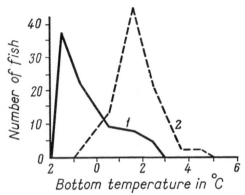

FIG. 9. The distribution of: 1, *Ulcina olriki* (Lütken) (Agonidae); 2, *Eumesogrammus praecisus* (Kröyer) (Stichaeidae) in relation to the distribution of bottom temperatures (from Andriashev, 1939).

Secular changes in the temperature (as occurred, for example, in the North Atlantic in relation to the dynamics of the Atlantic current) affect the distribution of fishes considerably (Helland-Hansen and Nansen, 1909). In the warm years there were cases of the capture of such relatively warm-water species as the mackerel, *Scomber scombrus* L. in the White Sea, and of the garpike *Belone belone* (L.) at Cape Kanin. During the warm period the cod penetrates into the Kara Sea, and its commercial concentrations even appear at the coasts of Greenland.

Conversely, during periods of cooling, arctic species spread to the lower latitudes. For example, the polar cod, *Boreogadus saida* (Lep.), penetrates into the White Sea in massive quantities.

Sharp changes in the water temperature often lead to mass mortalities of fishes. As an example of this we may mention the case of the chamaeleonhead *Lopholatilus hamaeleonticeps* Goode et Bean (Fig. 10). This species was known

up to 1879 from the southern coast of New England. In later years, in relation
to the warming, it appeared there in large quantities and became the object
of a fishery. As a result of the sharp cooling, which set in in March, 1882,
many individuals of this species died. The dead fish covered the sea surface
for many miles. After this the chamaeleonhead disappeared completely from
this region and has only recently reappeared there in significant quantities.

Mortalities of cold-water fishes—trout, whitefish—may be caused by
rising temperatures, but usually the temperature causes the mortality
indirectly, acting through changes in the oxygen content and so destroying
the respiratory conditions.

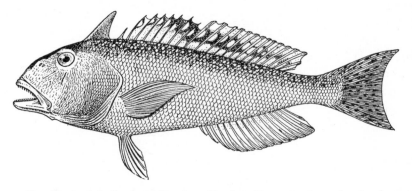

FIG. 10. *Lopholatilus hamaeleonticeps* Goode et Bean, the chamaeleonhead.

Changes in the distribution of fishes, brought about by variations in the
temperature, also occurred in foregone geological epochs. It has been
established, for example, that in the water-bodies along the basin of the
present-day river Irtysh, there occurred in the Miocene fishes of considerably
warmer-water species than those which now inhabit the Ob basin. Thus the
neogenic Irtysh fauna included representatives of the genera *Chondrostoma*,
Alburnoides, *Blicca*, which do not occur in the Ice Ocean basin in Siberian
territory at present, but are distributed mainly in the Ponto-Aralo-Caspian
province and were apparently displaced from the Ice Ocean basin as a
result of the climate changing to a cooler one (V. D. Lebedev, 1959).

We also find examples of changes in the areas inhabited by species, under
the influence of changes in the environmental temperature, in more recent
times. The cooling caused by the spread of the ice sheet at the end of the
Tertiary and the beginning of the Quaternary periods enabled the representatives of the salmon family, which were adapted to cold water, to spread

considerably southward as far as the Mediterranean Sea basin, including the rivers of Asia Minor and North Africa. At that time this family was also far more abundant in the Black Sea, as indicated by the large quantities of their bones in the remains of food of palaeolithic man.

Climatic fluctuations also led to changes in the composition of the ichthyofauna after the Ice Age. During the climatic optimum of about 5000 years ago, when the climate was somewhat warmer, the fish fauna of the White Sea basin included some 40% of warmer water species, such as *Aspius aspius* (L.), *Scardinius erythrophthalmus* (L.), and *Abramis ballerus* (L.). These species no longer occur in the White Sea basin; they were undoubtedly displaced from it by the cooling which took place before the start of the present era (Nikolsky, 1943).

Thus the relation between the distribution of separate species and the temperature is very strong. The relation of the representatives of any faunistic complex to definite thermal conditions causes the frequent coincidence of the limits of separate zoogeographical areas in the sea with particular isotherms. For example, the Chukotsk temperate arctic province is characterized by very low temperatures and the corresponding predominance of arctic fauna. The majority of boreal elements only penetrate as far as the eastern part of Chukotsk Sea, with the streams of the warm current. The White Sea fauna, which formed in a separate zoogeographical area, is considerably more cold-water in its composition than the fauna of the neighbouring southern parts of the Barents Sea to the north of it.

The characteristic distribution of migrations, spawning and feeding grounds of any one species in different areas of its habitat can vary in relation to the distribution of temperatures and other environmental factors. Thus, for example, the spawning grounds of the Pacific cod *Gadus morhua macrocephalus* Til., are in the coastal zone at the coast of Korea, and in deep water in the Bering Sea; the feeding grounds are conversely distributed (Fig. 11).

Adaptive changes, occurring in fishes when the temperature varies, are connected with some morphological reconstruction. Thus, in many fishes, the adaptive reaction to variations in the temperature and the density of the water appears as variations in the number of caudal zone vertebrae (with closed haemal arches), in other words changes in the hydrodynamic properties as an adaptation to movement through water of different density. Similar adaptations are found in fishes developing at different salinities, and these are also related to variations in the density. In this connection, it should be noted that variations in the number of vertebrae occur when the temperature (or salinity) varies during the period of segmentation of the body. If such an effect occurs at a later stage of development, the number of metameres does not vary (Hubbs, 1922; Täning, 1944). A similar phenomenon

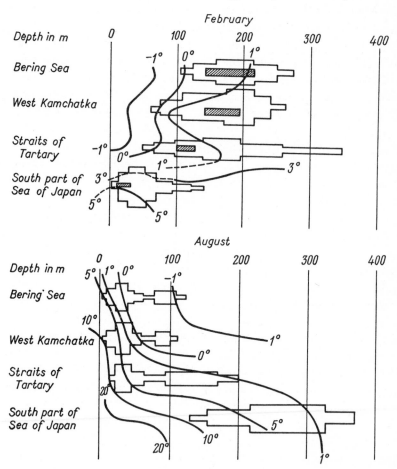

Fig. 11. Distribution of the Pacific cod *Gadus morhua macrocephalus* Til. in various parts of its habitat in relation to the distribution of temperatures; hatched blocks: spawning grounds (from Moissev, 1960).

has been observed for a number of species of fish (salmon, cyprinoids, etc.). A similar type of variation occurs in several species of fish in the number of rays in the unpaired fins, which is also related to adaptation to movement in water of various densities.

It is particularly necessary to consider the influence of ice on the life of fishes. This is a direct temperature effect, because when the water freezes its temperature rises, and when the ice melts its temperature falls. But another effect of ice is of even greater importance. The ice cover forms an important insulation against the atmosphere. During the period of ice cover the effect of winds upon the water practically ceases, the access of oxygen from the air greatly decreases, and so on (see later). By isolating the water from the air the ice makes the penetration of light into it more difficult. Finally, the ice sometimes has a mechanical effect upon the fish. Cases have been recorded of fish and spawn which were in the inshore region being carried on shore and crushed by ice there. Ice also plays some role in altering the chemical composition of the water and its salinity. The salt content of ice differs from that of sea-water, and in mass ice-formation not only does the salinity of the water increase, but also the proportions of the salts are altered. Melting of the ice, conversely, reduces the salinity and has the opposite effect upon the salt composition.

SALT CONTENT OF THE WATER

The total amount of salts dissolved in the water affects fishes mainly through changes in the osmotic pressure and density of the water. But the salt content of the water has a great direct significance for the life of the fish.

It is usual to call fish that can withstand considerable fluctuations of salinity, euryhaline, while those that cannot withstand great changes in the amounts of dissolved salts are called stenohaline. The first group includes many gobies, as for example *Pomatoschistus caucasicus* (Kawr.), which can withstand a range of salinity of from a few tenths to $60^0/_{00}$; the Caspian pipe-fish, *Syngnathus nigrolineatus caspius* Eichw., can live in water of salinity $0·27$ to $38^0/_{00}$ and higher. Many of the percomorphs which live among coral reefs, and also apparently deep-sea fish, can be quoted as stenohaline forms. Among freshwater species some of the cyprinoids cannot tolerate an increase in salinity. Although some fish are able to live at a salinity of $70^0/_{00}$ and higher, life is by no means possible at all values of the salinity.

The salts dissolved in the water permeate into the body of the fish comparatively easily, mainly through the gills. In 1909 Pütter suggested that aquatic organisms can live not only by eating particulate food, but also by assimilating the salts and organic matter dissolved in the water, which permeated into the body across its walls. In other words, according to

Pütter, aquatic organisms can feed as heterotrophic plants, and endoparasites, which live continuously surrounded by dissolved food. Pütter also applied his theory to fishes, believing that in them the absorption of nutrient matter takes place across the gills and in the alimentary tract.

Later work, particularly by Krogh, showed that Pütter's theory scarcely corresponded with the facts, at least in the dimensions which its author claimed for it. Krogh demonstrated that in fish the ingestion of nutrient matter can occur only through the intestinal tract and that, in addition, the organic matter dissolved in the waters of the earth's sphere represent compounds which cannot be used by fishes.

However, it was later shown that the presence of certain mineral salts in the water does ensure a more rapid growth in fish. Karzinkin and Shekhanova (1957), using radioactive phosphorus P_{32}, discovered that its salts do enter the body of the fish not only through the buccal cavity, but also across the gills and the skin. In the scaly carp the gills and buccal cavity absorb about 93 % of these salts, and the body surface about 6·3 %; in the mirror carp the gills and buccal cavity absorb 87·9 %, and the body surface 12·1 %. Apparently the smaller amount of coverage by scales in the mirror carp facilitates the absorption by the body surface.

The same authors showed that when the concentration of phosphorus salts in the water rises to 10 mg/l, there is a significant increase in the growth rate of young sturgeon, *Acipenser güldenstädtii* Brandt. However, when the phosphorus concentration is raised still further, there is no further increase in the growth rate (Fig. 12).

Naturally, many of the salts dissolved in the water exert a fundamentally indirect effect upon fish, by influencing the food organisms or even their food. The organic matter transported by rivers, particularly during the flood period, ensures a rich development of the various organisms which form the food of fishes in the estuarine regions. Thus, for example, before the mouths of the Ganges in the rainy period, when this river transports enormous amounts of biogenic salts into the Bay of Bengal, there develops an extremely rich phytoplankton, which attracts crustaceans, which in their turn form the food of the Bombay duck, *Harpodon nehereus* Buch. During the rainy season massive shoals of this fish appear in the estuarine regions of the Ganges, and form the basis of an important fishery (Hora, 1934a).

This phenomenon has found its reflection in the Indian epics "Mahabharata" and "Ramayana," in which a legend in allegorical form is told concerning the role of the biostock in the productivity of the water.

The salts transported by rivers play an important role in the productivity of the seas, particularly in determining to a significant extent the highly nutrient qualities of the southern Soviet seas. Regulation of the flow of rivers by the construction of dams across them leads to a considerable accumulation of salts in reservoirs and thereby to a sharp reduction in the

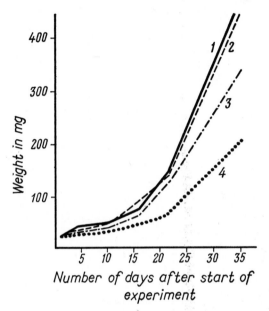

FIG. 12. Growth in weight of young sturgeon in relation to the concentration of phosphorus in the water. Concentrations of phosphorus—1, 20 mg/l; 2, 10 mg/l; 3, 2 mg/l; 4, control, 0·005 mg/l (from Karzinkin and Shekhanova, 1957).

amounts of salts flowing out to sea. Thus, for example, following the construction of the Tsimliansk hydroelectric scheme, the biomass of the phytoplankton in the Sea of Azov was reduced by 2–3 times, and that of the zooplankton from 600 mg/m³ to 24–50 mg/m³. Naturally, this had a sharply adverse effect upon the feeding condtions of fishes, and also on the size of their stocks (Karpevich, 1958).

In the open sea an increase in the transport of biogenic salts from the deposits takes place in regions of intensive vertical circulation of water, particularly in the regions of the "polar fronts," where cold and warm waters flow together. In these areas there usually develops a rich plankton and benthos, and they naturally form the feeding grounds of fishes (Zenkevich, 1947).

Tidal currents, like the vertical circulation, also cause the mixing of bottom sediments, thus bringing about a better assimilation of their mineral salts by organisms, and thereby increasing the productivity of the water. Thus, in one of the inlets of the Bay of Fundy, where the tidal amplitude is very great (a mass of water of about 2 billion tons transported four times a day), there is a very rich development of plankton and exceptional catches of fish. In regions where the bottom is continuously disturbed, causing the salts to be washed out of the deposits, there usually develops a rich plankton and benthos, and many fish accumulate there, Of particular importance to the life of fishes are the phosphates and nitrates because the presence of these

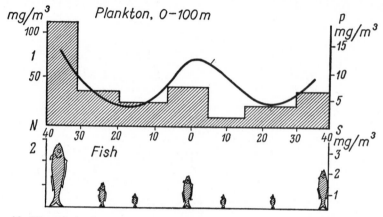

FIG. 13. The relation between the distribution of phosphates, plankton, and the catches of pelagic fishes in the Pacific Ocean (according to Bogorov).

compounds particularly favours the development of organic life in the water (Fig. 13). As Bogorov has shown, in the Pacific Ocean there is a direct relation between the distribution of phosphates, plankton, and the catches of pelagic fishes. It is noteworthy that the numbers of young of certain marine commercial fishes are in close dependence upon the amounts of phosphates in the water. In regions where sea-birds nest *en masse* the enormous amount of excrement falling into the water forms an excellent fertilizer and favours the development of organisms upon which fish feed (see page 133).

Under the conditions of pond farming, fertilization with various mineral salts, including phosphates, is frequently used, and causes a significant increase in the production of fishes.

The basic aim of fertilization is the provision of favourable salt conditions for the development of the organisms upon which the fish feed, or for the food of these organisms (for example, phytoplankton), but there is no doubt, as can be seen from the above, that the mineral salts are to some extent assimilated by the fish.

Certain dissolved mineral salts, particularly those of iron, are very important for the life of fishes. As the experiments of Minkina (1949) showed, a concentration of iron of 0·2 mg/l causes a sharp reduction in the metabolic rate of fishes and slows down their growth; conversely, a concentration of 0·1 mg/l stimulates their growth. An increase in the concentration of iron in the water leads to some reduction in the rate of oxygen consumption of fishes.

The presence of iron salts at a certain concentration is essential for the normal development of fish eggs. According to Cheprakova (1960), at a concentration of iron salts ($FeCl_3$) of 10·3 mg/l all the eggs of the perch died. At concentrations of 3·94 mg/l and 1·92 mg/l, hatching started earlier than in the controls. But at 3·94 mg/l there was a partial mortality of the embryos before hatching. When iron salts are added to the water the blood pigments appear earlier in the embryos.

Compounds of various metals, particularly those of the heavier ones, can cause the death of fishes at various concentrations. One part of lead in 3 million parts of water causes death (Carpenter, 1930). Iron and aluminium at high concentrations also cause death (Minkina, 1946). Doses of iron higher than 0·2 mg/l sometimes cause the death of fishes. Aluminium compounds at concentrations higher than 0·5 mg/l can be fatal.

Naturally the action of metallic salts upon fishes varies with the temperature. The higher the temperature (up to certain limits), the higher the metabolic rate of fishes, and the greater the effect on the organism of the salts dissolved in the water. The interaction of ions in solution is particularly important in this respect. Loeb (1926) showed that the toxic effect of an isotonic solution of NaCl on fish embryos (experiments on *Fundulus heteroclitus* [L.]) is reduced by the addition of a series of bivalent ions—Ba, Sr, Ca, Mg, and others. At later stages of development there appears to be a certain amount of specificity, and the toxicity of sodium can only be reduced by the addition of Ca ions.

Changes in the survival of embryos of *Fundulus heteroclitus* (L.) in relation to changes in the proportions of Na to Ca ions are shown in Fig. 14.

It should be noted that cations have a considerably greater effect upon fish than do anions.

The toxic effect of metallic compounds leads firstly to the coagulation of the mucous secretion of the gills and the protoplasm of living cells, which disrupts the metabolism. In iron-poisoning the gills become covered with a dense brown coating, which makes respiration difficult.

In recent times the presence of substances dissolved in the water which are not normal constituents of sea- or fresh water, but which enter it as the result of various human activities such as tree-felling, industrial effluents, pollution by oil, processing of mineral ores, and so on, has become particularly important to fishes. The list of substances which enter the water as a result of human activities and which affect the aquatic fauna, including fishes, is very large (Beak, 1958). Ellis (1937) listed up to a hundred such substances.

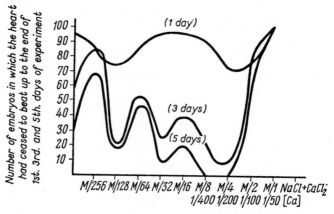

FIG. 14. Changes in the survival of embryos of *Fundulus heteroclitus* (L.) in solutions of KCl with increasing concentrations of NaCl+CaCl₂ (from Skadovsky, 1955).

The effect on fish of acids which enter the water is very great, but the investigation of their toxic effect is made difficult by the fact that the acids do not affect fishes in the same way in relation to the hardness of the water and the concentration of hydrogen ions. Thus, for example, sulphuric acid at a concentration of 1:7450 in soft water causes the death of goldfish in 6–9 hours; in hard water the fish can survive this concentration for many days. Tartaric acid at a concentration of 1:1000 in soft water kills goldfish in 20–25 minutes, but the fish can survive 200 minutes in hard water at the same concentration. This is apparently explained by the fact that the carbonate salts of calcium and partly of magnesium, which cause the hardness of water, "buffer" it, i.e. they reduce the change in pH at low acidities (and also in alkaline conditions). In soft water, which is practically unbuffered, negligible amounts of acids (and of alkalis) cause a strong change in the pH up to the lethal limit for fishes and other aquatic animals. In the majority of cases the acid is not lethal of itself (i.e. as the carrier of certain cations), but acts through changing the pH of the water.

Acids can be arranged according to their toxic effect, from experiments on goldfish, into the following series (the figures refer to the concentration of the substances in mg/l at which the fish died):

tannic	10	nitric, oxalic,	
chromic	100	benzoic	200
sulphuric	130	acetic	348
hydrochloric	159	lactic and citric	625

The acids differ in the mechanism of their action on fishes. Certain acids, such as acetic, which burn the gills, bring about the disruption of respiration and thus cause the death of the fish; others act through the alimentary canal, penetrating through the intestinal wall into the body fluids and disrupting the normal course of metabolism. Usually the toxic effect of acids upon fish is a combination, not only the gills being damaged or the body fluids affected via the intestine, but both effects occurring together.

Industrial effluents containing sulphuric acid affect the eggs and larvae of the perch at pH less than 6·5, and the young of the carp at pH less than 5·0. Both the H and the SO_4 ions affect the fish. The effect of the SO_4 anion is particularly great on developing eggs, destroying their normal metabolism (N. Mossevich, Dragulin, Kushnareva, and M. Mossevich, 1952).

The effects of other dissolved compounds which enter the water, both organic and inorganic, are also rather variable. In fact, in the majority of cases they affect primarily the course of respiration. Therefore, the slower the respiratory processes of a fish the more slowly does the toxic effect of any dissolved substance act. When the temperature is reduced, which slows down the rate of respiration, the action of toxic substances is usually reduced. Other substances, such as phenol, cause paralysis of the fishes' neuro-muscular apparatus and haemolysis of the blood. Amyl alcohol destroys the coordination of movements in fish and also produces a semiparalytic condition.

Naturally the substances dissolved in the water affect not only the adult fish but their spawn as well. Thus, for example, papermill effluents which contain sodium sulphate, mercaptans, and other substances, disrupt the normal course of division of the eggs and the development of the embryos, even when present in negligible quantities, and rapidly kill them at higher concentrations. It is interesting that fish embryos at different stages of development are not equally sensitive to the action of various toxic substances. Experiments have shown that the action of dinitrophenol on the earliest stage of development of fishes causes a significantly higher mortality and a larger number of freaks than it does in larvae which have already developed eyes.

The toxic effect of dissolved substances also varies seasonally. The greatest susceptibility to the action of poisons occurs when the fish are feeding heavily, and usually coincides with the warmer parts of the year; this is very likely due to the increase in the rate of interaction between the poison and the protoplasmic proteins at higher temperatures. Although the nature of the effect of the various substances contained in effluents is extremely variable, the fundamental nature of their adverse effects is that, as they oxidize in the water, they rapidly deplete the water-mass of oxygen. The water, particularly in winter under ice, then develops an oxygen deficit, which leads to the death of fishes and other aquatic organisms.

In order to protect fishes from the effect of effluents, special settling tanks or other purifying installations are set up at factories. In many cases the water is used several times over in the factories.

If industry were properly organized, it should be possible to protect the water-masses from pollution by industrial effluents and to preserve them for fish production.

GASES IN SOLUTION

Like all other animals, fishes cannot live without the access of oxygen to the organism through its blood, which ensures the metabolism and thereby the life of the fish. Naturally, therefore, the cessation of access of oxygen to the blood leads to the death of the fish in a short time.

The majority of fishes are adapted to absorbing the oxygen dissolved in the water, and only a few are able to assimilate oxygen from the atmosphere. In fishes which are taken out of the water, as experiments on the spurdog, *Acanthias acanthias* (L.), and the cod, *Gadus morhua* L., have shown, there is a very rapid increase in the amount of lactic acid both in the blood and in the muscles. Whereas in the cod before the experiment the concentration of lactic acid in the muscles was 5–45 mg %, after 4 minutes exposure to the air it increased to 60–120 mg %. On being returned to the water the amount of lactic acid in both the muscles and the blood gradually decreased, but very slowly. In the muscles it dropped in various individuals to 25–65 mg %

30 minutes after returning to the water (Levestad, Andersen, and Scholander, 1957).

Only a few species, living in waters in which for various reasons there frequently develops an oxygen deficit, are adapted to breathing atmospheric air.

The normal respiration of fishes takes place through the access of water via the mouth and its passage out via the gill clefts (Fig. 15). But in the

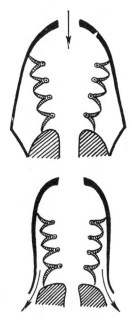

Fig. 15. Scheme of respiration of adult fishes. Above, inhalation; below, exhalation (from Voskoboinikov, 1928).

Cyclostomes and certain fishes this scheme is somewhat altered; thus, in the hagfish the water reaches the gill sacs not through the buccal cavity, but through an unpaired nostril which is connected to the pharyngeal cavity. This change is an adaptation to a semiparasitic mode of life, in which the mouth is frequently occupied in burrowing into the body wall of its prey, and respiration would otherwise be interrupted. Another feature in the structure of the respiratory apparatus of the hagfish is also connected with its semi-parasitic mode of life. The apertures of the gill sacs open into a common canal which, in turn, opens far behind the head in a single aperture. This structure enables the hagfish to bury its head deeply into the body of its prey without disrupting its own normal respiration. In the lamprey, which also sometimes leads a semiparasitic life, but in contrast to the hagfish has no nostril connected to the pharyngeal cavity, respiration takes place by means of sucking water in and driving it out again through the gill apertures.

In skates, when they are lying on the sea-bed and the mouth is turned to the ground, water reaches the gills through a spout. In fishes whose head and body are covered with a dense armour and the gill aperture is small, and the covers immobile, exchange of the water over the gills takes place by means of currents of water produced by constant movements of the pectoral fins. This is the mode of respiration of the trunk fish, moon-fish, and certain others.

FIG. 16. Head of *Gyrinocheilus* (from Hora, 1933).

In the fresh waters of south-eastern Asia there lives a fish of the suborder Cyprinoidei, *Gyrinocheilus* in which the mouth often functions as a sucker. When this happens, of course water cannot pass normally to the gills. To allow normal respiration to be maintained the gill apertures of this fish are divided into two parts, so that each side of the head has two gill apertures, one upper and one lower (Fig. 16). When the mouth is closed the water reaches the gills through the upper apertures and leaves through the lower ones (Hora, 1933).

In many fishes the skin also serves as a supplementary respiratory organ, the skin of fishes having a particularly great significance in the excretion of CO_2. The loach *Misgurnus* excretes up to 92 % of its CO_2 through the skin. In the loach also 63 % of its oxygen is obtained through the skin, and 37 % through the gills. If the gills are occluded (by tying the pharynx and gills) the consumption of oxygen through the skin increases to 85 %. The remainder is obtained through the intestine.

The respiratory organs change very profoundly during the process of individual development of the fish, and this is related to changes in its mode of life. In many larvae and embryos of fishes, before the definitive gills have developed as organs for the assimilation of oxygen from the water, the blood-vessels in the yolk-sac and fin-folds perform this function. The more favourable the respiratory conditions under which the embryos and larvae develop, the less strongly developed is their capillary respiratory system.

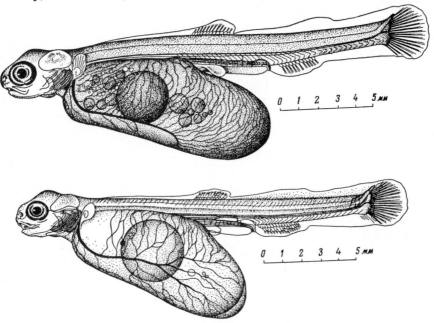

Fig. 17. Free-living embryos of chum (top) and humpback (bottom) salmon (from Nikolsky, 1954).

As the yolk-sac is absorbed and its respiratory blood-vessel network is reduced, there is a corresponding increase in the blood-vessel network in the fin-folds. Even in closely related species, in which development proceeds under different respiratory conditions, there are substantial differences in the degree of development of the larval respiratory organs. Thus, for example, as can be seen in Fig. 17, in the humpback salmon, *Oncorhynchus gorbuscha* (Walb.), the eggs and embryos of which usually develop in water that is more highly saturated with oxygen than is the case for the chum salmon *O. keta* (Walb.), the capillary system on the yolk-sac is less well developed (Nikolsky and Soin, 1954).

In some larvae (dipneusts, gymnarchids, etc.), until the definitive respiratory organs develop, special larval gills perform this function (Fig. 18).

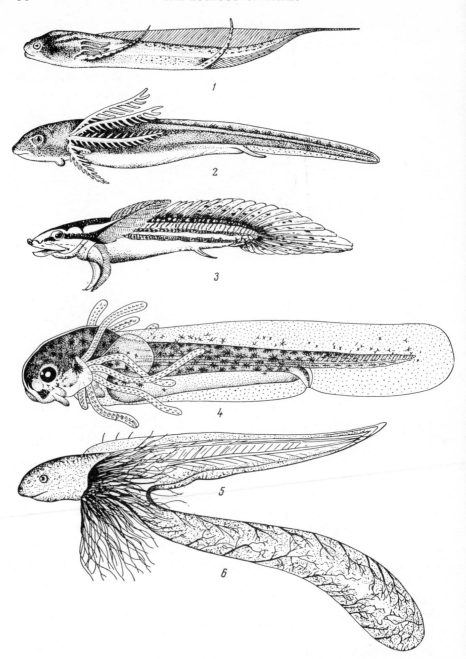

FIG. 18. Larval gills of various fishes (not to scale): 1, The African lungfish *Protopterus*; 2, the American lungfish *Lepidosiren paradoxa* Fitz.; 3, the bichir *Polypterus* sp.; 4, the loach *Misgurnus fossilis* (L.); 5, *Gymnarchus niloticus* Cuv.

In many larval fishes a pseudobranch functions in place of the larval respiratory organs.

Various species of fishes are adapted to living at different concentrations of dissolved oxygen. Salmonids can live at a concentration of 7–8 cc of oxygen per litre of water, while many cyprinoids can easily survive a reduction to 3 cc/l.

According to the amount of oxygen which is essential for normal respiration of fishes, they may, to some extent conditionally, be separated into four groups (Wunder, 1936):

1. Fishes which require very large amounts of oxygen; the normal condition for them is 7–11 cc/l, and at 5 cc/l some of them begin to suffer. These include the trout, *Salmo trutta* L., the minnow, *Phoxinus phoxinus* (L.), the loach, *Nemachilus barbatulus* (L.), bullhead, *Cottus gobio* (L.), and many other species inhabitants, chiefly, of fast, cold rivers.

2. Fishes which demand a large amount of oxygen, but which can live at 5–7 cc/l. This group includes the grayling, *Thymallus thymallus* (L.), the chub, *Leuciscus cephalus* (L.), *Chondrostoma nasus* (L.), the gudgeon, *Gobio gobio* (L.), burbot, *Lota lota* (L.), etc.

3. Fishes which demand a relatively small amount of oxygen and are able to live even at 4 cc/l, as, for example, the roach, *Rutilus rutilus* L., ruff, *Acerina cernua* (L.), etc.

4. Fishes which can survive very low oxygen saturation when there remains only $\frac{1}{2}$ cc/l. Such fish are the carp, tench, crucian carp, etc.

The above division applies mainly to freshwater fishes, because marine fishes are only subjected to very slight fluctuations in oxygen content. Sea-water is usually either fully saturated, or even frequently super-saturated, with oxygen. An oxygen deficit can only rarely be found in the sea, mainly in enclosed bays and inlets or at night in places where there is a mass development of planktonic algae. Oxygen deficit can also occur in deep trenches such as the deep layers of the Black Sea or in certain deep parts of the Caspian. This is connected with the presence of water of higher salinity at the bottom and the consequent absence of a vertical circulation. In the Sea of Azov an oxygen deficit in the bottom layers sometimes occurs in summer during calm weather, when there is, similarly, a cessation of the vertical circulation, and the process of decomposition of organic matter leads to the disappearance of oxygen from the bottom layers, which causes the death of the bottom fauna, including bottom fish, such as the gobies.

The amount of oxygen used by fishes is not constant. It varies with age in relation to the changes in the activity of the fish and of the conditions under which it lives. In fishes which are adapted to living under conditions of a periodical onset of oxygen deficit, the activity is reduced in these periods, the metabolic rate falls, and the amount of oxygen used for respiration is reduced.

TABLE 1

Amount of Oxygen used by Fishes per 1 g Live Weight per Hour at a Temperature of 18–20°C (According to G. G. Vinberg, 1956)

Species of fish	Amount of O_2 in mg
Ladoga whitefish *Coregonus laveretus* (L.)	0·396
Common bullhead *Cottus gobio* L.	0·355
Bleak *Alburnus alburnus* (L.)	0·282
Common gudgeon *Gobio gobio* L.	0·281
Salmon 3-yr old *Salmo salar* L.	0·257
Salmon 4-yr old *Salmo salar* L.	0·229
Sterlet *Acipenser ruthenus* L.	0·204
Burbot *Lota lota* L.	0·173
Crucian carp *Carassius carassius* (L.)	0·133
Loach *Misgurnus fossilis* (L.)	0·123

However, just as in the case of the minimal amounts of dissolved oxygen at which a fish can live, so in relation to the amount of oxygen used by a fish in respiration, there is a clear species specificity. Oxyphilic fishes, as Table 1 shows, use more oxygen than fishes which can live at low concentrations of dissolved oxygen.

It is well known that many water-masses, in winter and even sometimes in summer, completely lose their dissolved oxygen as a result of the process of decomposition. In winter-time the depletion is particularly great, because the presence of ice cover hinders the access of atmospheric oxygen. At such times fishes strive, if possible, to leave the depleted water mass, entering the rivers which flow into it, aggregating at the mouths of rivers and rising through ice holes. Depletion setting in in lakes and fish-farms, causing the deaths of many fishes, sometimes causes very heavy losses to the fish industry. To combat winter depletion it is usual to make ice holes in order to admit the air to the water. However, this precaution is frequently ineffective. Whenever possible the flow of water through the lake must be increased. Such measures usually lead to the cessation, or in the worst cases to a reduction, of the depletion.

To combat depletion, particularly in fish-farms, various methods of aeration of the water, mainly by the use of pumps to force air under the ice, are in use nowadays.

In the Soviet Union the most serious depletion occurs in the river Ob. In winter-time it involves an enormous area from the Vasiugan, or even higher, down to the lower reaches of this river. The reason for the depletion of the Ob is the transport from the marshlands of the Vasiugan basin and other rivers of humus material and iron oxides, which when oxidized use up all the dissolved oxygen. Since the ice cover makes it impossible for oxygen to enter the water from the atmosphere, the depletion spreads very rapidly and, beginning in the region of Vasiugan at the end of December or in early January, it reaches the Obsk inlet by February and the beginning of March. The fish escape from the depletion by entering the tributary system, or else they pass into the Obsk inlet. All the same a small part of the Ob fish die annually because of the depletion (Mossevich, 1947).

In the summer-time depletion usually occurs at night. Its main cause is the rich development of aquatic vegetation, which rapidly uses up the oxygen at night. Oxygen is also used up in the oxidation of organic matter, which is abundant in water-masses "in bloom." By day the consumption of oxygen is compensated by photosynthesis. At night, when the photosynthetic processes cease to function, but the consumption of oxygen continues at the same rate, this can cause a deficit and lead to the death of fishes, particularly in small water-bodies. While winter deficits occur only in temperate and cold climates and require the presence of ice cover for their development, summer deficits also develop in the tropics, in which they naturally occur even more frequently than in temperate latitudes. The scale of summer nocturnal deficits is, however, significantly less than that of the winter ones.

A number of species of fish, which live under the conditions of a periodical oxygen deficit in the water, have evolved an adaptation for breathing atmospheric oxygen. The simplest method of breathing atmospheric oxygen is found in one of the American electric eels, *Hypopomus*. This eel swallows bubbles of air and brings them into contact with the gills, across the surface of which the atmospheric oxygen is absorbed. Some fishes use the skin surface for the absorption of atmospheric oxygen (the eel, *Anguilla*, the mud-skipper, *Periophthalmus*).

Fishes which possess a swim-bladder soon use up all the oxygen contained in it when there is an oxygen deficit. This is a rather primitive way of using the swim-bladder for respiration. But in certain fishes, such as dipneusts, the bicher, and others, the swim-bladder has actually become converted into an organ for the respiration of atmospheric air. The structure of the swim-bladder in these cases has become considerably modified, being spongy and reminiscent of the lungs of higher vertebrates. The conversion of the swim-bladder into "lungs" has enabled the dipneusts to inhabit very marshy lakes, where there is often a complete lack of oxygen in the water. When this happens the fish breathes the atmospheric air. *Protopterus* survives when the lake dries up completely, and at such times it burrows into the mud, where it remains in a state rather like that of hibernation. *Lepidosiren* uses atmospheric air throughout its life and cannot live even in water which is rich in dissolved oxygen, merely by aquatic respiration.

Another method whereby fishes use atmospheric air is in intestinal respiration, which has been developed in various groups of fish, as for example among the cyprinoids (sheat-fish, loaches), or among the Symbranchidae. Intestinal respiration also occurs as a supplement to gill respiration and usually takes place in an oxygen deficit. In fishes with intestinal respiration the intestine undergoes certain modifications compared with closely related species without this function. The length of the intestine is usually increased, the blood capillaries approach its inner surface closely, and the digestive function is lacking in certain parts, the villi are absent, and the intestine here performs a strictly respiratory function. In some fishes part of the stomach is so adapted. Thus, in the tropical sheat-fish, *Otocinclus*, there is a special blind outgrowth of the stomach, which is usually full of air and performs the respiratory function. The air swallowed by fishes in respiration loses about 5 % of its oxygen and acquires about 3 % of carbon dioxide. The used air leaves either through the mouth, as in many sheat-fish, or else through the anal aperture, as for example in the loach.

Some fishes which breathe partly through atmospheric air have developed various types of epibranchial chambers, which serve as reservoirs for air (Fig. 19). The oxygen is absorbed from the swallowed air either by the walls of the epibranchial chambers, as in the Anabantidae and Ophicephalidae, or else by the ventrally placed gills. The epibranchial organ varies considerably in structure in the various species (Fig. 19).

In *Anabas* this consists of paired outgrowths of the branchial cavities, placed symmetrically above the gills. Inside each of these cavities there are folds, the walls of which are permeated with minute capillaries. The air swallowed by the fish enters these cavities, which function as lungs by virtue of the rich network of capillaries, which absorb the oxygen from the air and give up carbon dioxide. In the snakeheads (Ophicephalidae) the epibranchial organ is represented by paired outgrowths in the pharynx. The walls of these outgrowths, as in *Anabas*, are very rich in blood capillaries. A similar type of epibranchial organ is found in representatives of the family Symbranchidae, for example *Amphipnous couchia* Ham. In the sheat-fish *Clarias* there is an

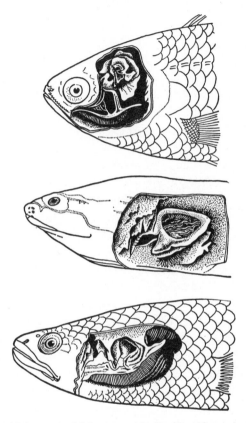

Fig. 19. Epibranchial organs of fishes: top, *Anabas* (Perciformes); middle, *Amphipnous* (Symbranchiformes); bottom, *Ophicephalus* (Ophicephaliformes) (from Hora, 1933).

unpaired epibranchial organ situated above and behind the gills. The greatest development of the epibranchial organ is found in the sac-gilled sheat-fish, *Heteropneustes*, in which there is a long sac situated above the very small swim-bladder and stretching right back into the caudal region. In some fishes the epibranchial organ plays only an accessory role in respiration, and functions only at such times as when the fish gets into water which is poor in oxygen. In others the epibranchial respiration is basic. Such a fish, when it is unable to rise and swallow air, inevitably dies in a short time; *Amphipnous* will die under such circumstances in less than a day. It is interesting that the gills of this fish are very much reduced, and undoubtedly are unable to supply the blood with sufficient oxygen. The snakehead, *Ophicephalus striatus* Bl., also dies from lack of oxygen in 30–197 minutes when prevented from reaching the surface. Apparently young snakeheads die sooner from suffocation than older ones.

Such Indian fishes as *Anabas*, *Heteropneustes*, and certain others, can live freely in well-aerated water without rising to the surface to swallow air. The epibranchial organ in these fishes is an accessory respiratory organ and functions basically only in exceptional circumstances, which enables such fish as the climbing perch *Anabas* to escape from dried-up lakes and travel overland to find others.

As may be seen from Table 2, the great majority of fishes which are adapted to breathing atmospheric air are inhabitants of subtropical and tropical latitudes, and only a few live in the waters of temperate and high latitudes.

In the majority of fishes which breathe atmospheric air, such respiration is an adaptation to surviving an oxygen deficit in the waters which they normally inhabit, and only in a few species is aerial respiration an adaptation to travelling over dry land from one water-mass to another (the common eel, the climbing perch, *Anabas*, *Periophthalmus*).

Apart from oxygen, other gases are also of considerable importance to fishes. As was stated above, CO_2 in even relatively small doses causes the death of fishes. The mechanism of the action of carbon dioxide upon fish as upon other animals, consists of the reduction of the blood's capacity to absorb oxygen. Admittedly the amount of free carbon dioxide in water is very small, especially in sea-water, because magnesium, calcium, and other cations rapidly combine with it. The amount of CO_2 in the water is directly proportional to the pH, changes in which also have a serious effect upon fishes. As the acidity of the water increases the rate of metabolism falls, although the respiratory rhythm increases in more acid water compared to either neutral or alkaline.

Hydrogen sulphide also has a very adverse effect upon fishes. It can only develop and accumulate in water when there is no oxygen in the water, because in the presence of oxygen it is rapidly oxidized. The effect of hydrogen sulphide varies. Such species as the tench, *Tinca tinca* (L.), and the crucian carp *Carassius auratus* (L.), will die after 8–10 days following immersion for 3 hours in water containing hydrogen sulphide at a concentration of 1:10,000, the trout dies after 15 minutes in a hydrogen sulphide concentration of 1:100,000. The American eared perch, *Eupomotis gibbosus* (L.), dies within one hour at this concentration. The strength of the action of hydrogen sulphide, as of other gases, varies considerably as the temperature varies. Death occurs more quickly at higher temperatures.

TABLE 2

Fishes which Breathe Atmospheric Air (According to Carter; see Brown, 1957)

Species	Respiratory organ	Distribution
Neoceratodus	"Lungs"	Tropical Australia
Protopterus	"Lungs"	Tropical Africa
Lepidosiren	"Lungs"	Tropical S. America
Polypterus	"Lungs"	Tropical Africa
Lepidosteus	Swim-bladder	Temp. and tropical N. America and Cuba
Amia	Swim-bladder	Temp. N. America
Gymnarchus	Swim-bladder	Tropical Africa
Erytrinus	Swim-bladder	Tropical S. America
Electrophorus	Pharyngo-epibranchial organ	Tropical S. America
Hypopomus	Gills	Tropical S. America
Misgurnus	Intestine	Temp. and tropical Asia and Europe
Clarias	Epibranchial organ	Tropical Asia and Africa
Doras	Stomach	Tropical S. America
Callichthys	Stomach	Tropical S. America
Hoplosternum	Stomach	Tropical S. America
Hypostomus	Stomach	Tropical S. America
Ancistrus	Stomach	Tropical S. America
Plecostomus	Stomach	Tropical S. America
Heteropneustes	Epibranchial organ	Tropical Asia
Umbra	Swim-bladder	Temp. Europe and N. America
Monopterus	Epibranchial organ	Tropical Asia
Amphipnous	Epibranchial organ	Tropical Asia
Anguilla	Skin	Europe, Asia, and N. America
Ophicephalus	Epibranchial organ	Tropical Asia
Parophicephalus	Epibranchial organ	Tropical Africa
Anabas	Epibranchial organ	Tropical Asia
Osphronemus	Epibranchial organ	Tropical Asia
Betta	Epibranchial organ	Tropical Asia
Periophthalmus	Skin	Africa, Asia, Australia

LIGHT, SOUND, OTHER VIBRATIONS AND FORMS OF RADIANT ENERGY

Light and, to a lesser extent, other forms of radiant energy play a very significant role in the lives of fishes. Other types of low-frequency vibrations, such as sound and both infra- and ultrasonic vibrations, are also of importance in their effect upon fishes. Electrical currents, both natural ones and those radiated by fishes, are also of considerable importance. The fish is adapted to sensing all these influences with its sense organs.

LIGHT

Illumination, both direct and indirect, is of great importance in the lives of fishes. In the majority of fishes the visual organs play a substantial role in orientation, during swimming, towards prey, predator, other individuals of the same species in a shoal, or immobile objects, etc.

Only a very few fishes are adapted to living in complete darkness in caves and artesian waters, or in the very weak natural light produced by organisms at very great depths.

The structure of the fish—its visual organs, the presence or absence of luminescent organs, the development of other sense organs, pigmentation, etc.—is connected with the features of illumination. The behaviour of the fish, particularly its diurnal rhythm of activity and many other aspects of its life, are significantly related to the degree of illumination. Light exerts a definite influence both on the course of the fish's metabolism, and on the maturation of its gonads. Thus, for the majority of fishes light is an essential element of the environment.

The state of illumination in the water may be extremely variable and depends, apart from the strength of the illumination, on the reflection, absorption, and dispersion of light, and many other factors. A substantial factor in determining the illumination of water is its transparency. This is extremely variable, from the opaque, coffee colour of the rivers of India, China, and Central Asia, in which an object submerged in the water becomes invisible as soon as it is covered with water, and ending with the transparent waters of the Sargasso Sea (transparency 66·5 m), the central part of the Pacific Ocean (59 m), and a number of other places, where a white Secchi disc becomes invisible to the eye only at a depth of more than 50 m. Naturally, the condition of illumination of various waters varies considerably, even at the same latitude and depth, because the amount of light decreases rapidly with depth. Thus, in the sea off the English coast 90 % of the light is absorbed in the top 8–9 m.

The fish senses light with its eyes and light-sensitive spots. The special features of the illumination determine the specific structure and function of the eye. As the experiments of Beebe (1936) showed, the human eye can perceive traces of light under water at a depth of over 500 m. At a depth of 100 m a photographic plate is darkened after exposure for 1 hour and 10 minutes, at a depth of 1700 m a photographic plate is not affected by an exposure of two hours. Thus animals which live at depths beginning around 1500 m and down to the greatest depths of the world's oceans, more than 10,000 m, are never subjected to the effect of daylight and live in complete darkness, which is disturbed only by the light given out by various deep-sea animals.

By comparison with man and other terrestrial animals, the fish is more short-sighted; its eye has a considerably shorter focal distance. The majority of fish can clearly perceive objects at a distance of 1 m, but the maximum visual distance is apparently not greater than 15 m. Morphologically this is determined by the lens being more spherical than in terrestrial vertebrates. In bony fishes the eye accomodates by means of the so-called crescent-shaped organ, in sharks by the ciliary organ.

The horizontal field of vision of the adult fish is 160–170° (data for trout), i.e. more than in man (154°), and the vertical field is 150° (134° in man). However, this vision is monocular. The binocular field of vision of the trout is only 20-30°, whereas in man it is 120° (Baburina, 1955). The maximum acuity of vision in fishes is attained at 35 lux (in man, at 300 lux), which is connected with the lower illumination of the water as compared with the air. The quality of the sight is also connected with the structure of the eye.

Fishes whose eye is adapted to seeing in air have a flatter lens. In the American four-eyed fish, *Anableps tetrophthalmus* (L.), the upper part of the eye (lens, iris, cornea) is separated from the lower by a horizontal partition. The upper part of the lens is flatter than the lower, which is adapted to seeing in water. This fish, which swims along the surface, can observe both the air and the water at the same time.

In one marine species of seahounds, *Dialommus fuscus* Clark, the eye is divided by a vertical partition, and the fish can see out of water with the anterior part of its eye, and in water with the posterior part. Living in depressions in the littoral, it frequently sits with the fore part of its head out of the water (Fig. 20). However, fishes can see out of the water without having their heads in the air.

In the water the fish can only see objects which are out of the water if they are within an angle of 48·8° of the vertical. As Fig. 21 shows, the fish sees aerial objects as if through a circular window. This window widens as the

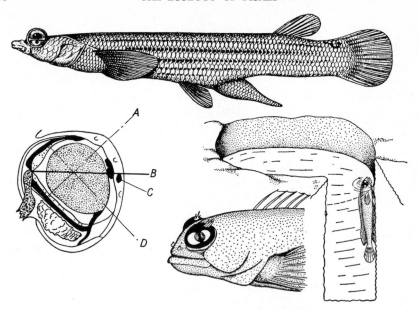

FIG. 20. Fishes which have eyes adapted to seeing in both water and air. Above, the four-eyed fish *Anableps tetrophthalmus* L.; left, a section through its eye; below, the four-eyed sea-hound *Dialommus fuscus* Clark. A, axis of aerial vision; B, dark threshold; C, axis of underwater vision; D, lens (from Schultz, 1948).

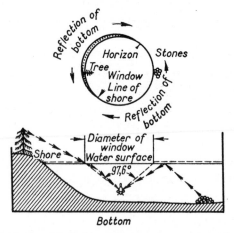

FIG. 21. Visual field of a fish looking up through a calm surface. Above, the water surface and air space visible from underneath; below, the same scheme from the side. Light rays falling on the surface of the water within the "window" are refracted and reach the fish's eyes. The fish can see a space above the water within an angle of 97·6°; outside of this angle it sees the images of objects on the bottom reflected from the surface of the water (from Baburina, 1955).

fish sinks, and narrows as the fish rises to the surface, but the fish sees always through the same total angle of 97·6° (Baburina, 1955).

Fishes have special adaptations for seeing under various illuminations. The rods in the retina are adapted to sensing weak light, and in daylight they become buried in between the pigment cells, which cover them from the light rays. The cones, which are adapted to sensing brighter light, approach the surface of the retina in bright illumination.

Since the upper and lower parts of the eyes of fishes receive different amounts of light, the upper part senses more dispersed light than the lower part. In relation to this fact, in the majority of fish the lower part of the retina possesses more cones, and fewer rods, per unit area than the upper part.

The eye undergoes considerable structural modifications in ontogeny. In young fishes, which feed near the water surface, the region of the greatest sensitivity to light is in the lower part of the eye, but when the fish starts to feed upon benthos the sensitivity of the upper part of the eye increases, so that objects lying below may be perceived.

The nature of the reaction to light also changes in ontogeny. The young of the salmon, trout, and certain other fishes hide from the light under stones, thus protecting themselves from predators. In the ammocoetes larva of the lamprey (Cyclostomes) in which the tail carries light-sensitive cells, this is related to living in the soil. When the tail is illuminated the ammocoetes reacts with swimming movements, by which they burrow further into the bottom deposit.

The light intensity perceived by the eyes varies according to species. In the American fish *Lepomis* of the family Centrarchidae the eye can perceive light at an intensity of 10^{-10} of normal daylight. Such light intensity is found in the Sargasso Sea at a depth of 430 m below the surface. The bluegill sunfish *Lepomis*, a freshwater fish, is an inhabitant of comparatively shallow waters. It is therefore most probable that deep-water fishes, especially those with telescopic eyes, are able to react to very low illumination (Fig. 22).

Deep-water fishes have evolved a number of adaptations in connection with the weak illumination in deep water (Fig. 22). In many of them the eye attains to an enormous size. For example, in *Bathymacrops macrolepis* Gelchrist, fam. Microstomidae, the diameter of the eye comprises about 40 % of the length of the head. In *Polyipnus*, fam. Sternoptychidae, the diameter of the eye is 25–32 % of the length of the head, while in *Mycto-phium rissoi* (Cocco), fam. Myctophidae, it is even as much as 50 %. Often the shape of the pupil is abnormal in deep-water fishes; it becomes elongated, and extends beyond the lens, and because of this and of the increase in the total size of the eye, its light-absorbing properties are increased. In *Argyropelecus*, fam. Sternoptychidae, the eye possesses a special luminescent organ which maintains the retina in a state of permanent stimulation and thereby

FIG. 22. Visual organs of certain deep-water fishes. 1, *Argyropelecus affinis* Garm.; 2, *Myctophium rissoi* (Cocco) (from Fowler, 1936).

increases its sensitivity to light rays from without. The eyes of many deep-water fishes are telescopic, which increases the sensitivity and widens the field of view. The most peculiar changes in the visual organ occur in the larvae of the deep-water fish *Idiacanthus* (Fig. 23). In these, the eyes are placed

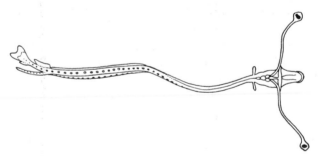

FIG. 23. Larva of the deep-water fish *Idiacanthus* (order Stomiatoidei) (from Fowler, 1936).

on long stalks, which considerably increases the field of view. The eyes of the adult are not on stalks.

Whereas some deep-water species have the eyes very well developed, in others, as has already been stated, the eyes are either considerably reduced

(*Benthosaurus*, etc.), or else completely lacking (*Ipnops*). Beside having reduced eyes, these fishes usually develop various outgrowths on the body: the rays of the paired and unpaired fins become very elongated. All these outgrowths serve as organs of touch, and to some extent they compensate for the reduction of the eyes.

The development of eyes in fishes which live at depths to which no light ever penetrates is related to the fact that many abyssal animals are luminescent.

Luminescence is a very common property of animals which live at great depths in the sea. Nearly 45 % of fishes which live at depths greater than 300 m have light-producing organs. These occur in their simplest form among fishes of the family Macruridae. Their epidermal mucus glands contain a phosphorescent substance which gives out a weak light, so that the whole fish appears to glow. The majority of other deep-water fishes have special light-producing organs, sometimes of fairly complex structure. The most complicated light organ in fishes consists of an underlying layer of pigment, covered by a reflector and luminescent cells, the whole being covered by a lens (Fig. 24). The distribution of the light organs varies so much among the species that it can often be used for systematic purposes (Fig. 25).

Usually the light is the result of a reaction between the secretion of the luminescent cells and the water, but in the fish *Acropoma japonica* Günth. it is due to microorganisms in the organ. The intensity of the light depends upon several factors and varies even in one fish. Many fishes are particularly luminescent during the reproductive period.

It is not yet well known what the biological significance of the luminescence of deep-water fishes is, but there is no doubt that the role of the light organs varies from one species to another. In the Ceratiidae the light organ, which is placed at the end of the first dorsal fin-ray, apparently serves for the attraction of prey. Possibly the luminescent organs at the end of the caudal fin of *Saccopharynx* has the same function. The distribution of light organs along the sides of the body in *Argyropelecus*, *Lampanyctes*, *Myctophium*, *Vinciguerria*, and many other species enables them to find other individuals of the same species in the dark at great depths. Apparently this is of great importance to shoal-forming fishes.

Cave-dwelling fishes live in complete obscurity, which is not even broken by luminescent organisms. According to the closeness of their relation to life in caves, it is customary to subdivide them into the following groups:

1, troglobionts, those which constantly inhabit caves; 2, troglophils, those which mostly inhabit caves but occur elsewhere; 3, trogloxenes, species with a wide distribution but which also enter caves.

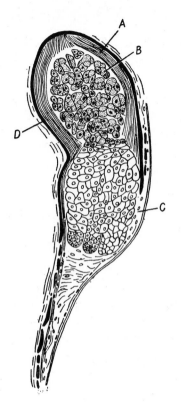

FIG. 24. The light organ of *Argyropelecus*. A, reflector; B, light cells; C, lens; D, basal layer (from Brauer, 1906–08).

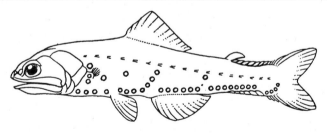

FIG. 25. Scheme of distribution of the light organs in the shoal-forming deep-water fish *Lampanyctes* (from Andriashev, 1939).

Like the deep-water fishes, cave-dwelling species have undergone considerable changes in their organization in relation to the character of the illumination. There occur among cave fishes all the transitional stages from fishes with well-developed eyes to completely blind ones. Thus, the eyes of *Chologaster cornutus* Agass. (fam. Amblyopsidae) are normally developed and function as visual organs. In the closely related *Chologaster papilliferus* For., although all the elements of the eye are present the retina is degenerate. In *Typhlichthys* the pupil is still open, and the neural connection of the eye

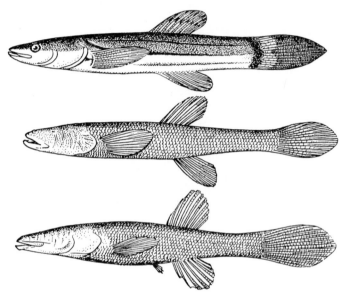

FIG. 26. Cave fishes. Top, *Chologaster*; middle, *Typhlichthys*; bottom, *Amblyopsis* (Cyprinodontiformes) (from Jordan, 1925).

with the brain is still present, but rods and cones are lacking. In *Amblyopsis* even the pupil is closed, and, finally, in *Troglichthys* the eye is very greatly reduced (Fig. 26). It is interesting that in the young *Troglichthys* the eyes are better developed than in the adults.

As a compensation for the degeneration of the visual organs in cave-dwelling fishes the lateral line organs are usually very well developed, particularly on the head, and so are the organs of touch such as the long whiskers in the cave-dwelling Pimelodid sheat-fishes of Brazil.

Cave-dwelling fishes are extremely variable. They include at present representatives of the Cypriniformes (*Aulopyge, Paraphoxinus, Chondrostoma,*

American sheat-fishes, etc.), Cyprinodontiformes (*Chologaster*, *Troglichthys*, *Amblyopsis*), several species of gobies, etc.

The light conditions in the water differ from those in the air not only in the intensity, but also in the depth of penetration of the various parts of the spectrum into the water. It is well known that the coefficient of absorption of light rays of different wavelengths by the water is extremely variable. Red light is the most strongly absorbed by water. At a depth of 1 m 25 % of the red light rays are absorbed, and only 3 % of the violet. However, even the violet light becomes indistinguishable at a depth of 100 m or more. Consequently, fishes can only feebly discern colours at great depths.

The visual spectrum to which fishes are sensitive is slightly different from that to which terrestrial vertebrates are sensitive. Differences occur among fishes, which are related to the nature of their habitat. Species which live in the inshore zone and near the surface of the water have a wider visual spectrum than those which live at great depths. The sea-scorpion, *Myoxocephalus scorpius* (L.), which lives in shallow water, is sensitive to light of wavelengths from 485 to 720 mμ, the starry ray (*Raja radiata* Donov.) which lives at great depths, from 460 to 620 mμ, the haddock (*Gadus aeglefinus* L.), from 480 to 620 mμ (Protassov and Golubtsov, 1960). It should be realized in this respect that the sensitivity to the longer-wave part of the spectrum is reduced first of all.

The fact that the majority of species of fishes can distinguish colours is indicated by a large number of observations. Only certain cartilaginous fishes (Chondrychthyes) and ganoids (Chondrostei) cannot distinguish colours. The remaining fishes can distinguish colours well, as has been indicated, particularly by many experiments using the conditioned reflex method. Thus, the gudgeon, *Gobio gobio* (L.), can be trained to take food from a cup of a certain colour.

It is well known that fishes can vary the colour and pattern of their skin in relation to the colour of the background on which they are placed. When a fish which has become adapted to a black background, and has altered its coloration correspondingly, is given a choice of a series of backgrounds of various colours, it will usually choose the background of the colour to which it had been adapted and the colour of which corresponds to that of its skin. Particularly sharp changes in the colour of the body on different grounds occur in the flounder. Not only the tone, but the pattern as well, depend on the character of the background against which the fish is placed. The mechanism responsible for these changes is not perfectly understood. It is only certain that the changes in the coloration result from stimulation of the eyes. By placing transparent coloured blinkers over the eyes of a fish, Sumner (1933) caused it to change its colour to that of the blinkers. A flounder with its body against a background of one colour, and its head against another, changes its body colouration to correspond with the background of its head (Fig. 27).

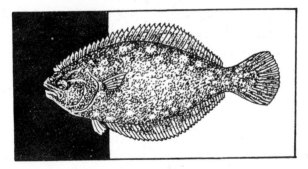

FIG. 27. The dependence of the body coloration of the flounder upon the colour of the background against which the fish's head rests (from Knipovich, 1939).

Naturally the coloration of a fish's body is most closely connected with the conditions of illumination.

It is usual to distinguish the following basic types of coloration among fishes, which are adaptations to particular habitats.

Pelagic coloration—bluish or greenish back and silvery sides and belly. This type of coloration occurs among fishes which inhabit the water column (herring, anchovy, bleak, etc.). The bluish back makes the fish less conspicuous from above, while the silvery sides and belly are difficult to see against a background of a mirror surface.

Vegetal coloration—brownish, greenish, or yellowish back and usually transverse stripes or blotches on the sides. This coloration is the property of fishes which inhabit weeds or coral reefs. These fishes can sometimes be very brightly coloured, particularly in the tropical zone.

In fresh water, fishes with vegetal coloration include the common perch and pike, and in the sea the sea-scorpion and coral-fish.

Demersal coloration—dark back and sides, sometimes with darker blotches and light belly (in the plaice the side nearest to the ground is light). In bottom fishes which live above stony river beds with transparent water, there are usually dark spots on the sides of the body, and these may often be distributed in the form of longitudinal stripes (the so-called stream coloration). Such a coloration is a property, for example, of young salmon in the river phase of life, young grayling, the common minnow, and other fishes. This coloration makes the fishes less conspicuous against the background of the stony ground in clear running water. Bottom fishes of stagnant waters do not usually have dark bright spots, or else they only have a washed-out appearance.

Shoaling colorations of fishes are particularly distinctive. This coloration facilitates the orientation of individuals to each other in a shoal (see page 88). It appears in the form of either one or several spots along the sides of the body or on the dorsal fin, or else as a dark stripe along the body. As examples we may mention the Amur minnow *Phoxinus lagowskii* Dyb., the young of the spiny bitterling, *Acanthorhodeus asmussi* (Dyb.), certain clupeoids, haddock, etc. (Fig. 28).

The coloration of deep-water fishes is very specific. Usually these fishes are either coloured dark, sometimes almost black, or else in red tones. This is explained by the fact that even at comparatively small depths red under water appears as black and is not easily discerned by predators.

A rather different type of coloration occurs among deep-water fishes, which possess light organs on their bodies. In these fishes the skin contains guanin, which gives the body a silvery appearance (*Argyropelecus*, etc.).

It is well known that the coloration of a fish varies during its individual development. It changes when the fish moves from one habitat to another in the process of development. Thus, for example, the coloration of the young salmon in the rivers is of the stream type, as it migrates to the sea it changes to the pelagic type, and when the fish returns to the river to spawn it once again assumes the stream character.

There may also be diurnal variations in the coloration; in certain representatives of the Characinidae (*Nannostomus*) the daytime coloration is that of the shoal—a black stripe along the body—while at night there appears a series of transverse stripes, i.e. a changeover to the vegetal coloration.

Nuptial coloration frequently occurs as a protective adaptation in fishes. It is lacking in fishes which spawn in deep water, and is usually feebly expressed in fishes which spawn at night time.

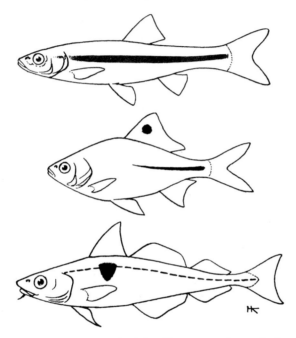

Fig. 28. Types of shoal-coloration in fishes (from top to bottom): the Amur minnow *Phoxinus lagowskii* Dyb.; the spiny bitterling (young) *Acanthorhodeus asmussi* (Dyb.); the haddock *Gadus aeglefinus* L.

The significance of light in the life of fishes is not only restricted to its visual importance. Illumination also has a considerable significance in the development of fishes. In many species the normal course of metabolism is disturbed if they are reared in light conditions which are abnormal for them (rearing those which are adapted to developing in the light, in the dark, and vice versa). This was graphically shown by Dissler (1953) who reared chum salmon in the light (see page 182).

Light also influences the course of the maturation of the gonads of fishes. Experiments on the American char *Salvelinus fontinalis* (Mitchill) showed that in experimental fishes exposed to intensified illumination ripening sets in earlier than in the controls kept at normal illumination. However, in fishes which live at high altitudes, as apparently in certain mammals under conditions of artificial illumination, the light, having stimulated an increased development of the gonads, may bring about a sharp reduction in their activity. Ancient species in high altitudes have evolved an intense coloration of the peritoneum, which protects the gonads from the excessive influence of the light.

The dynamics of the light intensity throughout the year determines the course of the maturity cycle in fishes to a considerable extent. The fact that tropical fishes reproduce throughout the year, while fishes of temperate latitudes reproduce only at particular times, is to a significant extent connected with the intensity of insolation.

Peculiar protective adaptations against the light are found in the larvae of many pelagic fishes. Thus, in the clupeoid larvae of the genera *Sprattus* and *Sardina* black pigment develops above the neural canal, which protects the nervous system and the underlying organs from the excessive influence of light. As the yolk-sac is absorbed, the pigment above the neural canal in the larvae disappears. It is interesting that in closely related species which have demersal spawn and larvae, there is no such pigment.

The solar radiation has a particularly serious influence upon the course of metabolism in fishes. Experiments carried out with *Gambusia affinis* Baird et Gir. showed that if this fish is deprived of light avitaminosis rapidly develops, and this leads first of all to the loss of the capacity to reproduce.

SOUND AND OTHER VIBRATIONS

Sound travels much more rapidly through water than through air. Also water absorbs some of the sound.

Fishes are sensitive to mechanical, infrasonic, sonic, and also, apparently, ultrasonic, vibrations. Water currents, mechanical and infrasonic vibrations of frequency from 5 to 25 hertz[1] are sensed by means of the lateral line organs, and those from 16 to 13,000 hertz by the auditory labyrinth, more strictly its lower part, the sacculus and lagena (the upper part serves as an organ of balance). In some species of fishes the vibrations of wavelength

[1]The hertz equals one vibration per second

from 18 to 30 hertz, i.e. those at the limit between infrasonic and sonic waves, are sensed by both the lateral line organs and the labyrinth. Differences in the character of the sensitivity to vibrations in various species of fishes are brought out in Table 3.

TABLE 3

Nature of Sound Vibrations to which Various Species of Fishes are Sensitive

Species of fish	Frequency in hertz	
	from	to
Phoxinus phoxinus (L.)	16	7000
Leuciscus idus (L.)	25	5524
Carassius auratus (L.)	25	3480
Nemachilus barbatulus (L.)	25	3480
Ameiurus nebulosus Le Sueur	25	1300
Anguilla anguilla (L.)	36	650
Lebistes reticulatus Peters	44	2068
Corvina nigra C. V.	36	1024
Diplodus annularis (L.)	36	1250
Gobius niger (L.)	44	800
Periophthalmus koelreiteri (Pallas)	44	651

A substantial role in the sensing of sound is played by the swim-bladder, which apparently acts as a resonator. Since sound travels both faster and further in water, so sensing it in water is also easier. Sound scarcely penetrates into water from the air. Penetration from water to air is slightly easier, because the pressure of the sound is much greater in water than in air.

Not only can fishes hear, but many of them can also produce sounds. The organs which produce the sounds are varied. In many fishes the swim-bladder serves for this purpose, and is often surrounded by a special musculature. The swim-bladder is used for sound production by the Sciaenidae, Labridae, and others. In the sheat-fish (Siluroidei) the sound is produced by the thoracic rays in combination with the bones of the pectoral girdle. In some fishes the sound is produced by the pharyngeal and buccal teeth (Tetrodontidae).

The character of the sounds produced by fishes is extremely variable: they are reminiscent of drum beats, croaking, snorting, whistles, growling. It is usual to divide the sounds produced by fishes into "biological," i.e. specially produced by the fishes and having some adaptive significance, and "mechanical," produced during movements, feeding, burrowing in the ground, and so on. The latter usually have no adaptive significance and may in fact even expose the fish.

There are more species of fishes which produce "biological" sounds in the tropics than in waters of higher latitudes. The adaptive significance of the sounds is variable. Sometimes the sounds are produced more frequently at the spawning times and apparently serve to attract the sexes to each other. This is true of the Sciaenidae, Siluroidei, and a number of other fishes. These sounds may be so strong that they enable fishermen to locate concentrations of spawning fishes. Sometimes it is not necessary to immerse the head in order to hear them.

In certain Sciaenidae the sounds also have some significance in feeding shoals. Thus, in the Bofors region (Atlantic coast of U.S.A.) the most intensive period of sound production falls in the dark part of the day from 21.00 to 02.00 hours and coincides with the period of most intensive feeding (Fish, 1954).

In some cases the production of sound has a frightening significance. While protecting their nests, the catfishes (Bagridae) apparently scare predators away by making scraping noises, which they do by means of the fins. The species *Opsanus tau* (L.), fam. Batrachoididae, also makes special noises when protecting its spawn.

The same species of fish may produce different sounds, varying not only the intensity but the frequency as well. Thus, *Caranx crysos* (Mitchill) produces two types of noise—a croaking and a rattle. These sounds differ in wavelength. The noises produced by males and females also differ in strength and frequency. This has been noted, for example, in the sea-perch, *Morone saxatilis* Walb. in the fam. Serranidae, the males of which produce the more intense sound with the greatest amplitude of frequencies (Fish, 1954). Young fishes also differ from older fishes in the character of the sounds they produce. The difference between the character of the sounds produced by males and females of the same species of fish is frequently connected with the difference in construction of the sound-producing apparatus. Thus, in the male haddock (*Gadus aeglefinus* L.), the "drum muscles" of the swim-bladder are considerably better developed than in the females. These muscles are particularly well-developed in the spawning season (Templeman and Hodder, 1958).

Some species react very strongly to sound. While some sounds frighten fishes away, other attract them. Salmon in rivers before the spawning season will frequently leap out of the water at the knock of an engine or a blow of an oar on board a boat. The Amur bighead *Hypophthalmichthys molitrix* (Val.) also leaps out of the water when frightened by noise. The reaction of fishes to noise may form the basis of a method of fishing. Thus, when fishing for grey mullet by the bass-matting method, the fishes, frightened by noise, leap out of the water and fall into a special mat placed on the surface, usually in the form of a semicircle and with edges turned up. Fishes which fall into such a mat cannot jump back into the water. In fishing for pelagic fishes by means of the purse-seine a special bell is sometimes lowered into the water at the mouth of the purse, and switching this on and off frightens the fishes away from the mouth of the net when it is being pursed up (Tarasov, 1956).

It is possible that the noises produced by fishes are used by them as echo-sounders. Location by means of sound production is apparently widespread among deep-water fishes.

It has been observed in the Atlantic in the Puerto Rico region that biological sounds, produced apparently by deep-water fishes, were repeated later as a weak echo from the sea-bed (Griffin, 1950).

ELECTRICAL CURRENTS, ELECTROMAGNETIC VIBRATIONS

In natural waters there are weak natural electrical currents, partly due to the earth's magnetism and partly to solar activity. Natural telluric currents have been established for the Barents and Black Seas, but they apparently exist in all the larger water-masses. These currents undoubtedly have a considerable biological significance, but their role in the aquatic biological processes has received only slight attention (Mironov, 1948).

Fishes react delicately to electrical currents. But many fishes are able not only to produce electrical discharges, but also to set up an electromagnetic field around their body. Such a current is developed around the head region of the lamprey *Petromyzon marinus* (L.).

Fishes are able to produce and detect electrical discharges by means of their tactile organs. The discharges may be of two types: strong ones, which serve for offence or defence (see page 99), or weak ones, which are used for signalling. In the sea lamprey (Cyclostomi) the production of a tension of 200–300 mv near the front of the head apparently serves for the detection (by the change in the field produced) of objects close to the head of the lamprey. It is possible that the "electric organs" described by Stensio in cephalaspids had a similar function (Kleerekoper and Sibakin, 1957). Many of the electric eels produce weak rhythmical discharges. The rate of discharge varied, among six species which were investigated, from 65 to 100 per second. The rate of discharging also varies according to the condition of the fish. Thus, in a quiescent state *Mormyrus kannume* Bul. produces one impulse per second; when disturbed it produces up to 30 per second. A swimming *Gymnarchus niloticus* Cuv. sends out impulses at the rate of 300 per second.

Mormyrus kannume Bul. senses electromagnetic vibrations by means of a series of receptors distributed at the base of the dorsal fin and ennervated by cranial nerves from the posterior end of the brain. In the Mormyridae the impulses are sent out by the electrical organ on the caudal stem (Wright, 1958).

From the character of the reaction of the fish to electrical current its effect can be divided into three phases.

In the first phase the fish, on entering the field of influence of the current, appears to be disturbed and attempts to swim away from it; in so doing, the fish tries to take up a position in which its body lies parallel to the direction of the current. The fact that the fish does react to an electromagnetic field has recently been confirmed by the observation that fishes have a reflex reaction to it (Kholodov, 1958). When the fish enters into the field of action of a current its respiratory rhythm speeds up. Fishes have a species specificity in their reaction to electrical current. Thus, the American sheat-fish *Ameiurus nebulosus* Le Sueur reacts more strongly than does the goldfish *Carassius auratus* (L.). Apparently fishes with well-developed skin receptors react most acutely to electrical currents (Bodrova and Kraiukhin, 1958). In any species, the larger individuals react earlier than the smaller ones.

The second phase of the action of a current upon the fish is marked by the fact that the fish turns its head to the anode and swims towards it, reacting very delicately to even negligible changes in the direction of the current. It is possible that the orientation of the fish to telluric currents in its migrations through the sea is related to this effect.

The third phase is the galvanic narcosis of the fish and its subsequent death. The mechanism of this action is connected with the formation of acetylcholin in the blood, which acts as a narcotic. This disrupts the respiration and heart action of the fish.

In electrical fishing the movements of fishes are directed towards the fishing gear, or else the current is used to produce a state of shock. Electrical currents are also used at electrical barrages to prevent the passage of fishes into the turbines, in irrigation canals, for guiding fishes into the mouths of fish-passes, and so on (Giulbadamov, 1958; Nusenbaum, 1958).

X-RAYS AND RADIOACTIVITY

X-rays exert an acutely adverse effect upon adult fishes, and also upon spawn, embryos, and larvae. As Samokhvalova (1935, 1938) showed, in experiments on *Lebistes reticulatus*, a dose of 60 units is lethal for fishes. Smaller doses acting on the gonads of *Lebistes reticulatus* cause a reduction in the brood-strength and a degeneration of the gonads. Irradiation of the young immature males leads to an incomplete development in them of the secondary sexual characteristics.

X-rays rapidly lose their power on penetrating into water. It has been shown with fishes that at a depth of 100 m the activity of X-rays is reduced by half (Folsom and Harley, 1957; Publ. 551).

Radioactive irradiation has a greater effect upon spawn and embryos of fish than on the adult animals (Golovinskaya and Romashov, 1960).

The development of the atomic industry and also the testing of atomic and hydrogen bombs have led to a significant increase in the radioactivity of the atmosphere and water and the accumulation of radioactive elements in aquatic organisms. The most important radioactive element which has a significance in the life of organisms is strontium 90 (Sr^{90}). Strontium enters the body of the fish chiefly through the intestines (mainly through the small intestine), and also through the gills and skin (Danil'chenko, 1958).

Most of the strontium (50–65 %) is concentrated in the bones, considerably less in the viscera (10–25 %) and gills (8–25 %) and only a little (2–8 %) in the muscles. But the strontium deposited mainly in the bones causes the appearance of radioactive yttrium, Y^{90}, in the muscles.

Fishes accumulate radioactivity, both directly from the water and from other organisms which form their food.

Young fishes accumulate radioactivity more rapidly than adults, because of their higher metabolic rate.

More active fishes (tunnies, Cybiidae, etc.) excrete radioactive strontium from their bodies more rapidly than less active ones (such as, for example, *Tilapia*), which is related to their higher metabolic rates (Boroughs, Chipman, Rice, Publ. 551, 1957). Fishes of the same species, occurring together, may vary by a factor of five times in the amount of radioactive strontium in the bones, as has been shown on the blue-gill sunfish, *Lepomis* (Krumholz, Goldberg, Boroughs, Publ. 551, 1957). The radioactivity of a fish may exceed that of the water of its environment. Thus it was established for *Tilapia* that if the fish were kept in radioactive water their radioactivity became equal to that of the water within 2 days, while in 2 months it was six times as great (Moiseev, 1958).

The accumulation of Sr^{90} in the bones of fishes causes the development of a disease which is related to the disruption of calcium metabolism. The use of radioactive fish as food by humans is controversial. Because the half-life period of strontium it is very long (nearly 20 years), and it is very firmly retained in the bone tissues, fishes remain contaminated for a long time. However, the fact that strontium concentrates mainly in the bones makes it possible to consume fish fillets, cleaned off the bone, after they have been kept for a comparatively short time in a refrigerator, because the yttrium concentrated in the flesh has a short half-life period.

Bottom Deposits and Particles Suspended in the Water

Fishes are less closely dependent upon the substrate for support than other groups of vertebrate animals. Many species of fish never touch the bottom at any time of their lives, but a significant and probably greater part of them have some sort of connection with the bottom. Most frequently the interrelation between the ground and the fish is not a direct one but comes about through the preference of the food species for a particular type of substrate. For example, the preference of the bream in the Aral Sea for grey muddy grounds at certain times of the year is completely explained by the high biomass of benthos on this ground (benthos is the food of the bream). But in certain cases there is a direct connection between the fish and the nature of the ground, due to the adaptation of the fish to a particular type of substrate. Thus, for example, burrowing fishes are always adapted in their distribution to soft grounds; fishes which are adapted to stony grounds often have a sucker to enable them to adhere to bottom objects, etc. Many fishes have evolved somewhat complicated adaptations for crawling over the ground. Certain fishes, which sometimes have to move over dry land, also have a number of features in the structure of their extremities and tail, which are adaptations to moving over firm substrates. Finally, the coloration of fishes, as we saw above, is to a considerable extent determined by the colour and pattern of the ground. Not only adult fishes, but demersal eggs (see later) and larvae are also very closely connected to the bottom, on which the eggs are laid or over which the larvae move.

There are comparatively few species of fish which lead a considerable part of their lives burrowing into the ground. Among the cyclostomes a considerable part of the time is spent in the ground by, for example, the ammocoetes larvae of the lamprey, which can remain below its surface for

several days. The European loach, *Cobitis taenia* (L.), also spends a considerable part of its time in the ground. Like the ammocoetes, it can also even
feed when buried in the ground. But the great majority of fishes only burrow
into the ground in times of danger or when the water-mass dries out.

Nearly all these fishes have a snake-like form and various other adaptations
to burrowing. Thus the Indian fish *Phisoodonophis boro* Ham., which makes
burrows in liquid mud, has tubular nostrils placed on the ventral side of the
head (Hora, 1934). This adaptation enables the fish to make its burrows
rapidly by means of its pointed head, while its nostrils do not become
clogged with mud. The burrowing process consists of undulating movements
of the body, similar to the swimming movements of the fish. Standing head
downwards at an angle to the ground, the fish, as it were, screws itself into it.

The other group of burrowing fishes have flattened bodies, like the flatfish
and skates. These fishes do not usually burrow very deeply. Their method of
burrowing is different—they throw soil over themselves and do not usually
cover themselves completely, leaving the head and part of the body uncovered.

Fishes which burrow into the ground are mainly the inhabitants of either
shallow internal waters or else of the inshore parts of the sea. This adaptation does not occur among deep-water fishes. Among freshwater fishes
adapted to burrowing into the ground, one may mention the African representative of the dipneusts, *Protopterus*, which enters into a form of
aestivation in the mud when the lake dries out. Among freshwater fishes of
temperate regions we may mention the loach, *Misgurnus fossilis* L., which
usually burrows when the water dries up, and the loach, *Cobitis taenia* (L.),
for which burrowing into the ground serves mainly as a form of protection.

The sand-eel, *Ammodytes*, is an example of a sea-fish which burrows,
usually to protect it from pursuit. Some gobies hide from danger in shallow
burrows which they make. Flatfishes and skates also burrow mainly in order
to make themselves less conspicuous.

Many fishes which do not themselves burrow into the ground are able to
penetrate into it quite deeply in search of food. All benthophagic fishes
burrow into the ground to some extent. Their method of burrowing is
usually by means of currents of water ejected from the buccal cavity, and
carrying small soil particles away to the side. Direct burrowing is rare among
benthophagic fishes.

Churning in the ground is frequently connected with the construction of a
nest. Thus, for example, nests in the form of a ditch, into which the eggs are
spawned, are constructed by certain representatives of the family Cichlidae,

in particular *Geophagus brasiliensis* (Quoy et Gaimard). Many fishes protect their spawn from predators by covering it with deposit, in which it develops. Spawn which develops in the deposit possesses a number of special features, and develops badly out of the deposit (see page 153). Among marine fishes which bury their spawn, we may mention *Leuresthes tenuis* (Ayres), and among freshwater species, the majority of the salmon family, in which both the spawn and the larvae in the early stages of development are buried among shingle, being thereby protected from their numerous enemies. Fishes which bury their spawn in the deposit usually have an extremely long period of incubation (from 10 to 100 days or more).

In many species the egg membrane, on reaching the water, becomes sticky, so that it adheres to the substrate.

Fishes which inhabit hard grounds, particularly in the inshore zone or else in fast currents, often have various organs for attachment to the substrate (see pages 74, 81) either in the form of a sucker which is a modification of the lower lip, thoracic or pelvic fins, or else in the form of thorns and hooks, which usually develop on the bony parts of the pectoral or pelvic girdles, and also on the gill covers.

As we have already stated, many species of fishes inhabit particular types of bottom, and in some cases different species of the same genus may inhabit different bottoms, For example, the bullhead *Icellus spatula* Gilb. et Burke occurs over stony-shingly grounds, while the closely related species *I. spiniger* Gilb. occurs over sand and mud. There may be various reasons for the adaptation of fishes to particular types of substrate. It might be a direct adaptation to the type of ground (soft for burrowing species, hard for attaching species, etc.) or else, since a particular type of ground is related to a particular type of water-mass, there is in many cases a connection between the distribution of the species and the type of ground through the medium of the hydrographical regime. And, finally, a third form of connection between the distribution of fishes and the bottom is through the distribution of the food organisms.

Many fishes which are adapted to crawling over the ground have undergone very profound changes in the structure of the extremities. The thoracic fin serves to support the fish on the ground, as in the larvae of *Polypterus* (Fig. 18, *3*), certain Labyrinth fishes, as for example the climbing perch *Anabas*, the gurnard *Trigla*, the mudskipper *Periophthalmus*, and many of the Lophiiformes, such as the angler-fish *Lophius piscatorius* L. and the stars, *Halientea*. In connection with the adaptation to moving over the ground the anterior extremities undergo very profound modifications (Fig. 29). The most substantial modifications are found in the Lophiiformes, in the anterior extremities of which there is a series of features which are analogous to those which occur in the tetrapods. In the majority of fishes the dermal skeleton is well developed, the primary skeleton being greatly reduced, while in the tetrapods the reverse occurs. *Lophius* occupies an intermediate

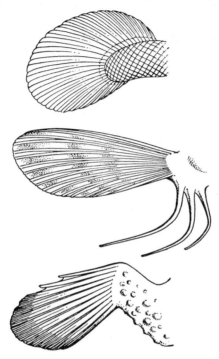

FIG. 29. Thoracic fins of fishes which walk along the bottom (from top to bottom): of a lungfish (Polypteri); a gurnard (Perciformes); *Ogcocephalus* (Lophiiformes).

position in respect of the structure of its extremities, having both its dermal and its primary skeletons equally well developed. The two *radialia* of *Lophius* are similar to the tetrapod *zeugopodium*. The musculature of the extremities in the tetrapods is divided into the proximal and distal, which is transferred to the edges, thus making pronation and supination possible. The same is found in *Lophius*. However the musculature of *Lophius* is homologus to that of other bony fishes, and any changes in the direction of the extremities of the tetrapods is the result of adaptation to a similar function. Using its extremities as legs, *Lophius* moves very easily over the bottom.

There are many common features in the structure of the pectoral fins in *Lophius* and *Polypterus*, although in the latter the musculature is transferred from the surface to the edges of the fins to a lesser extent than in *Lophius*. A similar type of change from a swimming organ to one for support is also found in the mudskipper, *Periophthalmus*. The mudskipper lives in mangrove swamps and spends quite a lot of its time on land. On the shore it chases after terrestrial insects, on which it feeds. This fish moves by leaping, which it does by means of the tail and the thoracic fins. The gurnards have a peculiar adaptation to crawling over the ground. The first three rays of the pectoral fins have become separated and acquired mobility. The gurnard moves over

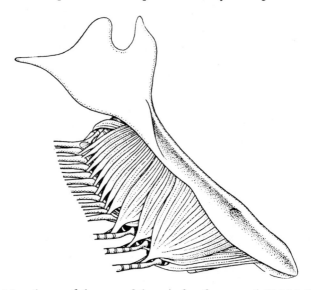

FIG. 30. Musculature of the rays of thoracic fin of a gurnard (*Trigla*). The enlarged muscles of the free rays are seen (from Belling, 1912).

the ground by means of these rays. They also serve as raptorial organs. There are also certain anatomical modifications in respect of the particular function of the first three fin rays; in particular, the muscles which produce the movement of the free rays are much better developed than in all the others (Fig. 30). The climbing perch *Anabas*, a representative of the labyrinthids, which moves over dry land, uses the thoracic fins for movement, and also sometimes the gill covers.

Not only the ground, but also the suspended solid particles, play a considerable role in the lives of fishes. The significance of the transparency of the water to fishes was noted above. In small internal water-masses and the coastal regions of the seas the transparency is mostly determined by the admixture of suspended mineral particles.

The suspension of particles in the water has the most various effects upon fishes. The greatest effect occurs when the water contains up to 4 % by volume of solid particles. Here the greatest effect is the mechanical influence of the mineral particles of various sizes—from a few microns to 2–3 cm in diameter—carried in the water. Fishes of turbid rivers have a number of adaptations, such as a great reduction in the size of the eyes. Small eyes are characteristic of such turbid-river species as the shovel-nose, various sheatfish, and *Nemachilus*. The reduction in the size of the eyes is explained by the need to reduce the unprotected surfaces, which could be damaged by the suspended particles carried by the current. The small size of the eyes of *Nemachilus* is also related to the fact that this bottom-dwelling fish orientates toward its food mainly by means of its tactile organs. In its development the eye becomes relatively reduced in size as the fish grows and its barbels appear and the fish changes over to bottom feeding (Lange, 1957).

The occurrence of large quantities of suspensions in the water would also hinder the respiration of fishes. Apparently in fishes which live in turbid waters the mucus secreted by the skin has the property of rapidly sedimenting the particles suspended in the water. This has been studied in greatest detail in the American lungfish, *Lepidosiren*, in which the coagulating properties of the mucus enables it to live in the thin mud of the Chaco. It has been established also for *Physoodonophis boro* Ham. that its mucus has a well-developed property of sedimenting suspensions. The addition of one or two drops of the mucus secreted by the skin of this fish to 500 ml of turbid water causes sedimentation in 20–30 seconds. With such a rapid rate of sedimentation, the fish is always surrounded, as it were, by an envelope of clear water, even in turbid waters. The mucus itself, when brought into contact with turbid water, changes its chemical reaction. It has been established that the pH of the mucus, on being brought into contact with water, falls sharply from 7·5 to 5·0. Naturally, the coagulating property of the mucus is important as a means of protecting the gills from being choked by the suspended particles. But in spite of the fact that fishes which live in turbid waters have a number of adaptations for protection against the action of suspended particles, the death of the fish may ensue if the concentration of the suspension should exceed a definite limit. In this case the death is due to suffocation as a result of the gills becoming clogged. Cases are known in which there has been a mass mortality of fishes during the period of the monsoon rains, when the turbidity of the currents increases by ten times. Such phenomena have been recorded from the mountainous regions of Afghanistan and India. Even fishes such as the Turkestan sheat-fish, *Glyptosternum reticulatum* McClel., which is well adapted to living in turbid waters, died under these conditions.

MOVEMENT OF THE WATER AND MODES OF MOVEMENT IN FISHES

Fishes are adapted to moving through both still and flowing water. Both progressive and fluctuating movements of the water play a significant role in the lives of fishes. Fishes are adapted to moving through the water by various means and at various speeds. The body shape, fin structure, and certain other features in the structure of the fish are connected with this.

Fishes may be divided into several types according to the body shape (Fig. 31) :

1. Torpediform—the best swimmers, inhabitants of the water column. This group includes the scombriids, mullet, dogfish, salmon, etc.

2. Arrow-shaped—close to the preceding, but the body is more elongated and the unpaired fins are moved further back. Good swimmers, inhabitants of the water-column: garpike, pike.

3. Flattened laterally—this type varies considerably. It is usually sub-divided into (a) bream-type, (b) moon-fish type, and (c) pleuronectiid type. The fishes which belong to this type also vary considerably in their modes of life—from inhabitants of the water column (moon-fish), to demersal (bream and pleuronectiids).

4. Snake-shaped—body much elongated, transverse section almost circular; usually inhabitants of weeds—eels, needlefish, etc.

5. Ribbon-shaped—body much elongated and flattened laterally. Poor swimmers: *Regalecus*, *Trachypterus*, etc.

6. Sphere-shaped—body almost spherical, caudal fin feebly developed: puffer-fish, certain lumpsuckers, etc.

7. Flattened—body flattened dorso-ventrally: various skates, etc.

Of course all these body types are interrelated by intermediate stages. Thus, the common loach, *Cobitis taenia* L., occupies an intermediate position between the snake- and ribbon-shaped types.

In the majority of fishes progressive movements are accomplished by means of bending the whole body as a wave, which passes along the body of the fish (Fig. 32). Other fishes move with a rigid body by means of vibrations of the fins—the anal in the case of the electric eel *Electrophorus electricus* (L.), or the dorsal as in the mudfish *Amia calva* (L.) Pleuronectiids swim by making

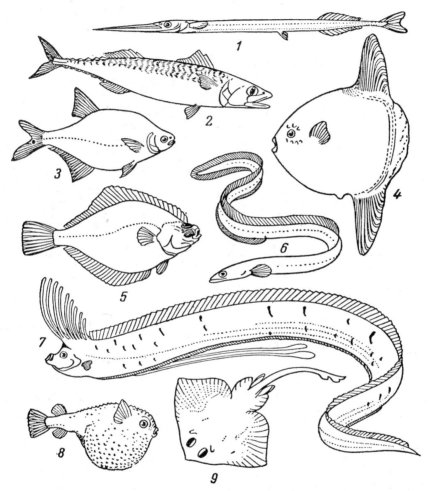

Fig. 31. Various types of body shape in fishes. 1, Arrow-shaped (garpike); 2, torpediform (mackerel); 3, laterally flattened, bream-type (common bream); 4, moon-fish type; 5, flatfish type (flounder); 6, snake-shaped (eel); 7, ribbon-shaped (king-herring); 8, spherical (globe-fish); 9, flattened (skate).

vibratory movements of both the dorsal and anal fins simultaneously. In the skate swimming is by means of vibratory movements of the greatly enlarged thoracic fins (Fig. 33).

The caudal fin mainly cancels the dragging movements of the end of the body and weakens the returning waves. It is customary to subdivide fishes as follows according to the mode of action of the tail: (1) *isocercal*, in which the dorsal and ventral blades are of equal size; this type of tail occurs in the

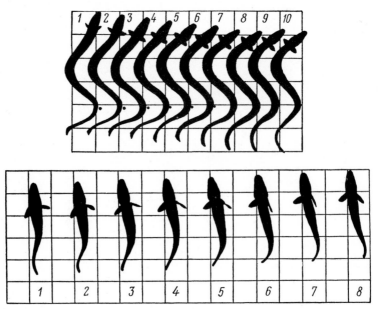

FIG. 32. Swimming movements. Top, the eel; bottom, the cod. A wave is seen to pass along the body of the fish (from Gray, 1933).

scombreids, tunnies, and many others; (2) *epicercal*, in which the upper blade is larger than the ventral; this type of tail facilitates upward movement; it is characteristic of sharks and sturgeons; (3) *hypocercal*, in which the lower

FIG. 33. The swimming movements of fishes by means of the anal fin (electric eel) and the thoracic fin (skate) (from Norman, 1958).

blade is better developed and facilitates downward movement; the hypocercal tail occurs in the flying fishes, breams, and certain others (Fig. 34).

The basic function of a rudder is fulfilled by the thoracic and pelvic fins. These also assist in turning the fish in a horizontal plane. The role of the unpaired fins (dorsal and anal), if these do not perform the function of forward movement, consists of assisting in upward and downward turning and only occasionally do they act as stabilizing keels (Vasnetsov, 1941).

The ability to bend the body is, of course, closely related to its structure. Fishes with the greater number of vertebrae can bend the body more than those with fewer vertebrae. The number of vertebrae in fishes varies from 16 in the moon-fish, to 400 in the strap-fish. Also fishes with small scales are able to bend the body further than fishes with large scales.

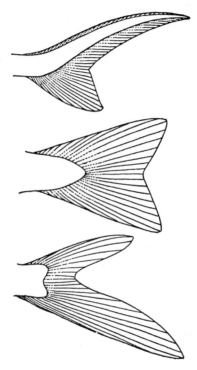

FIG. 34. Various types of tails of fishes (from top to bottom): epicercal, isocercal, hypocercal.

To overcome the resistance of the water the reduction of the drag of the body to a minimum is extremely important. This is obtained by means of the maximum smoothness of the surface and its lubrication with substances which reduce the drag. The skin of fishes usually has a large number of goblet-shaped glands, which secrete mucus to lubricate the surface of the body.

The best swimmers among fishes have a torpedo-shaped body. According to the data of A. N. Krylov, the swordfish *Xiphias gladius* L. can move at a velocity of up to 90 km/hr, i.e. up to 15 m/sec. The blue shark *Carcharinus glaucus* L. swims with a velocity of about 10 m/sec, the tunny *Thynnus tunnus* L. at 20 m/sec, the salmon *Salmo salar* L. at 5 m/sec. The actual velocity of a fish depends upon its size. For this reason, in order to compare velocities it is usual to employ a coefficient of velocity, which represents the ratio of the absolute velocity of the fish to the square root of its length ($v/\sqrt{L}$).

For very fast-swimming fishes (sharks, tunnies) the value of the coefficient is about 70. For fast-swimming fishes (salmon, mackerel) the coefficient is 30–60; moderately fast swimmers (herring, cod, grey mullet) 20–30; fairly slow (for example, bream) 10–20; slow (gobies, scorpaenids) 5–10; and very slow (moon-fish) less than 5.

Good swimmers in flowing water differ in some respects from good swimmers in still waters, in particular in the former the caudal stem is usually considerably higher and shorter than in the latter. As an example one may compare the shape of the caudal stem in the trout, which is adapted to living in water with fast-flowing current, and that of the mackerel, an inhabitant of slow-moving and still sea-waters.

Fishes which swim rapidly, overcoming rapids and rollers, become exhausted. They cannot swim for long periods without resting. At high activity the blood of fishes accumulates lactic acid, which disappears again when the fish rests. Sometimes fishes, for example, on traversing a fish-pass, become so exhausted that they die (Black, 1958, etc.). In this connection, when constructing fish-passes it is essential to provide sufficient places for fishes to rest in.

There are some types of fishes which have become adapted to a peculiar form of flight through the air. This property is best developed among the flying fishes—the Exocoetidae; actually, this is not true flight, but soaring like a glider. In these fishes the thoracic fins are very well developed and perform the same function as the wings of an aeroplane or a glider (Fig. 35). The basic locomotor, which gives the initial velocity in flight, is the tail-fin and particularly its lower blade. On jumping out of the water the flying fish continues for a time to slide along the water surface, leaving ring-shaped waves behind it, which move outward. As long as the body of the fish is in the air and only its tail is in the water, its velocity continues to increase, and it only starts to decrease when the body is completely free of the water surface. The flying fish can remain in the air for about 10 seconds, and in this time it flies more than 100 m.

The flight of the flying fishes has evolved as a protective adaptation, which enables the fish to leap away from its pursuing predators—tunnies, coryphaenids, the swordfish, etc.

Among Characinoid fishes there are representatives (the genera *Gastero-pelecus, Carnegiella, Thoracocharax*) which are capable of active, flapping flight. These small fishes, 9–10 cm in length, inhabit fresh waters in South America. They can leap out of the water and fly for 3–5 m by flapping the elongated pectoral fins.

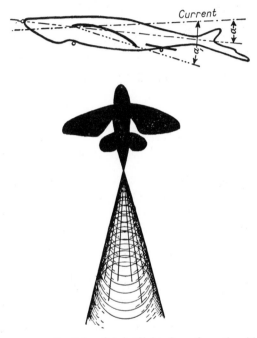

Fig. 35. The movement of a flying fish in flight. Seen from the side and above (from Shuleikin, 1953).

Although the pectoral fins are smaller in the flying Characinoids than in flying fishes of the family Exocoetidae, the pectoral muscles which cause the movement of the pectoral fins are much better developed. In the Characinoids they are adapted to flapping flight, and they are attached to the well-developed bones of the pectoral girdle, which bear some resemblance to the pectoral keel in birds. The pectoral fin muscles weigh up to 25 % of the body weight in the flying Characinoids, while in the closely related non-flying genus *Tetragonopterus* they are only 0·7 %.

As was stated above, life in flowing waters is related to the evolution in fishes of a number of special adaptations. Particularly fast currents occur in rivers, in which the water velocity sometimes almost equals that of a falling body. In rivers which take their source from mountains, the water velocity is a basic factor in determining the distribution of animals, including fishes, along the course of the stream-bed.

There are various courses of adaptation in different representatives of the ichthyofauna to life in the currents of rivers. The Indian investigator Hora (1930) divides all the fishes which inhabit fast currents into four groups, according to the nature of the habitat and the relevant adaptations:

1. Small species, living in stagnant places: in the flanks, under waterfalls, creeks, etc. Structurally these fishes are the least adapted to life in fast currents. Examples of this group are the bleak *Alburnoides bipunctatus* (Bloch.), *Danio rerio* (Ham.), etc.

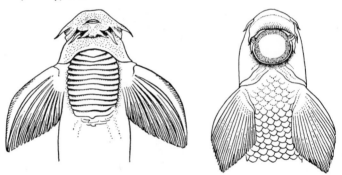

FIG. 36. Suckers in freshwater fishes for attachment to the substrate. Sheat-fish, *Glyptothorax* (left) and *Garra*, a cyprinoid (right) (from Hora, 1933, and Annandale, 1919).

2. Good swimmers with a strongly cylindrical body, which can easily stem fast currents. This group includes many river fishes—the salmon *Salmo salar* L., *Schizothorax*, species of barbels both Asian (*Barbus brachycephalus* Kessl., *Barbus tor* Ham.) and African (*Barbus radcliffi* Blgr.), and many others.

3. Small bottom fishes, which usually live under stones in currents swim from stone to stone. These fishes usually have a spindle-shaped, somewhat elongated shape. This group includes many loaches (*Nemachilus*), the gudgeon *Gobio*, etc.

4. Forms which possess special organs of attachment (suckers, hooks), by means of which they attach themselves to bottom objects (Fig. 36).

Usually the fishes belonging to this group have a dorsoventrally flattened body. The sucker occurs either on the lip (*Garra*) or between the thoracic fins (*Glyptothorax*), or else they are formed by the fusion of the pelvic fins. This group includes *Discognathichthys*, many species of the family Sisoridae, the distinctive tropical family Homalopteridae, etc.

As the current slows down on passing from the upper to the lower reaches of a river, fishes start to appear which are not adapted to stemming very fast currents. In fishes which inhabit waters with slow currents, the body is more flattened, and they are not such good swimmers as the inhabitants of fast streams (Fig. 37). The gradual changes in the body form of fishes from

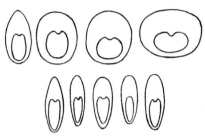

FIG. 37. Transverse sections of various fishes from fast-flowing waters (upper row) and slow-flowing or stagnant waters (lower row). Left to right above: trout, minnow, loach, bullhead; below: bream, crucian carp, carp, roach, rudd. Fishes of the same depth of body were used (from Hesse, 1924).

the upper to the lower reaches of a river, in connection with the gradual changes in the velocity of the current, are of a regular character. In those parts of a river in which the current slows down the fishes are unadapted to life in fast currents; in places with very fast currents only species which are adapted to stemming currents can remain; the typical inhabitant of a fast current are rheophiles. Van-dem-Borne divides the rivers of Western Europe into separate sections according to the distribution of fishes along the stream:

1. Trout section—the mountain part of a stream with fast currents and stony bottom is characterized by fishes with cylindrical bodies (trout, loach, minnow).

2. Barbel section—moderate currents, but still with a considerable velocity; the appearance of species with a taller body, as, for example, the barbel, dace, etc.

3. Bream section—slow currents, bottom partly of silt, partly of sand, with waterweeds in the stream-bed, and a predominance of fishes with laterally flattened bodies, such as the bream, roach, rudd, etc.

Of course, it is extremely difficult to draw the distinction between these separate ecological sections, and the replacement of one type of fishes by another usually takes place extremely gradually, but in general the sections defined by Borne can be distinguished fairly clearly in the majority of rivers with a mountain source, and the principle which he put forward for the rivers of Europe also holds for those of America, Asia, and Africa.

Forms belonging to the same species, but living in flowing and stagnant waters, differ in their adaptation to currents. Thus, for example, the grayling *Thymallus arcticus* (Pall.) in Baikal has a taller body and longer caudal peduncle than representatives of the same species from Angara, which are more narrow-bodied and have shorter tails, these being the properties of a good swimmer. The weaker young individuals of river fishes (barbels, loach) usually have a more narrow, cylindrical body, and shorter caudal stem than the adults. Apart from this, in mountain streams the larger and stronger adult individuals usually live higher up in the current than the young ones. As one moves upstream, the average size of the individuals of the same species, as for example, the comb-tailed and Tibetan loaches, increases, and the largest individuals are found close to the upper limits of the distribution of the species (Turdakov, 1939).

River currents can also affect the fish's organism not only mechanically, but indirectly, through the medium of other factors. Usually, water masses with fast currents are characterized by supersaturation with oxygen. For this reason rheophilic fishes are also at the same time oxyphilic, i.e. they require plenty of oxygen, and conversely, fishes which inhabit slowly flowing or stagnant waters are usually adapted to a different oxygen regime and can withstand an oxygen deficit better.

Currents that affect the character of the stream bed, and thereby the character of the bottom fauna, naturally exert an influence upon the nutrition of fishes. Thus, in the upper reaches of rivers, where the bed usually contains fixed boulders, there can usually develop a rich periphyton, which serves as the basic food of many fishes in this section of the river. In connection with this, the fishes of the upper reaches are usually characterized by very long intestinal tracts, adapted to the digestion of plant food, and also by the development of a horny cover on the lower lip. Further downstream the bed becomes finer and becomes mobile under the influence of the current. Naturally, it is impossible for a rich bottom fauna to develop on a shifting bed, and the fishes here feed upon other fishes or else upon food which falls into the river from the shore. As the current slows down the bed becomes silted up, the bottom fauna develops, and there again appear in the fauna fishes which feed on the vegetation and possess long intestinal tracts.

The currents in rivers do not only affect the structural organization of the fishes. Of primary significance are the changes in the reproductive behaviour of river fishes. Many of the inhabitants of fast-flowing rivers possess adhesive spawn. Several species cover the spawn by burying it in the sand. The American sheat-fishes of the genus *Plecostomus* spawn in special caverns; other genera (see section on reproduction) incubate their spawn on their ventral sides. The structure of the external sex organs also changes. In certain species the sperm is less mobile, etc.

Thus we see that the forms of adaptation to currents in rivers are extremely varied among fishes. In certain cases the unexpected transportation of large masses of water, as for instance, when the overflow of a mountain lake bursts, can lead to the mass mortality of the ichthyofauna, as happened for example in Chitral (India) in 1929. The speed of the current sometimes acts as an isolating factor, leading to the dissociation of the faunas of separate water-masses and contributing to their isolation. Thus, for example, the thresholds and waterfalls between the large lakes of eastern Africa do not form an obstacle to the large, strong fishes, but they are impassable for small fishes and lead to the isolation of the faunas of those parts of the water basins which are divided in this way.

Naturally, the most complex and peculiar adaptations to life in fast currents have evolved among fishes inhabiting mountain streams, in which the speed of movement of the water attains the highest values.

According to present-day opinions, the faunas of mountain rivers in temperate and high latitudes of the northern hemisphere are relicts of the Ice Age. (We use the term "relict" to include those animals and plants whose distribution is isolated either in time or in space from the basic areas of distribution of a given faunistic or floristic complex.) The faunas of mountain streams in tropical and, parts of, temperate latitudes did not have a glacial origin, but evolved as the result of a gradual migration of animals to the upland water-masses from the plains.

For a number of groups the course of adaptation to life in mountain currents can be followed quite clearly and established (Fig. 38).

As in rivers, so also in stagnant waters the currents exert a considerable effect upon the lives of fishes. But while in rivers the main adaptation has evolved in response to the direct mechanical influence of the moving current, in seas and lakes the currents have a more indirect effect, through the changes which they bring about in the distribution of other environmental factors (temperature, salinity, etc.). Naturally, adaptations to the direct mechanical influence of water movements have also evolved among fishes in stagnant water-masses. The mechanical influence of currents is expressed in the first place in the transport of fishes, their larvae, and spawn sometimes over considerable distances. Thus, for example, the larvae of the herring (*Clupea harengus* L.), which hatch on the coast of northern Norway, are carried far to

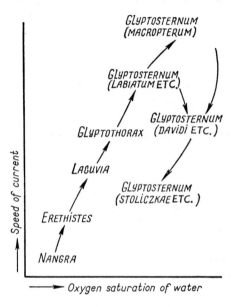

FIG. 38. A suggested scheme of adaptation of sheat-fishes of the fam. Sisoridae to the two basic factors in mountain streams. The diagram shows that a number of species became less rheophil (from Hora, 1930).

the north-east by the current. The larvae cover the distance between the Lofotens, where they are spawned, to the Kola meridian in about three months. The pelagic eggs of many fishes are similiarly carried over considerable distances. Thus, for example, the eggs of the plaice spawned on the French coast are transported to the Danish coast where the larvae hatch. The transport of the larvae of the eel from the spawning area to the mouths of European rivers depends over the greater part of its course on the Gulf Stream, by which the larvae are carried almost passively to the European coast. Adult fishes, particularly poor swimmers, are also frequently transported over considerable distances. Thus, there are several records of the transport of the moon-fish to the Vladivostock region by warm currents flowing from south to north.

The minimal current speed to which fishes react is apparently about 2–10 cm/sec. The anchovy, *Engraulis encrasicholus* L., begins to react to currents at a speed of 5 cm/sec, but this threshold reaction has not been established for many species.

The cells of the lateral line are the organs which sense water movements. In their simplest form, in the sharks, this consists of a row of sensory cells distributed along the epidermis. In the process of evolution (as, for example, in the chimaeriids) these cells become immersed in a canal, which gradually (in bony fishes) closes over and is connected with the environment only by means of tubes, which are covered in scales and form the lateral line, which varies in its state of evolution among different species of fish. The lateral line is ennervated by the facial and vagus nerves. In clupeoids the lateral line occurs only on the head; in certain other species the lateral line is incomplete (as, for example, in certain minnows). By means of the lateral line organs the fish can sense movements and vibrations in the water. In many marine fishes the lateral line is the main organ for sensing vibratory movements of the water, while in river fishes it enables them to orientate to the currents (Dissler, 1956, 1960).

The indirect influence of currents on fishes are far greater than the direct ones, mainly through changes in the environment. Cold currents, flowing from the north to the south, enable arctic forms to penetrate well into the temperate regions. Thus, for example, the cold Labrador current displaces the distribution of warm-water species far to the south, whereas on the European coast these species are displaced far to the north by the warm Gulf Stream. In the Barents Sea the distribution of several high arctic species of the family Zoarcidae is adapted to strips of cold water distributed between streams of warm currents. In the branches of this current there occur warm-water species, such as scombreids and others.

Currents can also radically alter the chemical regime of the water-mass, affecting in particular the salinity, by carrying in either more saline or fresh water. Thus, the Gulf Stream carries more saline water into the Barents Sea, and various species are adapted to living in it. The whitefish and Siberian sturgeons are adapted to a considerable extent in their distribution to the currents which originate in the fresh waters transported by the Siberian rivers. In the regions of confluence of cold and warm waters there usually develops a zone of high productivity, because there usually occurs in such regions a high mortality of invertebrates and planktonic plants, which gives an enormous production of organic matter, thus enabling a few eurythermal organisms to develop in massive quantities. Examples of such a confluence of cold and warm waters are fairly common, as, for example, near the western coast of South America near Chile, on the Newfoundland Banks, etc.

Vertical currents also play a significant role in the lives of fishes. The direct mechanical effects can only rarely be observed. Usually the vertical circulation causes the mixing of the lower and upper water layers, and thereby the evening out of temperature differences, salinity, and other factors, which in turn creates favourable conditions for the vertical migrations of fishes. Thus, for example, in the Aral Sea far offshore in spring and autumn the roach rises to the surface for food by night, and sinks to the bottom by day. In summer, however, when there develops a sharply expressed stratification, the roach always keeps to the bottom layers.

Vibratory movements of the water also play a considerable role in the lives of fishes. The main form of vibratory movement of the water, having the greatest effect, is waves. These have various types of influence upon fishes, both direct mechanical ones and indirect ones in relation to the evolution of various adaptations. When the sea is strongly disturbed, pelagic fishes go deeper down to regions where they cannot sense the water movements. Waves have a particularly great effect upon fishes in inshore regions, where the force of the blow of a wave attains to $1\frac{1}{2}$ tons per square metre. Fishes which live in the inshore zone are characterized by a number of adaptations which protect them and their spawn from the action of the surf. The majority of inshore fishes are adapted to remaining in one place during heavy surf; otherwise they would be injured by stones. Thus, for example, typical inhabitants of inshore waters, like various gobies, have the pelvic fins transformed into suckers, by means of which they attach themselves to stones; a somewhat different type of sucker occurs in the lumpsuckers, Cyclopteridae (Fig. 39).

Besides their direct, mechanical effect on fishes, waves also exert upon them a considerable indirect influence, allowing the mixing of waters and the sinking of the thermocline to greater depths. Thus, for example, in the last pre-war years, in relation to the lowering of the level of the Caspian Sea, as the result of an increase in the zone of mixing the upper limit of the bottom layer, in which biogenic elements accumulate, was also lowered. At the same time, part of the biogenic elements entered into the cycle of organic matter in the water-mass, bringing about an increase in the amount of plankton, and also, therefore, in the food supply of the Caspian planktophagic fishes.

Another type of fluctuating movements of the sea-water, which has a considerable significance for the lives of fishes, is tidal movements, which are of considerable amplitudes in certain parts of the sea. Thus, on the coasts of North America and the northern part of the Okhotsk Sea the difference between the tidal levels is more than 15 m. Naturally, the fishes which live in the tidal zone, which periodically dries out, or in the tidal parts of the sea, over which enormous masses of water are transported four times daily, possess special adaptations to life in small pools, such as are left when the tide

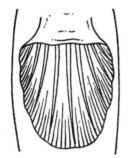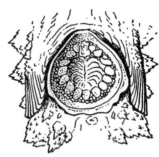

Fig. 39. Modification into a sucker of the pelvic fin of sea fishes. Left, the goby *Neogobius*; right, the spiny lumpsucker *Eumicrotremus* (from Berg, 1949 and Perminov, 1936).

recedes. All the inhabitants of the tidal zone (the littoral) have dorsoventrally flattened, snakelike, or cylindrical-shaped bodies. High-bodied fishes, apart from the flatfishes which lie on the bottom, are not found on the littoral. Thus, on the Murman coast the viviparous blenny, *Zoarces viviparus* L., and the gunnel, *Pholis gunnelus* L., species which have elongated bodies, and also the large-headed millers thumb, *Myoxocephalus scorpius* L., usually remain on the littoral.

Peculiar changes occur in the reproductive biology of tidal zone fishes. Many of them, particularly the millers thumb, leave the littoral zone at the time of spawning. Certain species have evolved the viviparous habit, as for example the viviparous blenny, the spawn of which undergoes an incubating period inside the maternal body. The lumpsucker usually spawns below the tidal level, but in those cases when the spawn does dry out it keeps pouring water over it, and lashing it with its tail. The most curious adaptation to reproduction in the tidal zone occurs in the American fish *Leuresthes tenuis*

(Ayres), which spawns on the spring tides in that part of the tidal zone which is not covered by the neap tides, so that the eggs develop out of the water in a humid atmosphere. The incubation period lasts until the next spring tide, when the larvae hatch and enter into the water. Similar adaptations to reproduction in the littoral are also found in certain members of the Galaxiiformes. Tidal currents, like the vertical circulation, also have an indirect effect upon fishes, by mixing the bottom deposits and thereby causing a better assimilation of their organic content, and thereby an increase in the productivity.

Such types of water movements as waterspouts have a rather unique effect upon fishes. Seizing up enormous masses of water from the sea or from inland waters, spouts transport them together with all the animals in them, including fishes, over considerable distances. In India during the monsoons, there frequently occur rains of fishes, when live fishes fall to the ground together with the rain-waters. Sometimes these rains cover rather large areas. Similar rains of fishes occur in the most varied parts of the earth; they have been reported from Norway, Spain, India, and a number of other places. The biological significance of rains of fishes lies primarily in the distribution of fishes, by enabling them to overcome obstacles which are normally impassable to fishes.

Thus, it can be seen that the types of effects of water movements upon fishes are extremely variable and impress an indelible imprint upon the organism of the fish in the form of specific adaptations, which enable the fish to exist under various conditions.

Biotic Inter-relationships Among Fishes

The biotic connections among fishes are also extremely variable. The fundamental forms of biotic connections, both interspecific and intraspecific, occur in relation to feeding. This is the relation of the predator and its prey, food and the consumer, parasite and host; competitive inter-relationships, caused by feeding on the same type of food (on the one hand, cooperation in searching for food among shoaling species and, on the other, the consumption of the same type of food and thereby when this is scarce the impoverishment of the feeding conditions of other individuals of the same species).

The type of relationships which develop in respect to feeding also includes symbiotic relationships, and many intraspecific groupings, such as shoals and colonies, particularly nesting ones—they originate for the purpose of simultaneous protection from enemies. As adaptations for protection against enemies, there are the different forms of adaptive colorations.

One of the most important forms of biotic connections is the formation of shoals. We have already remarked upon the protective and nutritional (searching) significance of the shoal. But it may also be an adaptation to the search for migration routes, and for wintering grounds.

Adaptation to the biotic environment originates in the process of evolution, in which there occurs a mutual adaptation of predator and prey, parasite and host, etc. The predator adapts itself to feeding upon one particular type of prey, which in its turn evolves an adaptation to protect itself from complete extermination by the predator. The inter-relationships between the parasite and the host are of two forms; they may be based on either the survival or the extermination of the host. In the first case the parasite species lives on its host without killing it, in fact it is concerned in the flourishing of the host species. In this case the parasite consumes the host's fluids or its food only to such an extent that it does no substantial harm to the host. Such an inter-relationship develops, for example, between intestinal parasites and their hosts, which are predatory fishes. In the optimal conditions, when the host does not become exhausted, these parasites do not cause them any substantial harm. They may cause the death of individual members of a population only if some other inter-relationships between the hosts and the environment is disrupted. It is another matter when the parasite has become adapted to exist by killing its host, as for example, the intermediate stage of ligulids which live in fishes. In this case the parasite species weakens the body of its host, making it more vulnerable to predators, and thereby improving its own chances of further development.

In parasitism based on the survival of the host, the infection may affect all the members of a population. In parasitism which kills the host, only a proportion of the population can be infected by the parasite, because if the infection exceeded a certain fraction and the reproduction of the host species population were to be disrupted, then it would disappear more or less quickly, and the parasite species population would, therefore, also disappear.

Finally, a complex system of intraspecific adaptations has evolved to facilitate the existence and reproduction of the population and to attain its maximal abundance under given conditions.

Both interspecific and intraspecific biotic relationships, as already stated, are mutual and in the closest possible way related to the abiotic environment.

For this reason, in dealing with them separately when considering particular problems, it should be borne in mind that biotic relationships, like abiotic ones, do not occur in isolation in nature; they are inseparably interdependent.

Intraspecific Relationships Among Fishes

The character of intraspecific relationships among fishes, as in other animals, develops during evolution. Intraspecific relationships are directed toward favouring the existence of the species under the conditions in which it originated and lives. The types and adaptive significance of intraspecific connections are extremely varied. They include, primarily, various forms of single-species groupings among fishes: shoals, elementary populations, schools, colonies, etc.

The *shoal* is a more or less prolonged grouping of mutually orientated fishes, of closely similar biological condition and age, united by similar behaviour.

The *school* is a smaller grouping within the limits of a shoal. In a school the fishes are usually within the range of interaction of their sensory organs at a particular time of day.

Elementary populations are usually of one age, frequently a life grouping of fishes in the same biological condition, and with the same rhythm of biological processes. According to N. Lebedev (1946) elementary populations usually originate on the spawning grounds and last for a long time, changing only through the dissemination of some of their individuals or by combining with individuals having the same biological rhythm and in a similar biological condition from other elementary populations.

The *race* is a single-species, self-reproducing group of fishes of various ages, inhabiting a definite region and associated with definite spawning, feeding, and wintering grounds. Each race is characterized by definite morpho-ecological features, which differentiates it from other races of the same species. Examples of distinct races are the east Sirdarian bream (Fig. 40) and the groups of herring of south-east Alaska (Fig. 41).

The *cluster* is a temporary union of a few shoals or elementary populations of fishes, due to various causes.

It is customary to distinguish:

1. *Spawning clusters*, which originate for the purpose of reproduction and consist almost exclusively of mature individuals. Young individuals get into them only accidentally. An example is the spawning clusters of cod at the Lofoten Islands or of the roach in the Volga delta, etc.

2. *Migrating clusters*, which form along the migration routes of fishes. It should be borne in mind that this type of cluster very often changes to another (for example, into a spawning one). An example is the clusters of salmon, rising to the spawning grounds up the rivers of the Far East, or of the anchovy, which pass through the Kerchensk Straits to winter in the Black Sea.

3. *Feeding clusters*, which develop on the feeding grounds and are due primarily to the concentration of food organisms. This type of cluster is more variable in its composition than the spawning or migrating ones, which usually comprise one species with only a very small admixture of others,

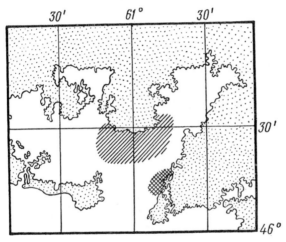

Fig. 40. Feeding grounds (single hatching) and spawning grounds (double hatching) of the east Sirdarian race of bream.

mainly predators feeding on either the shoaling species or their spawn. In addition, the first two types of clusters usually comprise specific age compositions—the spawning ones always consist of mature individuals, migrating ones either of adults or of young fish; mixed clusters of migrant fishes are comparatively rare. But feeding clusters can frequently consist of fishes of different species and ages (adult and young), although usually fishes of the same ages feed together, adults and young separately, not to mention the larvae.

4. *Wintering clusters*, which originate in the wintering grounds of fishes, are very clearly expressed in the Caspian Sea, in the mouths of the Volga, and in deep places in the Volga and Ural, in which enormous numbers

of various species of fishes gather for the winter. As diving work has shown, even when the fishes are gathered together in pits they still maintain a strict specific identity.

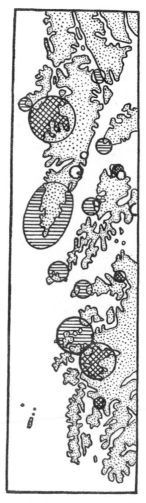

Fig. 41. Feeding grounds (horizontal hatching) and spawning grounds (cross-hatching) of the various races of Pacific herring *Clupea harengus pallasi* Val. near south-eastern Alaska (from Rounsefell and Dahlgren, 1935).

The *colony* is temporary, usually consisting of individuals of one sex, a protective grouping of fishes, which originates at the spawning grounds in order to protect the offspring from predators. Examples of the nesting colonies are the clusters of male mudfish (*Amia calva* L.) on the nests, and also the male catfish (*Pseudobagrus fulvidraco* Rich.), or the armoured American sheat-fish (fam. Loricariidae) on the burrows in which the spawn is laid.

As stated above, the shoal has a variable adaptive significance, including protection against predators, searching for food or migration courses, and finally, in wintering. Shoal-formation throughout the life cycle is by no means characteristic of all species of fishes. A shoaling mode of life is led throughout their life by small pelagic fishes, which feed on plankton (herring,

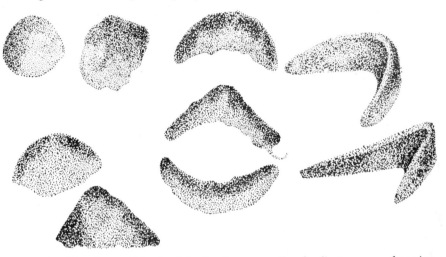

Fig. 42. The shapes of shoals of the Far Eastern sardine *Sardinops sagax melanosticta* (Schl.) (from Kaganovsky, 1939).

anchovy, etc.). In many species of fishes, shoaling behaviour appears only in the early stages of development, usually up to the attainment of maturity. In the adult state many fishes, such as the cyprinoids, *Aspius aspius* (L.), *Elopichthys bambusa* (Rich.), and many predatory fishes of other families, etc., only form temporary clusters.

The fish shoal has a definite structure, size and shape, which are connected with the provision of favourable hydrodynamic conditions for movement and orientation. The shapes of moving and stationary shoals differ in the same species of fish (Fig. 42). The moving fish develops around its body a definite field of force. Because of this, fishes moving in a shoal are attracted to each other in a definite manner (Fig. 43). The shoal is usually formed of fishes having similar size and biological condition. In shoals of fishes, in contrast to many mammals and birds, there is apparently no permanent leader, and they alternately orientate toward various members of the shoal Fishes orientate in shoals primarily by means of their visual organs (see later) and lateral lines.

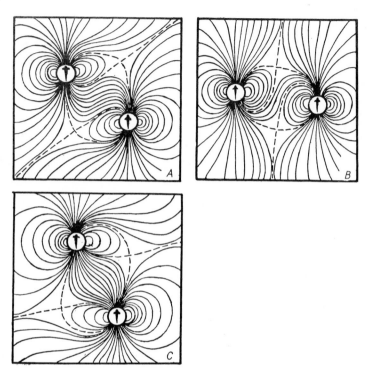

FIG. 43. Fields of force surrounding moving fishes. A, The fishes are mutually attracted; B, the fishes have no influence upon each other; C, the fishes repel each other (from Shuleikin, 1953).

A number of structural features, in particular the coloration (see above), are related to shoal-formation. The shoaling coloration enables the fishes to orientate toward each other. In species in which shoal-formation is a property of the larvae and fry only, the corresponding shoaling coloration may also only occur in the larvae. Thus, for example, in the young of *Acanthorhodeus asmussi* (Dyb.), there is a brilliant black spot on the dorsal fin, which disappears after the fish has attained a length of 5 cm and changed over to a solitary mode of life (Fig. 28). Sometimes the shoaling coloration develops at a particular period of the annual cycle. Thus the female chum salmon frequently develops in the spawning period a dark longitudinal stripe along the body, which apparently facilitates the orientation of the male toward them during spawning (Nikolsky, 1955).

The shoal usually includes only a single species of fishes, but cases are known in which individuals of one species are constantly included in shoals formed by another. Thus, according to Spanovsky, fry reared from solitary eggs of *Chilogobio czerskii* Berg have a dark longitudinal stripe along the body and up to a certain age they live in the shoals of other species of fry, such as the Amur minnow *Phoxinus lagowskii* Dyb., *Pseudorasbora parva* Schl., etc., which have a similar shoaling coloration.

The protective significance of the shoal cannot be doubted. As Radakov (1958) showed, single fish are more rapidly consumed by predators than fishes in shoals. In aquaria, single young coalfish were eaten by cod in approximately 26 seconds, but in shoals on the average in 2 minutes 15 seconds, although the concentration of the prey was, of course, much higher than when feeding upon single individuals.

The shapes of protective shoals vary. Fishes can appreciate danger (predators and nets) at greater distances in shoals and, therefore, can escape it more easily. This was observed, particularly, in the example of the pike searching for shoals and for single minnows. However, the shoal itself becomes noticeable to the predator at a greater distance compared to single individuals. When attacked by predators the shoaling fishes usually disperse, which disorientates the predator. The signal for this, apparently, is the sensing by them of the body fluids of the fishes captured by the predators. If the juice of a crushed specimen is dropped into a shoal of young roach, or a squashed specimen placed among them, the fishes, which were previously keeping together, rapidly disperse (Grbachek, 1953; Borisov, 1955).

Fishes of different ages react to the same danger signal differently. Larger fishes, as shown by Milanovsky and Rekubratsky, on the appearance of danger (for example, a shadow on the water), first of all quit the feeding clusters and hide in refuges. Small individuals in feeding clusters only react slightly to danger.

Since shoaling fishes mainly sense the presence of predators visually, the shoal cannot have any protective significance against predators which feed at night. In this connection many fishes which form shoals by day disperse by night into small schools or else remain solitary, as for example, the Caspian sardelle *Clupeonella delicatula caspia* Svetov., the oceanic herring *Clupea harengus* L., the anchovy *Engraulis encrasicholus* (L.), etc.

Sometimes the shoal has a direct protective significance against predators. Thus, the Black Sea anchovy on the approach of predators, such
as the horse-mackerel *Trachurus trachurus* (L.), aggregates into dense clusters
and sometimes starts to move around in a circle. Until the horse-mackerel
has managed to "break up" the cluster of anchovies, it is often unable to
seize even a single individual. In its own turn, when attacked by the pelamid,
Pelamys sarda (L.), the horse-mackerel aggregates into dense clusters, out of
which the pelamid can only sieze an individual with difficulty. The rate of
feeding of the pelamids increases sharply when the shoal of horse-mackerel
disperses (Tihonov and Paraketsov, 1955).

The shoal evades fishing gear better than do single fishes. When fishing
on shoals of fish, the catch usually increases significantly if the entire shoal
can be netted, because if only part is caught a larger number of fish manages
to escape from the fishing gear. For this reason, it is very important that the
shoaling behaviour of fishes should be studied in order to raise the fishing
efficiency. The basic factors to be taken into account in raising the efficiency
of fishing gear are as follows: (1) increasing the size of the gear to include
the whole shoal; (2) speeding up the detection; (3) disorientation of the
fishes at the moment of capture; (4) invisibility of the fishing gear (Radakov,
1956).

The adaptive nutritional significance of the shoal is most strongly expressed
in pelagic shoaling fishes, which feed upon zooplankton. In a shoal the fish
locates food organisms more rapidly and makes contact with them more
easily, thanks to which they feed more rapidly than when solitary (Welty,
1934; Nikolsky and Kukushkin, 1943). Young bream, according to the data
of Vorobiev (1937), feed more intensively in shoals than singly, but the
converse holds for the adults. Fishes in feeding shoals, as those in the larger
groups of elementary populations, frequently have the same diurnal feeding
rhythms, which causes them to start and finish their feeding together and,
thereby, to preserve the shoal as a complete unit (Novikova, 1956). Naturally,
this type of adaptation has its disadvantages, because the shoal of fishes will
consume the food organisms more rapidly than single fishes would.

The shoal also has an adaptive significance in migrations. Even fishes
which usually lead a solitary life form shoals when migrating. As N. Lebedev
(1946) has shown for the anchovy, a shoal of fishes locates its migration route
more rapidly, discovering particular orientations more easily.

The number of individuals in a shoal also has adaptive significance. The
size of a feeding shoal is to a great extent related to the pattern of distribution

and concentration of the food organisms. Thus, in benthophagic fishes such as the Caspian roach, *Rutilus rutilus caspicus* Jak., or the haddock, *Gadus aeglefinus* L., the larger the feeding ground the larger the shoal of feeding fishes. There is no doubt that the number of individuals in migrating and wintering shoals also has an adaptive significance. But this problem has hardly been investigated.

The nature of intraspecific relationships among fishes is extremely variable. Fishes also react upon each other through changes in the abiotic conditions. It is well known that many species of fishes cause currents of water by movements of their fins when protecting their spawn (pike-perch, gobies, etc). When protecting its spawn the male of the American representative of the dipneusts (*Lepidosiren paradoxa* Fitz.) (Cunningham and Reid, 1932) develops thread-like outgrowths on the pelvic fins, which secrete oxygen from the blood into the nest containing the eggs.

Even the eggs which lie together in the nests, such as those made in the ground by the salmon, affect each other. An interesting adaptation has evolved in the salmon to protect the eggs from fungi when unfertilized eggs are spawned. In the salmon the unfertilized eggs which get into the nests together with the fertilized ones do not die but develop parthenogenetically for quite a long time, until the fertilized eggs hatch and the danger of the products of decomposition affecting them has passed (Soin, 1953). If the eggs did not possess this property, the unfertilized eggs spawned in the nests would cause the death of the normally developing eggs through the products of their decomposition.

The fish produces around its body a region of chemically altered water. By secreting the products of its metabolism, the fish affects the other fishes in the water-mass. In natural conditions fishes very rarely die of suffocation caused by the exhaustion of all the oxygen in the water by the fishes themselves. Usually, as we have seen above, death of fishes through suffocation is the result of the disappearance of the oxygen due to putrefactive processes, which take place in natural water-masses. In aquaria, basins, fish-rearing apparatus, and other artificial water-masses, the death of the eggs and fishes due to an oxygen deficit caused by their own consumption because of dense population is fairly frequent.

As the experiments of Schuett (1933) showed, for a number of species of fishes—*Umbra limi* (Kirtland), *Carassius auratus* (L.), *Lebistes reticulatus* (Peters), and *Fundulus heteroclitus* (L.)—the amount of oxygen consumed by solitary individuals is greater than that consumed by grouped fishes. This principle holds, as established for goldfish, in both stagnant and flowing water. It is interesting that a reduction in the consumption of oxygen and of the total metabolism when individuals of the same species are placed together does not occur with all species and is mainly observed for passive ones. In the American sheat-fish, *Amiurus melas* (Rafinesque), isolated fishes use less oxygen than grouped ones. This is probably explained by the fact that in natural conditions *Amiurus* is a solitary fish, and when several are grouped together they become restless, starting to swim actively, which apparently causes an increase in their metabolism.

However, fishes may also have a positive effect upon each other. As the experiments of Allee and Bowen showed, increasing the density of a fish population lowers the harmful effect of lethal substances upon the fish. These authors showed that fishes placed in a vessel containing a solution of colloidal silver died sooner if they were isolated than when grouped, even if the volume of water per fish was the same in both cases. The mechanism of this effect has not been established yet, but when toxic substances are introduced into an aquarium, the fishes usually aggregate and remain close to each other.

It must be noted that water in which a fish has been kept undergoes a whole series of changes in its chemical and physical properties, and becomes "old water," or, in the terminology of English and American investigators, "fish-conditioned water," i.e. water which has been altered through the presence of fishes. This water has, for example, the property of fluorescing rather strongly under ultraviolet light, although distilled water does not fluoresce at all and the water of natural water-masses does so only to a very slight extent. The chemical changes in such water are mainly due to the absorption of the excretory products of the fishes. This leads to the fact that biologically conditioned water has a favourable effect upon fishes. But the mechanism of this effect has hardly been investigated yet.

Feeding relationships between the individuals of the same species are of the greatest significance. Cannibalism is a fairly widely distributed phenomenon among fishes. As Kliuchareva (1956) showed, cannibalism is found among many suborders of fishes. However, in the majority of cases this does not attain to any significant magnitude. In a number of species the transition to cannibalism has a considerable adaptive significance for the preservation of the species. In the smelt, *Osmerus eperlanus* (L.), cod, *Gadus morhua* L., navaga, *Eleginus navaga* (Pall.), the transition to feeding on their own young in years of peak year-classes effects a regulation of abundance and reduces the aggravation of the feeding relationships which might arise as a result of overpopulation. For the common perch, *Perca fluviatilis* L., feeding on its own young frequently enables it to live in water-bodies which contain no other species of fish and where the adult perch, by consuming its own young, actually lives at the expense of the plankton, which is the food of its young and on which it could not feed directly itself.

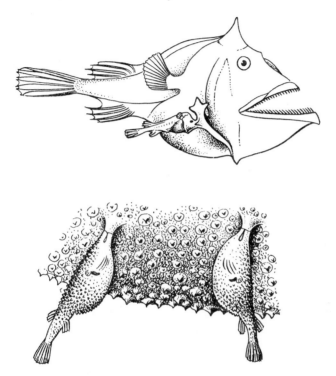

FIG. 44. Parasitic males in Ceratioidei. Top, *Edriolychnus schmidtii* Reg.; the lower part of the female's gill-cover is turned outwards and the male is seen to have become fused on to her body; bottom, males of *Ceratias*, attached to the ventral side of the female.

Sometimes intraspecific parasitism occurs among fishes. Thus, the males of many deep-water angler-fishes of the family Ceratioidei, being much smaller in size than the females, live as parasites upon them. Such dwarf males attach themselves by the mouth to the female and feed upon their body fluids (Fig. 44).

Both intraspecific predation and parasitism have considerable adaptive significance. In the case of intraspecific predation there is a reduction in the force of intraspecific feeding relationships when a peak year-class enters into the population. Frequently, through consuming their own young, the adult individuals are enabled to assimilate food which they are not adapted to consuming directly (as in the example just given of the common perch).

In the case of intraspecific parasitism among deep-water fishes, it is possible for the dwarf males to survive under the protection of the female, even with the general scarcity of food in great depths, and, being constantly connected to them, fertilization of the eggs at the appropriate time is assured.

INTERSPECIFIC INTER-RELATIONSHIPS AMONG FISHES

The character of interspecific connections, as that of intraspecific ones, develops during the process of evolution, as an adaptation to the new living conditions. The formation of new species proceeds by means of the development of adaptations to the abiotic and biotic conditions of the particular geographical zone in which they become established, and usually bears a group character. As a result there develops the so-called faunistic complex, a group of species connected by the generality of their geographical origin, particularly their development in one geographical zone, to the abiotic and biotic conditions of which the species making up the complex are adapted. In the process of the establishment of a faunistic complex regularities become established in the connections between the species making up the complex, namely, a reduction in feeding competition due to the divergence of their dietary spectra, particularly in fishes of mature age; definite adaptations in predators and their prey. The prey-species evolve the essential fecundity and protective adaptations—coloration, thorns, spikes, toxicity—which protect them from predators. It should be realized that protective devices are rarely absolute; they merely cause a relative reduction in the effectiveness of predators. Thus, for example,

TABLE 4

Ratio of Spiny and Common Bitterling in the Food of Predators and in Net Catches (as Per cent of Total Numbers of Bitterling) (from Lishev, 1950)

Name of fish	% in food of predators	% in catches
Spiny bitterling *Acanthorhodeus asmussi* (Dyb.)	19	70
Common bitterling *Rhodeus sericeus* (Pall.)	81	30

the presence of spines on the dorsal fin of *Acanthorhodeus asmussi* (Dyb.) reduces its consumption by predators in comparison with the common bitterling, which has no spines (Table 4).

Spines on fishes are not only a form of armature. They increase the size of the fish and make them less available to the predators. As can be seen from the data presented below, when the Pacific sculpins spread out their gill-covers the width of the head is more than doubled (Paraketsov, 1958).

Increase in the Distance between the Ends of the Large Preopercular Spines when the Gill-Covers of Pacific Sculpins are Expanded (from Paraketsov, 1958).

Myoxocephalus jaok (Cuv. Val.)	2·5 times
Taurocottus bergi Soldatov et Pavlenko	2·4 times
Enophrys diceraus (Pall.)	2·3 times
Hemilepidotus gilbertii Jord. et Starks	2·2 times
Alcichthys elongatus (Steind.)	2·1 times

This adaptation leads to the fact that the armoured fishes pass beyond the influence of the predators at a smaller size than the unarmoured ones. Thus, for example, the Pacific skates of the family Rajidae eat armoured sculpins of up to 18 cm length, and unarmoured ones of up to 42 cm; while the predatory Scorpaenidae eat them up to 12 cm and 25 cm, respectively.

Predators also evolve adaptations for the capture of their prey.

It should be noted that there are certain differences in the nature of the interspecific relationships in faunistic complexes at different latitudes. Thus, the faunistic complexes of lower latitudes are characterized by intensive relationships of the type "predator→prey," and there is a corresponding increase in the development of protective adaptations (great fecundity, care of young, armour). In the North Pacific fauna "predator→prey" relationships are apparently more intensive than in the North Atlantic (Nikolsky 1950; Paraketsov, 1958).

In the complexes of lower latitudes the species are usually to a greater extent stenophagic, i.e. adapted to feeding upon a smaller variety of foods. Thus in these complexes there is a greater variety of feeding niches. There are also other differences (Nikolsky, 1947, 1953, 1956).

Having originated within the limits of a certain geographical area, the species which comprise the complex start to spread, occupying those places within the limits of other zones in which the conditions correspond to their morpho-biological properties. Naturally the representatives of different faunistic complexes come into contact with each other when they spread. Nowadays, the faunas of nearly every marine and continental water-mass consists of representatives of various faunistic complexes. The relationships which develop between the representatives of the different complexes are also subject to definite principles, namely, sharper competition for food develops between the representatives of the various complexes which occupy similar ecological niches.

Predators of lower latitudes, on mixing with prey species of higher latitudes, which are usually less well protected, start to feed on the latter. It is, conversely, considerably more difficult for the predator originating from higher latitudes to start feeding upon the prey species of the lower latitudes.

The nature of the interspecific relationships between fishes is extremely varied: it includes predation, parasitism, commensalism, competitive relationships over food, and a number of other connections.

In respect of the "predator→prey" type of relationships, predatory species evolve adaptations for the capture of their food and for its assimilation (see section on feeding), while the fishes which serve as the prey have evolved corresponding protective devices.

Protective adaptations are extremely variable. Many fishes have evolved some form of toxicity. Poisonous fishes may be either actively or passively toxic. Actively poisonous fishes are those which have poison glands, usually distributed at the bases of the fin spines or else on the gill-covers. Sometimes the mucus covering the body of the fish is poisonous.

The poison glands of fishes are epidermal glandular cells, which may or may not be isolated from the rest of the epidermal cells (Pavlovsky, 1931). In its mode of action the poison of these glands is somewhat like that of snakes. The most powerful poison is that of the sea-devil. There are frequent cases of death through being pricked by its spines. Death occurs within 2 hours to a day, and is very painful (Savchenko, 1886).

The most poisonous fish in European waters is the weaver, *Trachinus draco* L. The poison glands are at the base of the 13th spine of its dorsal fin, and also the spine of the gill-covers. When the spine is pressed the membranes of the poison gland cells burst, and the poison runs out along the spine into the wound. In European waters poison glands also occur at the bases of the spiny fin rays in the sea-hedgehog, *Scorpaena*, redfish, *Sebastes*, etc. In sheat-fish the poison glands are at the bases of the thoracic fins.

Poison glands are found in the representatives of various groups of fishes, namely, in the armoured-tailed skates *Masticura*, from the tropical parts of the Pacific ocean, at the base of the caudal spine; in sheat-fish, *Plotosus* and *Tachysurus*, close to the spines of the thoracic and dorsal fins; in representatives of the family Synanceidae (Fig. 45), in the sea-hedgehogs of the genera *Centropogon*, *Notesthes*, *Pterois*, etc., which are abundant in the tropical waters of the Pacific ocean, close to the spines of the dorsal fin; in the surgeon-fish, *Teuthidae*, on the caudal stem (Fig. 46).

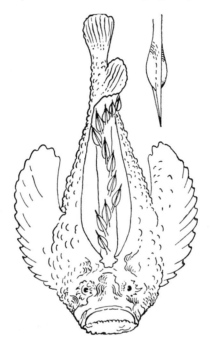

FIG. 45. Spines and poison glands in a representative of the fam. Synanceidae, the sea-devil *Synanceichthys verrucosus* (Schneider). The dorsal surface has been cut to show the poison glands; above, a ray with its poison gland (from Whitley, 1943).

Prickles and spines, either with or without poison glands, usually occur among slow-swimming demersal fishes. They are rather rare in pelagic fishes and usually occur in the caudal region. This is related to the differences in the method of protection: demersal fishes protect themselves without moving, while pelagic fishes try to evade encountering the predator. There are relatively more armoured fishes in the tropical regions, and the protective adaptations are more strongly developed than in temperate latitudes.

Passively toxic fishes have poisonous flesh, blood, skin, or eggs. The largest numbers of such poisonous representatives are members of the two families Tetrodontidae and Ostracionidae. In these the flesh and especially the skin are toxic. If the skin of these fish is peeled off, the flesh may sometimes be eaten.

The flesh of some tropical clupeoids is toxic only during the reproductive period, when these fishes, such as *Harengula punctata* (Rüppell), gather in considerable concentrations.

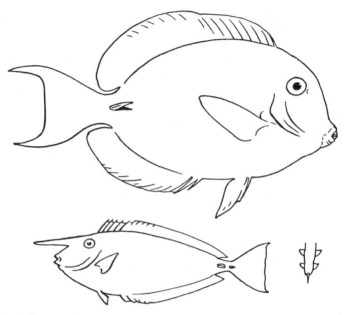

FIG. 46. Spines on the caudal stem in representatives of the order Perciformes. Top, *Teuthis*; bottom, *Naso*; bottom right, caudal stem of *Naso* with the spines, viewed from above (from Whitley, 1943).

These toxins affect man very powerfully and they may sometimes have a fatal effect. In 1774 Captain Cook, who was poisoned by the flesh of the toxic fish *Pleuranacanthus seleratus* (Whitley) (fam. Tetrodontidae), while sailing in the tropical waters of the Pacific Ocean, was ill for a long time.

In some species the spawn is toxic. The spawn of Schizothoracinae (fam. Cyprinidae) is toxic. In the Balkhash "marinka", *Schizothorax argentatus* Kessl., the spawn becomes toxic from the third stage of ripeness and remains toxic after being spawned (Kostin, 1953). The toxicity of the spawn is apparently a protective adaptation against fish-eating birds while spawning in shallow mountain streams. The spawn is also toxic to man, but loses this property when boiled. In conserves, which have passed through an autoclave, the spawn is also quite harmless. According to the observations of Kostin (1953) this spawn is harmless to certain fishes, particularly the loach (*Nemachilus*).

Some fishes, both hunters and hunted, can produce electrical discharges. The electric eel, *Electrophorus electricus* (L.), paralyses its prey by discharging its electrical batteries into it (Fig. 47). The electrical organs of *E.*

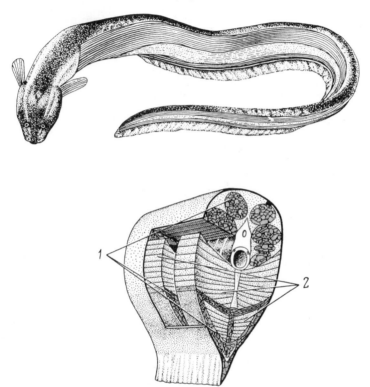

Fig. 47. Distribution of electric organs in the electric eel *Electrophorus electricus* (L.). 1, Muscles; 2, electric organ.

electricus and many other fishes (with the exception of the electric sheat-fish) are modified muscular tissue. Columnar cells which develop in the muscles have the property of acting as Leyden jars, accumulating muscular electricity which is discharged arbitrarily by the animal. The force of the electric cell's discharge is up to 300 V and can fell a large animal. Electric eels feed upon small fishes, which they first of all paralyse with their electricity and then swallow. The paralysed fish becomes convulsed, curls up and stiffens, spreading out the fins. The electric organs of the eel are distributed along the whole length of the body, including the head and the sides of the body, and are at the same time organs of offence and defence. In skates and the electric sheat-fish (in which the electric organs are modified glands) the electric organ also possesses this double function, and serves both to paralyse the prey, and for

FIG. 48. Armoured fishes (from top to bottom): pipefish (Syngnathiformes); coffer-fish (Tetrodontiformes); garpike (Lepidosteiformes); armoured sheat-fish (Cypriniformes).

protection against predators. The force of the discharge in the skate is up to 70 V. The electric organ is ennervated by the 8th, 9th, and 10th pairs of visceral cranial nerves. After a few discharges the fish loses its ability to produce electricity for some time.

For protection against predators many species also possess armour, which may be very powerfully developed. The armour of many different groups of fishes has evolved convergently (Fig. 48). In some cases it consists of out-growths on the scales, in others of bony plates. But the function of each is the same one of protection.

Naturally, all the protective adaptations which we have examined protect not only against predatory fishes, but against other predatory animals as well. We must, however, emphasize that we have not by any means mentioned all the protective methods which fishes have evolved, but only the most widely distributed ones.

Interspecific parasitism is rather rare among fishes. Two types of parasitism have been observed: (1) the parasitic fish more or less rapidly kills its host; (2) the parasitic fish does not kill its host. In the first type the interspecific parasitism of the cyclostomes borders on predation. We observe this in the hagfish. The common hagfish, *Myxine glutinosa* L., bores into the bodies of live fishes, gradually eating the contents and eventually leading to the death of their prey. The deep-water eels of the family Simenchelidae also lead a similar mode of life, boring into the bodies of large fishes and feeding on their contents. The semi-parasitic mode of life leaves its peculiar imprint on the hagfish and on the eel, *Simenchelys parasiticus* Gill. The modification of the respiratory apparatus in the hagfish in relation to the semiparasitic mode of life has already been described (page 33). In *Simenchelys* the gill cavity is only slightly and closely covered. As in the hagfish, though to a lesser extent, the skin of *Simenchelys* contains a large number of mucus glands, apparently to reduce the friction between the parasite and the host's body wall.

The inter-relationship between two species of American sheat-fish is an example of the second type of parasitism. The sheat-fish *Stegophilus* parasitizes the gill cavities of the larger sheat-fish *Platystoma* and feeds by sucking the blood of its host. In its mode of action it is reminiscent of the monogenetic trematodes.

Commensalism, a form of relationship between animals which is beneficial to one side and indifferent to the other, has been observed among fishes. The most characteristic example is the relationship between the shark and the sucker-fish *Echineis naucrates* (L.). In the sucker-fish (Fig. 49) the first dorsal fin is modified to form a sucker lying on the upper side of the head, by means of which this fish attaches itself to sharks and travels along with them, feeding on what the shark leaves over. The strength of such a sucker may be illustrated by the fact that the aborigines use the sucker-fish for catching turtles. They tie a thin string to the tail of the sucker-fish, and when they see a turtle in the water they throw the fish next to it. The sucker-fish immediately swims to the turtle and attaches itself to the shell, while the fisherman carefully pulls the fish in on his towing-line.

Very few cases of symbiosis between fish are known. It is possible that this is the type of relationship between the sharks and the pilot-fish, *Naucrates ductor* (L.). These small fish follow sharks and throw themselves on the food remains thrown out by ships, as though indicating the food to the sharks. The shark never eats the pilot-fish which swim close to it. It is possible that the pilot-fish does actually indicate the food to the shark by means of its sharper sight. Some authors state that the pilot-fish feeds on the parasitic crustaceans attached to the skin of the shark, but this problem has not yet been studied in detail.

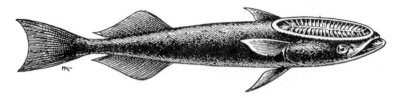

FIG. 49. The sucker-fish *Echeneis naucrates* L.

There are very complex relationships between fishes in respect to feeding on the same type of food. As stated above, the adult fishes belonging to one faunistic complex usually consume basically different foods. In adult fishes under natural conditions the nutritional spectra coincide only in respect to those foods which are of secondary importance to one of the species. Thus, as may be seen from the scheme presented in Fig. 50, in the two species of gobies *Neogobius fluviatilis* Pall. and *Benthophilus macrocephalus* Pall., both of which belong to the same marine Pontic complex, there is only a very slight coincidence in the composition of the food. A similar impression is given, for example, by the feeding relationships between the roach *Rutilus rutilus* (L.) and the perch *Perca fluviatilis* L., which belong to the same boreal plains complex. In rivers and lakes there is usually a divergence between the nutritional spectra of these species. However, the altered conditions of a reservoir may present a situation in which the feeding relationships between species of the same complex become more acute. For example, the water-weeds and their associated fauna frequently disappear owing to a change in water-level. If this happens, the species belonging to one complex are forced to feed on the same foods, which can lead to acute nutritional relationships if the food is not abundant.

As was stated above, the most acute feeding competition occurs between the species of fishes belonging to different faunistic complexes but the same food niche. For example, in the lakes of the European plain acute feeding competition arises over chironomid larvae between the ruff, *Acerina cernua* (L.) (a boreal plains complex species) and the bream, *Abramis brama* (L.) (ancient upper-Tertiary complex). A similar type of relationship has been observed in the Sea of Azov between the zooplankton feeders sardelle, *Clupeonella delicatula* (Nordm.) (Ponto-Caspian complex) and anchovy, *Engraulis encrasicholus* (L.) (Mediterranean complex).

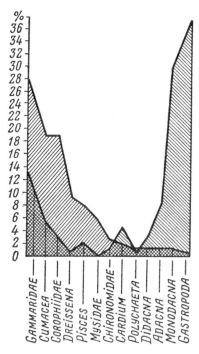

Fig. 50. Overlapping of the food spectra of *Neogobius fluviatilis* Pall. and *Benthophilus macrocephalus* Pall. (from Shorygin, 1939).

A knowledge of the principles of interspecific nutritional relationships is very important in the planning of the acclimitization of new species of fishes in various water-masses.

The foregoing applies, primarily, to the nutritional links between adult fishes. In young fishes, which have not yet started to consume the type of food which the adults use, there is usually, in addition to a greater degree of stenophagy, a greater degree of similarity in the food of the different species in a single complex. The larvae and fry of different species of fishes can avoid competition over food either if their food is very abundant or if they are spawned at different times. In the larvae of fishes belonging to different complexes, there is usually a divergence in the period of development, and therefore in the period in which they require the same type of food.

There are also other types of interrelationships between different species of fishes. For example, the utilization of the same spawning grounds and the consequent disruption by one species of the spawning conditions for the other (as, for example, occurs among Far Eastern salmons). Competitive interrelationships can also arise between different species of fishes in the overwintering grounds. But these types of relationships are not usually of very great magnitude and are not reflected in the dynamics of fish stocks.

Interspecific Relationships Between Fishes and other Organisms

Extremely varied connections occur in nature between fishes and other organisms, from viruses and bacteria to mankind, which are of substantial significance for fishes.

BACTERIA AND VIRUSES

In addition to their enormous significance in the lives of fishes, as in those of other organisms, by participating in the circulation of organic matter in nature, bacteria also have a special significance for fishes. There are the most varied forms of interrelationships between fishes and bacteria.

There are several serious bacterial and virus diseases of fish. Malignant red-spot of carps, a virus disease, is an example. The bacterium *Pseudomonas plehniae* also plays some role in its course. Other diseases of bacterial origin are dropsy, furunculosis, and a number of others (W. Schaperclaus, 1954), which frequently cause mass mortalities of fishes in fishponds.

Fishes have evolved a number of protective adaptations against bacteria. In particular, the mucus which covers the body, and also secretions from various organs (gills, liver), possess antibiotic properties (Zotov, 1958).

On the other hand, certain bacteria possess lysing, destructive properties in respect to a number of fungal diseases of fishes. Thus, Bacterium no. 29 suppresses the development and lyses the hyphae of the fungus *Saprolegnia*, which damages the egg membranes (Mazilkin, 1957).

Bacteria sometimes cause the flourescence of fishes; a special type of bacteria inhabits the light organs of certain fishes.

Bacteria apparently have a certain nutritional significance for fishes. Thus, in the Amur cyprinoid (*Xenocypris macrolepis* Bl.), the number of ingested bacteria is larger in the fore part of the gut than in the hind part, which indicates that they are assimilated by the fish (Borutsky, 1950).   Not only bacteria, but other microorganisms can also serve as food for fishes. Thus, the experimental feeding of a number of species (sturgeons, viviparous cyprinodonts) on the yeast *Candida* showed that fishes can assimilate them, although they grow less rapidly than when feeding on animal food (Assman, 1957). The bacteria are very important as food for the invertebrate food animals of fishes (Zhukova, 1957).

PLANTS

Among the lower plants the fungi are very important. Some fungi are pathogenic. True, fungi such as *Saprolegnia* usually only damage the spawn and fish when they are already weakened, or else when the conditions for metabolism are disturbed, i.e. the damage due to *Saprolegnia* is most frequently secondary. This fungus often settles on wounds on fish, and can cause the death of the fish through its rapid development, by destroying the tissues.

Chlorophyll-bearing plants are tremendously important for fishes. Giving out oxygen in light and absorbing carbon dioxide, plants can make the environmental conditions more favourable for fishes. In deep shade, when photosynthesis cannot proceed, plants only excrete carbon dioxide, and this process can sometimes attain to such magnitude that it leads to the death of fishes in the water-mass.

Plants are also used as substrate for their spawn by many fishes. By placing their eggs on plants, fishes, on the one hand, protect them to some extent from predators and, on the other, provide them with more favourable hydro-chemical conditions for development. Thus, for example, the carp frequently spawns on water-weeds, amongst which the oxygen saturation of the water is considerably higher both by day and by night than in the surrounding parts of the water-mass. Many fishes construct special nests out of plants, into which they spawn their eggs. This type of nest is constructed by the stickle-backs, *Gasterosteus* and *Pungitius*. Something like a nest is constructed by the mudfish, *Amia calva* L., etc.

Plants as an element of the landscape also have some significance for adult fishes. Many fishes are specially adapted to living among weeds. They possess camouflaging colorations (see above on weed-like colorations, etc.), or else a particular shape of body which resembles that of the weeds amongst which they live. Thus, the long outgrowths on the fins of the ragged sea-horse

Phyllopteryx eques Günther, in conjunction with the coloration, renders it completely inconspicuous among the water-weeds (Fig. 51).

The young of *Lobotes surinamensis* (Bloch.) and *Oligoplites saurus* (Bl.) and certain other fishes resemble the leaves of the mangrove tree floating in the water. The small fish *Chaetodipterus faber* (Broussonet) resembles pods floating in the water (Breder, 1942).

FIG. 51. *Phyllopteryx eques* Günther.

Chlorophyllous plants are also very important as food for fishes. It is true that in high latitudes where the vegetative period is short, there are no herbivorous fishes. But as the lower latitudes are approached there appear first of all facultative phytophages, such as the silver crucian carp, and the roach, for which plants have a subsidiary nutritional significance, because their main food consists of animals. In still lower latitudes, with even longer vegetative periods, plants come to play an increasing role as food of fishes. Some species of fishes feed entirely on plants, and have evolved a number of special adaptations for grazing, triturating, and assimilating plant food (see later in chapter on food, page 262 *et seq.*).

Planktonic algae form the food of such fishes as the Amur cyprinoid *Hypophthalmichthys molitrix* Val., the Pacific sardine *Sardinops sagax melanosticta* (Schl.), a clupeoid *Tilapia esculenta* Graham, a cychlid, and many others. Filamentous algae (*periphyton*) are eaten by *Varicorhinus heratensis* Keys. and

Chondrostoma nasus (L.), both cyprinoids. Finally, macrophytes are eaten by the grass–carp *Ctenopharyngodon idella* (Val.) and *Scardinius erythrophthalmus* (L.).

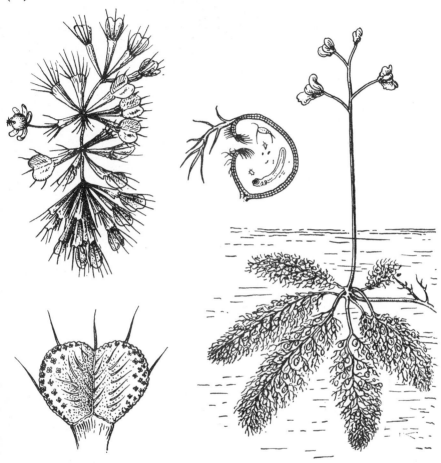

Fig. 52. Fish–eating plants. Left, *Aldrovandia*; right, the bladderwort *Utricularia* (from Lipin, 1950).

Herbivorous fishes are less numerous in the sea than in fresh water. Many fishes use plant detritus as food (*Xenocypris*, lamprey larvae, certain cychlids, etc.).

Apart from their considerable positive role in the lives of fishes, plants also have an adverse signiñcance. Certain plants, such as the bladderwort *Utricularia*, are specially adapted for feeding upon aquatic organisms, including fish larvae (Rodionova, 1959). This plant has branching leaves on fine stalks, bearing bladders. Each bladder has an entrance, which is closed by a valve in such a way that animals can only pass inward and not outward (Fig. 52). Various animals including the newly hatched larvae of fishes often get into these bladders. Unable to get out, these animals die, and the products of their decomposition are assimilated by the bladderwort. Fish larvae are also used sometimes by *Aldrovandia*, but the method by which this plant captures them differs from that of the bladderwort. The leaves of *Aldrovandia* fold together to form an expanded chamber, the interior of which is covered with hairs. When some animal touches these hairs, the leaf claps together and the animal is caught.

Besides the harm to fishes by consuming their larvae, these plants also exert a certain influence on their food supply by consuming planktonic crustaceans. Thus, the bladderwort in the Rybinsk reservoir exerts a strong influence on the quantities of zooplankton in the weed-beds. According to observations, from June 26 to July 19, 1957, 71·8–78 % of the bladders of these plants (average of several stations) contained planktonic crustaceans. The biomass of the plankton among the weeds where there was a lot of the bladderwort, was more than 10 times less than in regions close by but without bladderwort.

The average number of captured animals per plant was 1779 to 3570; their average biomass was 0·108 g (Rodionova, 1959).

However, the harm to fishes due to carnivorous plants is relatively slight.

Some harm is caused to fishes by the massive overgrowth of dense weeds on the water. Apart from taking mineral substances from the water, dense weeds impoverish the conditions in the water-mass. In connection with this, in many water-bodies the overgrowth is tackled both by removal and by means of herbicides.

FISHES AND OTHER ANIMALS

Nearly every group of animals has some sort of relationship with fishes.

Protozoa

Unicellular organisms play a considerable role in the lives of fishes. Many fishes in the early stages of their lives eat various protozoa, particularly infusoria. Thus, for example, both in natural conditions and in aquaria, young labyrinthodonts feed exclusively upon protozoa as soon as they hatch from the eggs. The young of many other fishes also feed upon protozoa, but they have no substantial significance as food for adult fishes. The Tintinnoidea play a rather substantial role as food of larval oceanic herring in their first stages of active feeding (Lebour, 1918, 1919, 1920; Hardy, 1924). Tintinnoidea are found in the stomachs of larval anchovies of up to 10 mm length; the frequency of occurrence of these protozoans in the stomachs is for fish 4–6 mm 100 %, 6–8 mm 60 %, and 8–10 mm 16.6 % (Bokova, 1955).

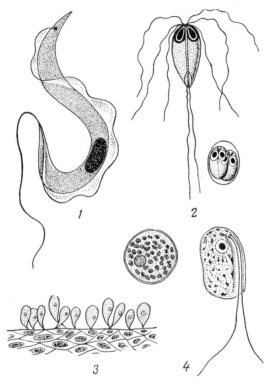

FIG. 53. Parasitic flagellates of fishes. 1, *Trypanosoma*; 2, *Octomytus* and its cyst; 3, *Costia* on the skin of a fish; 4, a cyst of *Costia* (from Dogel, 1939).

The fact that it is impossible to find protozoa in the stomachs of fishes by autopsy makes it very difficult to obtain precise data on their role as food, and they have not been studied from the point of view of food.

Protozoa have very great adverse effects upon fishes, many of them being the cause of serious diseases of fishes, and sometimes they cause considerable losses in fish-farms.

All the protozoan classes include fish parasites—flagellates, rhizopods, sporozoans, and ciliates.

Flagellate parasites occur on the skin, in the gut, and in the blood of fishes. A disease such as costiasis, caused by the flagellate *Costia nacatrix* (Henneguy), does enormous harm in fish-farms, killing many trout, carp, and other fish. This parasite damages the skin, destroying the epidermis. Intestinal parasites of fish include *Octomytus* in trout, and *Cryptobia* in the lumpsucker. Among flagellate blood-parasites of fishes, certain species of *Trypanosoma* are found in the blood of skates, sharks, bream, perch, flatfish, and others (Fig. 53).

Large numbers of *Trypanoplasma* occur in the blood of the humpback salmon, *Oncorhynchus gorbuscha* Walb., sometimes causing a mass pre-spawning mortality of these fish (Makeeva, 1957). These parasites have been

FIG. 54. A carp infested with the sporozoan *Myxobolus* (from Liaiman, 1939).

found in the blood of the tench, minnow, sterlet, and other freshwater fishes, and also in certain sea-fishes on the coast of Australia. The intermediate hosts of these parasites in fresh water are fish leeches.

Rhizopods mainly damage the digestive and excretory organs of fishes.

Pathologically, the most important parasitic protozoans are the various sporozoans (Fig. 54). Thus, *Myxobolus* parasitizes the skin of fishes, causing a puffy appearance and ulcers of various sizes. The cartilaginous parts of the skeleton and skull are attacked by *Lentospora*, which frequently cause the mass mortality of fishes in trout pond farms.

Ciliates are also parasitic in fish. Thus, *Chilodonella* and *Ichthyophthirus* occur on the gills, and *Balantidium* in the intestine.

Coelenterates

Coelenterates are unimportant as food of fishes. They are eaten by a number of tropical marine fishes, for example by members of the family Leiognathidae (Tham Ah Kow, 1950), but only in small quantities.

There are several endo- and ecto-parasites of fishes among the coelenterates. *Polypodium hydriforme* Uss. damages the sexual products of the Volga sterlet. Among colonial forms *Hydrichthys* parasitizes fishes in South Africa.

But the greatest harm to fishes is caused by both sedentary and free-swimming carnivorous coelenterates. *Hydra* and many colonial marine forms seize young fish with their tentacles and eat them. *Hydra* frequently

FIG. 55. A medusa with captured fishes.

causes noticeable losses in fish-farms, by killing the fish larvae. Medusae and certain ctenophores are very important as consumers of fish. Of the 700 or more known species of marine medusae it has been established that 27 of them do eat fish. But there can be no doubt that many others also consume fish. Beebe (1936) observed near the coast of Haiti thousands of the medusa *Linuche unguiculata*, many of which had seized larval fish (Fig. 55). The prey are first of all paralysed by the nematocysts, then held by the tentacles and led into the mouth. The species eaten most frequently by the medusa are young plaice, sandeels, and cod. Medusae also attack adult pipefish and many other fishes. Very often, small medusae attack fishes much larger than themselves. We also find cases of symbiosis between fishes and coelenterates. Thus, certain fishes of the family Pomacentridae live among the tentacles of the gigantic sea anemones *Stoichactis* and *Discosoma*, which are widely distributed in the Indopacific. The fishes *Amphiprion percula* (Lac.), *A. frenatus* (Brev.), *A. perederaion* (Bl.), *Premnas biaculeatus* (Bloch), etc., which live among the tentacles of sea-anemones, are of small size and very brightly coloured. There is no doubt of symbiosis here, because while any other animal which comes into the region of the spread-out tentacles of the anemone is rapidly killed, the *Amphiprion*, for example, swims among them completely unharmed, feeding on the "left-overs" of the anemone and even sometimes picking up food from the tentacles. The anemone in turn uses the left-overs of food obtained by the fish. It is interesting that *Amphiprion*, having seized its prey, brings it "home," where it eats it, the left-overs going to the anemone. Dutch investigators have also stated that the *Amphiprion* produces water-movements in front of the tentacles of the anemone. Each species of *Amphiprion* is connected with a particular species of anemone and, if placed in an aquarium containing a different species of anemone, will not approach it (Herre, 1936). As many as ten fishes may live in the vicinity of one anemone.

Another example of symbiosis between coelenterate and fish occurs in European waters. Under the bell of the large Arctic medusa *Cyanea capillata* L. there are often large numbers of young haddock, cod, and other species. Sometimes the young fish, like the *Amphiprion* in the actinian, eat the remains of food adhering to the tentacles of the medusa. The medusa does not touch the larvae. In this, as in the foregoing case, we have an example of symbiosis. Similar cohabitation between medusae and fish is known from tropical waters. Beebe and Tee Van (1928) state that near Haiti there may be as many as 300 larval fish under the hood of one medusa at the same time, and the medusa does them no harm whatsoever.

Certain coelenterates affect the food supply of fishes by consuming the same food. Thus, the ctenophore *Balinopsis*, which eats planktonic crustaceans in the north Atlantic, exerts a substantial effect upon the food supply of the oceanic herring.

It is interesting that another ctenophore *Beroe cucumis* Fabr., which eats *Balinopsis*, thereby has a favourable effect on the food supply of the herring, by killing an important consumer of its food (Kamshilov, 1955).

Rotifers

Rotifers are of substantial importance to fresh water fishes. For many fishes rotifers are a basic food in the earlier stages of external feeding. In the Volga the rotifers *Diurella*, *Brachionus*, *Asplanchna*, and their eggs are the basic food of young migrant shad of 6–10 mm length. (Sushkina, 1940). The same has also been observed in the case of the Dunai shad, *Caspialosa kessleri pontica* Eichv. (Zaitseva, 1955).

Rotifers are also the basic food of many young cyprinoids, and of the young of the majority of freshwater fishes. Thus, for example, rotifers form more than 50 % by numbers of the food organisms in the guts of *Hemiculter leucisculus* Bas. up to a length of 22 mm in the Amur. The main food of larval silver crucian carp up to 5·5–7 mm length in the Amur is also rotifers (Nikolsky, 1956).

Rotifers may also have a certain adverse effect upon fishes. Thus, the species *Proales daphnicola* Thomson lives on *Daphnia* and attaches itself by some special holding threads, in which larval carp can also easily become entangled. In experimental conditions with a concentration of not less than one rotifer *Proales* per cubic centimetre of water, carp larvae of 5–8 mm length quickly became entangled in such threads and perished (Bogoslovsky, 1955).

Worms

Worms are of substantial significance for both freshwater and sea fishes. Very many representatives of the various groups of worms are eaten by fishes.

Free-living nematodes play a substantial role in the food of freshwater fishes. Thus, in the Volga, according to the data of Aliavdina (1929), the bream and the blue bream consume fairly large numbers of nematodes. These worms were recorded from the guts of more than 17 % of blue bream and 8 % of bream. The predominant species in the food of the Volga fish was *Dorylaimus stagnalis* Dujardin.

Oligochaete worms are even more important as food for fishes. They are eaten by the majority of freshwater benthophagic fishes, which feed on the infauna, i.e. invertebrates which live in the ground. Thus, for example, they sometimes form more than 50 % of the food of the common gudgeon in the Moscow region. In parts of the Amur oligochaete worms form 100 % of the gut contents of *Cobitis taenia*. It should be noted, however, that because nematodes and, particularly, oligochaetes are very rapidly digested, their role in the nourishment of fishes (from the examination of gut contents) is usually somewhat underestimated.

Oligochaete worms are an important food for young fishes in fish-farms, where special techniques are used for breeding live worms. The oligochaete species usually cultured is *Enchytraeus albidus*, and in certain fish-farms a productivity of as high as 3–5 kg of worms per square metre of the ground is achieved in the cultures (Konstantinov and Konstantinova, 1957). To improve the nutritional value of the enchytraeid worms, essential salts and vitamins are added to the food.

In the sea the polychaete worms play a substantial role in the food of fishes. Thus, according to Zatsepin (1939) sedentary polychaetes form 10–20 % of the food of the haddock, *Gadus aeglefinus* L., in various parts of the Barents Sea.

The most important consumers of polychaetous annelids in the Sea of Azov are the sturgeon and bream. In order to improve the nutritional value of the Caspian, in 1934 the polychaete *Nereis succinea* Leuckart was transplanted from the Sea of Azov into the Caspian, where it became an important food for the sturgeon, and where certain other species of fish (bream, roach) also frequently consumed it. However, in the Caspian, *Nereis* also apparently exerts a certain adverse effect upon the numbers of bloodworms and oligochaetes by consuming them.

Besides the great importance of worms as the food of fishes, their adverse effect as fish parasites is also very considerable.

Among commercial species of fish, it is rare to find an individual which has no parasitic worms of any kind. Among the trematodes, for example, there are enormous numbers of species which parasitize both the internal and the external organs of fishes. Monogenetic trematodes usually parasitize the gills of fishes. Thus, for example, the gills of the sturgeons are parasitized by *Nitzchia sturionis* (Abildg.), which sometimes leads to the mass mortality of sturgeons through exhaustion caused by loss of blood. Some of the fishes may have as many as 500 specimens of this parasite on their gills, which consume an enormous amount of blood and disrupt the normal blood circulation. In 1936 there was a mass epizootic of the sturgeon *Acipenser nudiventris* Lov., large numbers of which died. The trematode *Dactylogyrus vastator* (Nybelin) parasitizes the gills of the carp. Infection takes place by means of free-swimming larvae, which at first move through the water by means of cilia. After a period of free life the larvae attach themselves to a fish, throw off the ciliated cover, and attach themselves to the body of the fish by means of hooks. This trematode mainly parasitizes young individuals of the carp, and is rarely found on older individuals. This may possibly be explained by the structural changes in the gills of the fish, which apparently make it more difficult for the parasite to attach itself. Recently it was discovered that the closely related species of monogenetic trematode, *Dactylogyrus solidus* Achmerow, had been introduced into the European part of the U.S.S.R., apparently with carp acclimatized there from the Far East. Very strict controls are essential in acclimatization of fishes, to ensure that parasites are not imported. New parasites, to which the local fauna is not adapted, may often cause a very strong epizootic.

The majority of the other Monogenetic trematodes are also located on the gills or skin of fishes. In contrast to them, the Digenea, whose development proceeds through one or two intermediate hosts, mainly parasitize the internal organs of fishes. Such digenetic trematodes as *Bucephalus polymorphus* Baer are located in the intestines, whence their eggs enter the water and infect various molluscs, in which they pass through a further stage of development, up to the cercaria stage. The cercariae, on emerging into the water, penetrate the skin of non-predatory fishes, where they become encapsulated. Predatory fishes which eat the non-predatory ones acquire this trematode as an intestinal parasite. For certain species of parasites, the final host is a water-fowl, which becomes infected through eating fish.

Certain digenetic trematodes occur in the kidney and urinary bladder. As an example we may examine *Catopteroides macrocotyle* Lütke. Infection with these worms takes place as follows: the eggs of the parasite in the water enter the intermediate host, the mollusc *Dreissena*. The cercariae emerge from the mollusc already in the form of a cyst with a reduced tail, and float up to the surface layers of the water, where they are accidentally swallowed with water by fishes; on reaching the intestines, they pass to the ureters and thence into the kidneys. Digenetic trematodes also parasitize the nervous system of fishes. Thus, many members of the genus *Tolyclelphus* occur in the cerebral fluid. Digenetic trematodes also occur in the gall bladder, blood system, and other organs of fishes.

The tapeworms, Cestodes, are tremendously important as parasites of fishes. The species *Ligula intestinalis* (L.) causes the greatest amount of harm to the fishing industry. Its final host consists of piscivorous birds, in which it parasitizes the intestines. It enters the bird from the body cavity of a fish. The primary host of this tapeworm is a copepod crustacean. The tapeworm causes considerable losses in fish-farms, through frequent mass mortalities. *Ligula* causes a reduction in the growth rate of fishes, disrupts their metabolic processes, and, when the parasite is well-developed, the death of the fish (see Fig. 56).

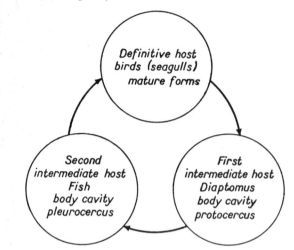

FIG. 56. Developmental cycle of *Ligula* (from Liaiman, 1939).

FIG. 57. A roach infested with the tapeworm *Ligula*; below, a specimen dissected.

When the coelomic parasites, which frequently parasitize a fish in large numbers, reach a large size, the fish becomes unable to swim (Fig. 57), and, floating up to the surface, becomes an easy prey for piscivorous birds.

The construction of a large number of reservoirs along rivers provides favourable conditions for the development of the ligulids, because the planktonic crustaceans are more abundant in the reservoirs than in rivers. At the

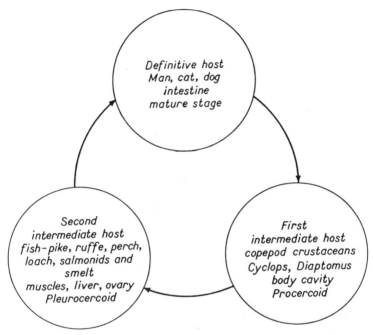

FIG. 58. The developmental cycle of the broad tapeworm *Diphyllobothrium latus* (L.) (from Liaiman, 1939).

same time, the reservoirs also provide favourable conditions for the waterfowl. Ligulids parasitize various species of fishes in reservoirs, particularly the bleak *Alburnus alburnus* (L.), and the roach *Rutilus rutilus* (L.). Such usually non-predatory fishes as the bream, crucian carp, etc. are also often parasitized by ligulids.

Many other tapeworms occur in the intestines of fishes. Sometimes the adults occur in the intestines, while the larvae occur in various other organs. Thus, in *Triaenophorus nodulosus* the adult individuals live in the intestines of the fish, while their larvae live in the liver. *Triaenophorus crassus* Ford in the cyst stage lives in the flesh of the whitefish in Canadian waters. For some species, such as *Coregonus tullibee* (R.), it is a normal parasite; for others, such as *C. clupeiformis* Mitch., it is accidental. In *C. tullibee* (R.), which is adapted to this parasite, an increase in the numbers of cysts in the flesh causes less reduction in the weight of the fish than in the unadapted *C. clupeiformis* Mitch. (Miller, 1945).

Many fishes are the intermediate hosts of tapeworms of which the final host is man (Fig. 58). Thus, *Diphyllobothrium latus* (L.) in the adult form lives in the human intestine, but its cysticerci occur in the muscle tissue of fishes. Infection occurs through the consumption of insuffiently cooked fish.

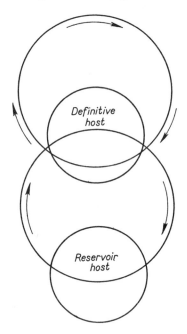

FIG. 59. The developmental cycle of *Raphidascaris* (in the presence of a reservoir host) (from Liaiman, 1939).

Another species, *Botriocephalus gowkongensis* Uch., is widely distributed in China. Young individuals of the grass–carp *Ctenopharyngodon idella* Val. infected by this parasite usually have a reduced feeding rate, and the erythrocyte count in the blood is lower than normal (Liao and Shih, 1956).

The roundworms or Nematodes also have a considerable significance as parasites of fishes. They occur in the most varied organs. They effect the intestines, swim-bladder, liver, peritoneum, muscles, skin, etc. Some of them develop through an intermediate host. Thus, for example, *Camallanus lacustris* (Loega), which occurs as adults in the intestines of fishes, has as intermediate host the water-louse, *Asellus aquaticus* L. In certain round-worms, as for example, *Raphidascaris acus*, the development occurs through an intermediate host, but a predatory fish becomes infected through eating a non-predatory fish, the liver and peritoneum of which contain the larvae of this worm (Fig. 59). Such a "semi-intermediate" host is termed a reservoir host.

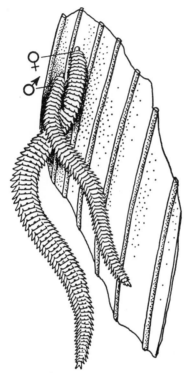

Fig. 60. The parasitic polychaete worm *Ichthyotomus sanguinarius* on the fin of a fish (from Fauvel, 1923).

The Acanthocephala also parasitize many fishes. They occur mainly in the intestines. They usually have one, sometimes two, intermediate hosts.

The harm caused to fishes by polychaetous annelids is relatively slight. Only a few species occur as external parasites of fishes. Thus, for example, representatives of the family Ichthyotomidae, in particular *Ichthyotomus sanguinarius*, occur as parasites on the fins of fishes (particularly the eels), to which they attach themselves by means of the mouth and feed upon the blood (Fig. 60).

In concluding this review of the role of worms as fish parasites, mention must be made of the leeches. These can affect fishes in various ways: distressing the fish by their bites, by sucking the blood, by acting as vectors for infection, and, finally, by creating favourable conditions for infection of the fish by bacteria and fungi. Various leeches may attack fishes. The most common species in European waters is *Piscicola geometra* L., which attaches itself at various points on the body. The fish dies if attacked by large numbers of leeches at the same time. Cases of the mass mortality of salmon, the gills of which were infected with the leech *Cystobranchus*, are known. The role of fish leeches as vectors of parasitic protozoa was mentioned above.

Molluscs

The types of relationships between fishes and molluscs are very varied. They are both of the type "predator → prey" (both the fish preying on the molluscs and vice versa), and of the form of parasitism and commensalism.

Both in the sea and in fresh waters, molluscs are an important food for fishes. The main kinds are bottom molluscs, but a certain part is played by pelagic ones (Pteropoda) such as *Clione limacina* Phipps in the food of the cod and haddock.

In the North Caspian various molluscs form a high proportion of the food of benthophagic commercial species of fishes (Table 5). Many species, such as the Caspian roach, feed almost exclusively on this group of animals.

In other inland seas the role of molluscs as fish-food is also very great. In the open parts of the Aral Sea *Acipenser nudiventris* Lov. in its feeding season feeds almost exclusively on the bivalve mollusc *Adacna minima*. Molluscs also play a substantial role in the nutrition of fishes in fresh water. Thus, the Sphaeriidae are one of the most important foods of the benthophagic fishes of the Great Lakes in North America.

Molluscs are the basic food of the species *Mylopharyngodon piceus* Rich. and *Hemibarbus labeo* Pall. in the rivers of the Far East. Fishes have evolved a number of adaptations related to feeding upon molluscs, mainly in connection with the crushing of the shells.

A number of species of fishes use bivalves as a spawning substrate. The eggs are placed in the mollusc's mantle cavity by the bitterlings *Rhodeus*, *Acanthorhodeus*, etc., and by certain species of *Chilogobio*. This represents a protection of the eggs from predators, and also a protection against desiccation due to fluctuations in the water-level, because when the water-level falls the majority of the molluscs manage to crawl into deeper water. The eggs and embryos have evolved a number of adaptations in connection

TABLE 5

Consumption of Molluscs by Fishes in the North Caspian

Food species	Roach	Bream	Russian sturgeon	Neogobius caspicus	Neogobius fluviatilis pallasi	Neogobius melanostomus	Benthophilus macrocephalus
Monodacna	16·0	1·0	—	—	0·6	3·4	29·6
Adacna vitrea minima	14·0	8·0	1·3	4·0	1·0	—	6·5
A. plicata, A. laeviuscula	1·5	—					
Didacna trigonoides	5·5	0·7	—	4·0	1·0	3·7	3·0
Cardium edule	1·3	0·003	—	10·0	2·0	20·5	5·0
Total Cardidae	38·3	9·7	1·3	18·0	4·6	27·6	44·1
Dreissena polymorpha	42·1	2·1	0·2	—	9·0	13·6	0·2
Mytiliaster lineatus	—	—	—	—	—	5·0	—
Gastropoda	2·0	0·1	—	—	0·7	8·0	35·0
Total molluscs	82·4	11·8	1·5	18·0	14·3	54·2	79·3

TABLE 6

Composition of the Food of the Cuttlefish *Illex* in the Newfoundland region (as Percentage Frequency)

Food species	Length of cuttlefish mantle 10–12	13–15	16–18	19–21	22–24	25–27	28–30
Capelan *Mallotus villosus* (Müll.)	—	9·9	9·3	16·5	4·7	1·4	—
Redfish *Sebastes marinus* L.	5·9	15·9	5·4	6·9	2·7	2·8	12·5
Gadoids (cod and haddock)	—	1·5	9·3	—	4·1	2·8	—
Unidentified fish	5·9	13·9	18·2	27·4	46·6	55·6	50·0
Total with fish	11·8	37·3	42·2	50·7	58·2	62·5	62·5
Total with invertebrates	88·2	74·3	84·3	43·8	37·8	26·4	25·0

with being spawned into molluscs (see page 153). This type of relationship between fish and mollusc comes under the heading of "commensalism." It apparently has no advantage for the mollusc.

In their own turn, certain molluscs consume fishes, sometimes in fairly large quantities. Thus, the North Atlantic cuttlefish *Illex illicebrosus* (Le

Sueur), as may be seen from Table 6, consumes a large number of commercial fishes in the Newfoundland region (Squires, 1957).

The cuttlefish *Sepioteuthis arctipinnis* Gould., which occurs in masses in Indian coastal waters, consumes fishes to a considerable extent. Of 485 which were examined, and which contained food in their guts, 73 % contained fish remains (Rao, 1954). Many other cephalopod molluscs also feed on fish. Some of them, which feed on the same food as fishes (for example, pelagic crustaceans, Euphausiidae) can exert an adverse effect on the food supply of pelagic fishes.

Molluscs have no great significance as parasites of fishes. Only certain larvae, bivalve glochidia (the genera *Unio* and *Anodonta*), parasitize fishes. The glochidia, on being released from the mother when a fish swims near, attach themselves to the gills or fins of their host. As a result of the irritation the epithelium of the fish starts to grow out in the region where the glochidium is attached and rapidly encloses it. The enclosed glochidia in the epithelium have the appearance of white spots or tubercles. They feed upon the tissues or fluids of the host. The duration of this phase varies, according to the species, from 10 to 75 days. Even in the same species the duration of this period varies according to the temperature and a number of other environmental factors. When the larva has finished its development, the tissues of the host surrounding it burst, and the larva emerges. The glochidia only cause the fish to become exhausted if they are present in large numbers. There are no known cases of the death of fish being caused by parasitization by glochidia in natural conditions. It is interesting that many species of fishes are immune to the glochidia, and the latter, if they become enclosed by the host's tissues, are gradually destroyed by leucocytes.

Crustaceans

The crustaceans are undoubtedly one of the most important groups of animals in relation to fishes, particularly in respect of their food.

The majority of fishes (benthophages, planktophages, and herbivores alike) pass through a stage in their development when they use planktonic crustaceans as food, and in particular, copepods. Crustaceans are the basic food of young predators such as the pike of 13–60–70 mm length (Shamardina, 1957) and the pike-perch of 5·5–25 mm; also the young of herbivorous fishes such as the grass-carp *Ctenopharyngodon idella* (Val.) 11–27 mm in length; young *Xenocypris macrolepis* Bl. of 6–15 mm length, the adult food of which consists of detritus; and many others.

But fishes do not only feed upon crustaceans in their larval stages. Plank-tonic crustaceans form the basis of the nourishment of such planktophagic fishes as the oceanic herring, *Clupea harengus* L., or the anchovy, *Engraulis encrassicholus* L., and many others. Oceanic herring in both the North Atlantic and the northern part of the Pacific Ocean feed mainly on the cope-pod *Calanus finmarchicus* Gunner *et al* and Euphausiacea.

Planktonic crustaceans are also eaten by freshwater fishes, such as the lake whitefish. It is interesting that the ripe eggs of many copepods are not digested on passage through the guts of fishes and do not lose their vitality. Because of this, if a ripe female with egg sacs is eaten by a fish the eggs do not die but continue to develop.

Crustaceans are eaten to some extent by the majority of benthophagic fishes of the Black, Azov, Caspian, and Aral Seas. Thus, in the Caspian (Zheltenkova, 1939) in the roach crustaceans comprise 6·8 % of the food, in the bream 54·0 %, in the sevruga-sturgeon 45·9 %, in the common sturgeon 19·8 %, in *Neogobius fluviatilis pallasi* Berg 70·5 %, and so on. In the Barents Sea the main consumers of crustaceans among demersal fishes are the cod, haddock, redfish, and small catfish. In fresh waters crustaceans are found more rarely in the food of adult benthophagic fishes, which is explained by their lower abundance there. Crustaceans play a large part in the nutrition of fishes (particularly trout) which inhabit mountain lakes and streams. Thus, for example, in Lake Sevan the main food of the local representatives of the genus *Salmo* consists of amphipods.

In the search for their crustacean food, fishes sometimes perform con-siderable journeys. Some of these movements have a diurnal rhythm; others are repeated at particular times of the year. Thus, for example, in the Aral Sea the amphipods rise to the surface by night and sink to the bottom by day. *Chalcalburnus chalcoides aralensis* Berg and *Pelecus cultratus* (L.), follow the amphipods. By day they feed in the bottom layers, but by night they rise to the surface. As an example of seasonal migrations performed by fishes in connection with the movements of crustaceans, we may mention the move-ments of the Bombay duck, *Harpodon nehereus* Ham., of the family Scopelidae (Hora, 1934a). During the rainy season in India, which lasts from June to October, enormous masses of water run into the rivers, carrying into them great quantities of biogenic materials. These biogenic materials, when they enter the sea, allow the development in the immediate vicinity of the mouths of the rivers, particularly the Ganges, of enormous masses of planktonic algae, which attract crustaceans from places far distant from the river mouths.

In places where there is a mass development of planktonic algae, enormous accumulations of crustaceans form, following which the Bombay duck also arrive. The local inhabitants know the time of appearance of this fish, and as soon as the rainy season sets in they start to prepare for the fishery.

Crustaceans are also used as food for young fish in fish-farms. Sometimes planktonic crustaceans (*Daphnia*, *Cyclops*, etc.) are specially cultured for this purpose.

Certain crustaceans can influence the food supply of fishes, by consuming the same food as eaten by the fishes. Thus, for example, the Chinese crab, *Eriocheir sinensis*, which feeds on molluscs and worms, can impoverish the feeding conditions of certain benthophagic fishes.

Crustaceans can also cause some harm, mainly to larval fishes, as predators. Thus, in the Dunai the copepods *Mesocyclops leucarti* (Claus) and *Acanthocyclops vernalis* attack larval shad (Fig. 61). Various other copepods also attack larval fish (Dziuban, 1939). This could happen in natural watermasses, when the development of the larvae gets out of phase and lags behind that of the plankton. Usually the mass development of the *Cyclops* coincides with the development of the fish larvae to a phase in which the larvae are able to feed upon the *Cyclops*.

In fish-farms, where sturgeon larvae are reared, cases are known in which the *Cyclops* put into the basins as food for the fishes have attacked the soft parts of their fins. Balanoid nauplii attack the pelagic larvae of fishes and feed on them, partially consuming them (Dolgopolskaïa, 1946).

To a lesser extent, crustaceans cause harm to fishes by attacking older individuals. Thus, certain crabs attack and consume diseased and dying fishes. Usually the crustaceans feed on weak or decomposing fishes, and do not attack strong healthy ones. The only exceptions are the swimming crabs, fam. Portunidae, which swim freely and some of which may occasionally catch even such a lively fish as the mackerel.

Commensalism also occurs between fishes and crustaceans. Thus, for example, the small fish *Careproctus sinensis* Gilb. et Burke, fam. Liparidae, lays its eggs under the claw of a crab. In connection with this the female of this fish possesses an ovipositor (Rass, 1950).

Parasitic relationships between fishes and crustaceans are of very great importance. There are no fishes parasitic on crustaceans. Crustacean parasites of fishes are very common.

Fishes are parasitized by representatives of three orders of the crustaceans: copepods, branchiurans, and isopods. All the crustaceans which parasitize

FIG. 61. Shad larvae being attacked by *Cyclops* in the Dunai River.

[*To face page* 124

fishes are external parasites, affecting the skin or the gills. They occur on both marine and freshwater fishes. Probably the most important ones are copepods. The U.S.S.R. fauna includes about 180 species of parasitic copepods (Markevich, 1951, 1956). Among freshwater copepods, mention must be made of *Ergasilus sieboldi* Nord., which can also tolerate slightly brackish water. In the Neva Bay, according to Dogiel's data, about 13 % of the pike and 6·5 % of roach are infected with this parasite. Each fish may carry from 1 to 213 parasites. The *Ergasilus* attaches itself to the gills of the fish by means of its second pair of antennae, which are modified to form

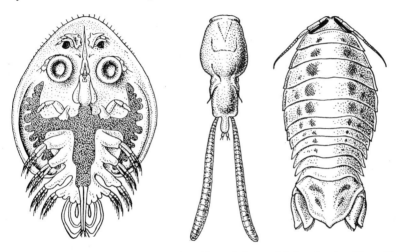

Fig. 62. Crustacean parasites of fishes (from left to right): *Argulus* (Branchiura), *Caligus* (Copepoda), *Aega* (Isopoda).

hooks. This parasite may cause serious harm, and sometimes bring about mass mortalities of fishes in fish-farms. The main copepod parasites of sea-fishes are members of the genus *Caligus* (Fig. 62). These crustaceans attach themselves to the fish by means of suckers and by the second antennae, which are modified to form a hook. The members of this genus are mainly distributed in northern seas. They occur on the cod, haddock, and other fishes in the Barents Sea. Temperatures above 18–20° are lethal for these parasites.

Some copepods are so extremely modified by their parasitic mode of life as to lose all appearance of being crustaceans. Thus, for example, *Lernaea branchialis*, which occurs on the gills of the cod, has undergone extreme modifications. The developmental cycle of this crustacean is rather complicated.

The larval stage develops on the gills of the plaice. When the larvae are ripe they live for some time in the water column, where the males fertilize the females and themselves die. The females attach themselves to the gills of gadoids, taking on a sac-like body shape and increasing considerably in size compared to that of the free-living stage. The main enlargement occurs in the first sexual segment of the thorax. The parasite roots itself deeply in the gill tissues and feeds on the host's blood, causing a slowing down of the fish's growth and its exhaustion.

One of the most serious pests of fish-farms is the branchiuran *Argulus foliaceus* L. (Fig. 62). This parasite causes particularly serious harm in carp farms, sometimes leading to the death of a considerable part of the livestock of young fish. The carp-louse attaches itself to the skin of the host, feeding on its body fluids, usually causing a considerable ulceration of the skin and exhaustion of the fish, finally leading to its death.

Certain isopods also occur as fish parasites. Isopods occur on both marine and freshwater fishes. Like the above-mentioned crustaceans, the isopods mainly feed by sucking the body fluids of their host. Large *Aega* (Fig. 62) very frequently occur on the gills, in the buccal cavity, and on the body of the fish, usually at the bases of the fins in cod and haddock. Certain representatives of this group occur on the gills of clupeoids and various other fishes. These are fairly large crustaceans, attaining to a length of 4 cm or more. They sometimes make deep wounds in the body of the fish, and may cause the fish to die.

In Far Eastern fresh waters there occurs on cyprinoids a parasitic isopod, *Livoneca amurensis* Gerfst. (Krykhtin, 1951). It attaches itself near the thoracic fin of the fish (in the Amur, mainly, on the ide, *Leuciscus waleckii* Dyb.), and buries itself inside the body cavity. Most of the fishes become infected at a length of 6–8 cm. The infected fish gradually dies. The great majority of infected fish die at a length of 8–10 cm. The parasite is usually absent in larger individuals, because the infected fish do not survive to such a size. Usually a male and a female parasitize the same fish.

Crustaceans are also important as vectors of helminth invasions toward fishes, being the intermediate hosts for several parasitic worms: ligulids, tapeworms, and others.

Insects

It should be noted that, in contrast to crustaceans, the insects play a considerably greater role in relation to fishes in fresh waters than in the sea.

Insects are of very great importance in fresh and brackish waters as food of fishes.

Aquatic insect larvae, particularly those of the chironomid midges, and also of the caddis-fly, mayfly, dragonfly, etc., form the food of fishes.

Chironomid larvae form the food of fishes principally in soft-bottomed water-masses, with stagnant or slowly flowing water. These larvae are most important as the food of freshwater fishes in the tropics, temperate latitudes, and in the arctic. They are also very important in the brackish waters of the Caspian and Aral sea-lakes.

Percentage of Chironomid Larvae in Food of the Bream
(From Shorygin, 1952, and Nikolsky, 1940)

	Spring	Summer	Autumn
Caspian	2	4	7
Aral	9·1	8·7	5·8

Because these larvae are a highly calorific fish food, they are specially cultured on fish-farms.

Caddis and mayfly larvae are mainly used as fish food in streams with a stony bed, fast current, and clear water. Thus, in the Amur, mayfly larvae comprise 80 % of the food of *Brachymystax lenok* (Pall.), and caddis larvae 8–15 %, while the food of the grayling in the Amur comprises 80–90 % mayfly larvae and 8–10 % caddis larvae.

In rivers with fast currents and a mobile sandy bottom, where the biomass of the benthos is small and cannot fully satisfy the food requirements of the fishes, they feed largely on the caddis larvae which grow in masses on obstacles which fall into the water. In the Ural River it is mostly the sturgeon which feeds on the caddis larvae on obstacles. The same is also true of Central Asian rivers.

Of considerable importance also as fish food are the insects which fall into the water from the shore. In summer the trout living in shallow hill streams feed mainly an aerial insects. Thus, in the English trout (Allen, 1938) aerial insects form the following percentage of the food by months:

Jan.	Feb.	Mar.	April	May	June	July	Aug.	Sept.	Oct.	Nov.	Dec.
0	0·7	1·7	21·5	52·5	32·2	25·0	93·0	73·4	1·7	1·5	0

At the time of mass-emergence of insects such as the mayfly and chirono-mid midges, even those fishes which do not normally feed on them start to do so. Naturally, in temperate and high latitudes the significance of aerial insects in the food of fishes bears a strictly seasonal character. In tropical waters the seasonal character of feeding upon aerial insects is much less pronounced.

Certain fishes specially hunt for aerial insects. Thus, the archer-fish of south-east Asian waters, *Toxotes jaculator*, splashes the insects sitting on plants suspended above the water with a jet of water from its mouth. The mud-skipper, *Periophthalmus*, which lives in mangrove swamps, actively hunts for terrestrial insects on dry land.

Insects, such as beetles, bugs, and midge larvae, which eat the same food as fishes, can deplete their food supply. Thus, for example, the predatory larvae of the midge *Procladius choreus* Meig. kills the larvae of other chirono-mid midges in quantities equivalent to 72–188 % of their own weight; and since the *Procladius* larvae are extremely abundant they can have a consider-able effect upon the food supply of fishes. The rate of consumption by *Procladius* of other midge larvae varies according to the nature of the bottom (Beliavskaia and Konstantinov, 1956).

Many insects and their larvae are predators which are capable of destroy-ing large quantities of spawn, larvae, and more rarely, adult fishes. Among the Dytiscid beetles many species attack and consume fish larvae. The harm due to these beetles, in particular the very widely distributed *Dytiscus marginalis* L., can be very appreciable. Cases are known when this species has completely exterminated the whole brood of salmon and carp in fish-farms.

According to the data of P. Petrovich (1939), different aquatic insects consume various amounts of fish larvae (Table 7).

Besides the water-beetles, as the table shows, very serious harm is caused to fishes by the water-bugs, particularly the water-scorpion and the water-boatman. The water-scorpion *Nepa* usually attacks young fishes and hardly touches adults, but if it gets into the spawning ponds in large numbers it can cause vary substantial harm, killing many larvae. In contrast to the water-scorpion the water-boatman *Notonecta* also kills small adult fish, by means of a poison which it injects into the wound by means of the proboscis. The bug *Corixa* also causes a certain amount of harm to fishes, by attacking their larvae. Young fishes are also eaten by the larger dragonfly nymphs.

In combating harmful insects in fish-farms various insecticides are used, particularly DDT. However, the DDT also affects fishes.

Recently the use of "black light" has been introduced for catching harmful insects; that is, the ultraviolet part of the spectrum, with a wavelength of less than 400 mϕ, which is perceptible to insects and attracts them (water-beetles, water-boatman, etc.). The rate of attraction of insects is very high. Thus, in one hour of work in the Azov region more than a thousand harmful aquatic beetles and bugs were attracted (Mazokhin-Porshniakov, 1957).

TABLE 7

Numbers of Fish Larvae Consumed by Aquatic Insects under Experimental Conditions

Species of insect	Number of larvae eaten	In experiments Number of days	Number per day
Dytiscus marginalis adults	102	22	4·5
Dytiscus marginalis larvae	91	12	7·6
Acilius sulcatus adults	18	8	2·2
Acilius sulcatus larvae	131	24	5·5
Notonecta glauca adult	45	9	5·0
Notonecta glauca nymphs	103	15	7·0
Nepa cinerea	17	8	2·1
Corixa	36	17	2·1

In fish-farms, one of the most widely used methods for combating harmful insects is the regulation of the filling of the ponds with water. The periods of filling are selected with respect to the life cycles of the various insects.

Echinoderms

In the sea the echinoderms play a substantial role in the lives of fishes. Many serve as food for them. In northern European waters, for example, echinoderms form the basic food of the striped catfish, *Anarhichas minor* Ol. Echinoderms also play a fairly substantial role in the nourishment of tropical fishes. Certain skates consume quite large quantities of them. In connection with feeding on echinoderms, fishes have evolved a number of adaptations, in particular the powerful terminal teeth in the catfish and the panel-like teeth of the skates are adapted for grinding up the armour of the echinoderms.

On the other hand, many echinoderms feed on fishes. Sea-stars, particularly *Asterias rubens* L., attack fishes by seizing them with their rays (Fig. 63).

Usually the sea-stars attack fishes which are no larger than the sea-star (from the end of one ray to that of the opposite one). An exception is the pipefish, which is preyed upon by the sea-star even when considerably larger than the sea-star. Occasionally a single fish will be seized by two sea-stars, which commence to swallow it from opposite ends. The sea-stars swallow the fish in the following manner: the fish, swimming about, touches a sea-star, which instantly seizes the fish by means of its pedicellariae and gradually moves it tail first toward the oral aperture. The fish is digested by parts, and while the hind part of the fish is being digested the fore part is still outside.

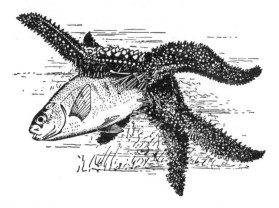

FIG. 63. Sea-star consuming a fish (from Gorce, 1939).

The main prey of sea-stars are those fishes which swim near the bottom of the sea. It is interesting that those fishes which live in close contact with the sea-star do not provoke any seizing reaction of the latter even when they touch them. Cases are known of the consumption by sea-stars of various species of *Sparus*, *Nerophis*, *Syngnathus*, *Syphonostoma*, *Fundulus*, and certain other fishes. Unfortunately, it has not yet been established what percentage of the food of sea-stars consists of fishes.

Sea-urchins also eat fishes which they seize by means of their pedicellaria. Sea-urchins have been recorded as eating the following species of fishes: *Gobius paganellus* L., *Labrus mixtus* Kröy., *Blennius*, *Pleuronectes*, and many others. As was mentioned for sea-stars, cases are also known of two sea-urchins attacking the same fish. At the same time that one urchin is digesting one end of the fish, the other end is being digested by another.

Echinoderms, particularly sea-stars and brittle-stars, are also important as consumers of fish food. According to the data of Thorson (1956), of all the fish-food organisms consumed by predators on the Danish coast only 2–5 % are actually eaten by fishes. The remainder are eaten by marine inverte-brates, primarily sea-stars and brittle-stars. The magnitude of the influence of sea-stars and brittle-stars upon the food supply of fishes is shown by the fact that the density of such predatory echinoderms as the sea-stars which feed, mainly, upon molluscs, sometimes exceeds fifteen individuals per square metre. Brittle-stars may be as dense as 400–500 per square metre, while the amount of food consumed daily per unit weight of these predators may be three to four times as great as that consumed by fishes. In some places the density of predatory brittle-stars is so great that they search with their rays every square centimetre of the surface of the sea-bed once daily (Thorson, 1956).

Something approaching commensalism between a fish and an echinoderm is the relationships between the small fish *Fierasfer* and a holothurian. This fish lives in the cloaca of the holothurian. Apparently this strange habitat serves the fish as a refuge from enemies. The *Fierasfer* feeds mainly on the small animals which also enter the gut of the holothurian. In the absence of the holothurian the *Fierasfer* sometimes inhabits the interior of a sea-star or the mantle cavity of a large bivalve mollusc. A species of fish which is a close relative of *Fierasfer* has been described by Sumner as a parasite of a holo-thurian. Penetrating into the interior of its prey, this fish gradually eats it from inside. *Fiersafer* lays demersal eggs, from which emerge larvae which have at first a pelagic life, then settle to the bottom and subsequently lodge inside the holothurian.

Other classes of vertebrates, besides fishes themselves, also play a very important role in the lives of fishes.

Amphibia

Amphibians are eaten by fishes only in fresh waters. Certain fishes, such as the snakehead, *Ophicephalus argus* Cant., eat tadpoles. The snakehead con-sumes large numbers of tadpoles in small water-masses. In fish-farm condi-tions the trout-perch *Huro floridana* (Le Sueur) readily eats tadpoles.

Frogs are eaten, to some extent, by pike. Thus, in various parts of the Pechora, frogs form 0·3–3·3 % of the food of pike (Teplova and Teplov, 1953). Large numbers of frogs are eaten by the sheat-fish, which in the Volga, Dnieper, and many other rivers specially approaches the banks in search of them. Frogs are regarded as one of the best baits on sheat-fish hooks. There is a special method of fishing for sheat-fish: in places where the hooks are set out, and baited with frogs, a peculiar noise is made by knocking the water-surface with an upturned wooden cup, in imitation of the noise made by the frogs, and the sheat-fish approach and seize the bait.

Amphibians may also exert a considerable adverse effect on fishes. Many frogs eat larval fishes, sometimes killing them in masses. Idelson and Vonokov (1938) showed that in the delta of the River Volga the green frog, *Rana ridibunda* Pall. consumes very large numbers of fry of commercial fishes. Thus, on the Loshtina mudflats, frogs killed in a period of 2 to 3 months an average of 110,000 fish fry per hectare, of which 75·4 % were roach, 6·3 % carp, 13·3 % bleak, 1·3 % bream, and 3·7 % white bream. Frogs consumed 58·7 % of the total numbers of fry descending from the flats. A similar picture is observed in other waters. Thus, in North America many fishes are killed by the bull-frog, *R. catesbiana* Schaw. Fishes are also eaten by the Japanese salamander, *Megalobatrachus maximus* Schl. and a number of other large amphibians.   There are indications that not only frogs but also newts eat the spawn.

Reptiles

Interrelationships between fishes and reptiles are mainly of the predator and prey type, the reptiles being the predators. Only a few freshwater fishes (such as the sheat-fish) ever consume reptiles, as when, for example, a lizard falls in when the river-bank gives way.

In temperate latitudes almost the only reptiles which eat fishes are the water grass-snake, *Natrix tesselata hydrus* Pall., and certain other grass-snakes. In some places, especially where fishes are cultivated in rice paddies, snakes may cause considerable losses. In tropical fresh waters snakes also cause serious harm to the fish populations. Thus, in East African lakes the water-snake *N. olivaceus* feeds on fish. In the sea fishes are attacked by representatives of the family Hydrophidae, which occur in the tropics. In contrast to freshwater species, the sea-snakes are poisonous.

Fishes form a substantial part of the food of crocodiles, especially the Nile crocodile of Lake Victoria Nyanza, although many individuals also eat large numbers of invertebrates. According to Graham (1929), the Nile crocodile easily captures swimming fishes and frequently causes substantial harm to the fisheries by tearing the fish out of the nets.

Both freshwater and marine turtles feed on fish. Among marine species the tiled turtle, *Chelone imbricata* L., and the green turtle, *C. midas* L., must be mentioned, and among freshwater species the members of the subfamily Emydinae (in European waters, *Emys orbicularis* L. and *Clemmys caspica* [Gmel.]) and the tropical and subtropical *Trionix*, which are even caught by the natives of China and Africa on hooks baited with fish.

However, it is not at present possible to estimate the destructiveness of reptiles toward fishes quantitatively. All the investigations of the feeding of aquatic reptiles on fish so far are only qualitative.

Birds

There are very complex and varied relationships between fishes and birds. Although fishes may frequently eat birds, they do not eat very many of them. Large pike in Siberian and North European rivers and lakes eat fairly large numbers of waterfowl. Some predatory sea-fishes also eat birds, and keep near to the bird colonies in order to feed on chicks which fly on to the water.

Sometimes birds facilitate the dispersal of fishes, by transporting spawn from one water-mass to another on their feet. Apparently this was the method whereby the southern stickleback, *Pungitius platygaster aralensis* (Kessl.), was introduced from the Aral Sea basin into the enclosed lakes of West Siberia.

Birds have a considerable significance toward fishes as fertilizers of the water. In the nesting places of aquatic birds enormous quantities of their droppings fall into the water every day, which causes a development of the phytoplankton and of the aquatic invertebrates on which fishes feed. For this reason, there are frequently masses of fishes in the vicinity of bird colonies, feeding on the rich plankton. Nowadays, the role of birds as fertilizers of the water is also exploited by mankind. Thus, in the U.S.S.R. there are beginning to come into practice fish-bird farms, in which ducks are kept on the carp ponds, which they fertilize with their droppings, leading to a significant increase in their productivity. The ducks also partially improve the ponds by eating surplus weeds.

On the other hand, there are very many species of piscivorous birds. Fishes form the basic, and even the only food of many birds. Among the hawk family, Accipitridae, several representatives have gone over to feeding almost exclusively on fishes. Thus, for example, the fish-hawk [*Pandion haliaetus* (L.)], the sea-eagles (white-tailed, *Haliaetus albicilla* L.; long-tailed, *H. leucoryphus* Pall.), and the Kamchatkan [*Thalassaetus pelagicus* (Pall.)], and several others. All these large predators mostly kill adult and often fairly large fishes. Most of the larger species of the orders Gaviiformes and

Colymbiformes also feed on fish, as for example, the eider-duck, sheldrake, and certain others. Fishes are also eaten by the various kingfishers, which are particularly widely distributed in the tropics. But the most important piscivorous birds are the cormorant, heron, pelican, gulls, and ducks. The species composition of the fishes consumed by the various species of birds, even in the same vicinity, can vary considerably according to their method of capturing the fish. Thus, for example, the cormorant does not usually eat pelagic fishes, which, however, make up a large part of the food of seagulls.

The numbers of fish consumed by piscivorous birds is very large, so that in places where they occur in large numbers these birds may cause serious losses to the fisheries. It is known that the food of the cormorant in the Volga delta comprises 23·4 % of carp, 22·5 % shad, 11·5 % perch, 10·3 % gobies, 9·1 % white bream, 6·6 % rudd, 6·6 % bream, 6·1 % pike, 3 % roach, i.e. the bulk of the heron's food consists of commercial fishes. According to Skokova (1955), the roach formed 37·6 % of the food of the cormorant in the Volga delta in 1952, and 27·8 % in 1953. In one day an adult cormorant eats about 700 g of fish, a young one about 500 g (Sushkina, 1932). Apart from this, when hunting, the cormorant injures enormous numbers of fishes, which ultimately die as a result of their injuries. In the region of the Volga delta it has been estimated that the cormorant kills 5000 metric tons of fish annually, i.e. nearly 1·5 % of the total catch in the North Caspian. In the bird colonies off Peru the birds annually consume up to 5·5 million kg of fish. Fishes, particularly pelagic ones, occupy an extremely important place in the food of the majority of colonial sea-birds in the Barents Sea (Table 8).

TABLE 8

Proportion of Fish in the Food of Colonial Sea-Birds in the Barents Sea (in %) (from Belopolsky, 1957)

Species of bird	% fish in food	Species of bird	% fish in food
Guillemot, *Uria aalge* Pont.	95·0	Glaucus gull, *Larus hyperboreus* Pall.	15·2
Guillemot, *Uria lomvia* L.	95·6	Great black-backed gull, *Larus marinus*	
Razorbill, *Alca torda* L.	92·0	L.	40·4
Puffin, *Fratercula arctica* L.	67·0	Herring gull, *Larus argentatus* Pont.	29·9
Black guillemot, *Cepus grylle* L.	58·6	Common gull, *L. canus* L.	22·2
Kittiwake, *Rissa tridactyla* L.	52·2	Tern, *Sterna paradisea* Brünn.	55·6
Arctic skua, *Stercorarius para-*		Common eider, *Somateria mollisima* L.	0·6
siticus L.	41·6		

The composition of the food of any one species of bird naturally varies according to the concentrations of the food species. Thus, for example, in the short-beaked guillemot *U. lomvia* in eastern Murman the bulk of the food consists of sandeels (23·1 %), herrings (38·5 %), and cod (20·5 %), while in the Novaya Zemlya region the food of this same species consists of polar cod (51·3 %) and cod (44·3 %). However, the biological type of the fishes consumed in various regions is more or less similar. There are strong seasonal variations in the composition of the fishes consumed by birds. As may be seen from the graph (Fig. 64), the bulk of the food of the long-beaked

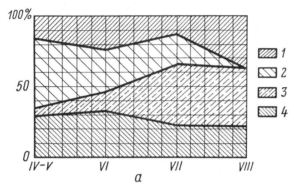

FIG. 64. Seasonal changes in the proportions of species of fishes consumed by the guillemot *Uria aalge* Pont on the east Murman coast (from Belopolsky, 1957). 1, Sandeels; 2, capelan; 3, herring; 4, juvenile cod.

guillemot *U. aalge* in the spring consists of capelan, which falls to zero in the autumn, which is related to the fact that the capelan leaves the areas inhabited by this bird. Conversely, the proportion of herrings in the food of this bird increases in the autumn.

Many piscivorous birds are so closely connected in their biology to particular species of fish, that it is possible to determine the approach of these fish by the appearance of the birds, which feed on them. For example, the wintering places of the shearwater in the Black Sea are close to those of the anchovy. Shearwaters can dive to very great depths when pursuing fish. Thus, in the Black Sea the Manx shearwater *Puffinus puffinus* Brünnich can dive to a depth of 70 m. The anchovy, *Engraulis encrasicholus* (L.), usually keeps to a depth of 20–40 m by day in winter, and the shearwater feeds intensively on it at this time; in the evening the fish rises closer to the surface and the shearwater, which feeds only by day, does not touch it (Salnikov, 1957).

Piscivorous birds such as the heron and water-swallow can cause some harm to hatcheries by consuming young fish. However, it must also be borne in mind that the water-swallow consumes predatory insects which feed on the fish (Borodulina, 1955).

Apart from the immediate harm caused to the fisheries by birds killing fishes, they also sometimes exert a direct effect on the fisheries. In particular, in some West Siberian lakes it sometimes becomes temporarily quite impossible to use stake nets for the capture of fishes, because the sea-gulls which nest in masses on these lakes tangle the nets in their efforts to get the fish out of them.

Birds also have a certain adverse effect on fishes as the vectors of helminth infections, particularly ligulids, the infection sometimes reaching such a magnitude that mass mortalities of fishes occur.

Mammals

Mammals, like birds, play a significant part in the lives of fishes.

Mammals have very slight significance as food for fishes. Certain sharks attack young seals; Caspian seal pups infrequently get into the stomachs of the white sturgeon. Mice, shrews, and other small mammals, which fall into the water, are often eaten by the pike, sheat-fish, and many other predatory fishes both in temperate latitudes and in the tropics. Among freshwater fishes the taimen, *Hucho taimen* (Pall.), *Brachymystax lenok* Pall., grayling *Thymallus*, and the pike, *Esox lucius* L., regularly feed on mammals in certain waters.

In the Pechora, and the Siberia and Amur Rivers, the taimen frequently eats mice, shrews, sometimes even squirrels. *Brachymystax* regularly eats small mammals (mice, shrews), but in small numbers. Thus, in the Amur, terrestrial mammals occur in only 10 % of the guts of *Brachymystax*.

Grayling regularly consume small mammals in certain waters. In the Pechora the grayling, *Thymallus thymallus* (L.), eats mainly shrews, *Sorex*, particularly in their migratory period when they swim across the water in large numbers. A special method of fishing for the taimen and grayling, using an artificial mouse consisting of felt shaped like a mouse and enclosing the hook, is based on the fact that these fishes will feed on small mammals.

In certain waters many mammals are eaten by the pike. It is of interest that such aquatic mammals as the water-rat are only rarely eaten by predatory fishes. Usually fishes eat only such small terrestrial mammals that accidentally fall into the water.

Fairly large mammals may be attacked by the sheat-fish, *Silurus glanis* L., which occasionally drowns dogs swimming across rivers. Certain members of the suborder Characinoidei attack large mammals. Thus, for example, the Amazonian pirhana, *Rooseveltiella piraya* Cuv. (see Fig. 65), swims in shoals and attacks large mammals which swim across the river. Despite their small size (up to 30 cm), these fish can severely wound the animals with their sharp teeth, tearing off pieces of flesh. If an animal, even of such a large size as a bull or a tapir, is attacked by these predators in midstream, very often it is unable to reach the bank through exhaustion, weakened by loss of blood, and finally falls prey to the small predators.

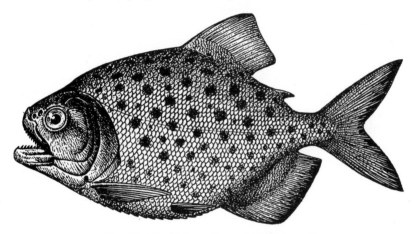

FIG. 65. The pirhana *Rooseveltiella piraya* Cuv.

Some beneficial effect on fishes is caused by mammals consuming organisms (mainly cephalopod molluscs) which otherwise feed on the same food as the fish. In European and North Pacific waters cephalopods are eaten by approximately 40 % of species of toothed whales.

However, mammals have a far greater effect on fishes as consumers. Thus, fishes play a very substantial part in the nutrition of the Cetacea (whales), Pinnipedia (seals), certain carnivores, insectivores, and even bats.

Many whales consume enormous quantities of shoal-forming fishes: anchovies, herrings, sardines, and other fishes, shoals of which they usually follow. Fifty per cent of the European whalebone whales feed on fishes. The herring whale, *Balaenoptera physalus* L., eats mainly capelan and herrings. *B. acutirostrata* Lac. and *Megaptera nodosa* Bonnaterre also eat fishes. The latter eats in particular the Far Eastern salmon in its marine phase of life

(Tomilin, 1957). Among the toothed whales of the European fauna some 45 % of species use fishes as food to quite a large extent. The sperm-whale, *Physeter*, feeds on fishes, especially *Sebastodes* and skates (Tomilin, 1957).

The white whale, *Delphinapterus leucas* Pall., eats salmon (chum, humpback, etc.) and gadoids (mainly polar cod, cod, and navaga), and also representatives of other groups of fishes. The narwal, *Monodon monoceros* L., eats plaice, gadoids, and skates. Fishes also comprise a significant part of the food of the dolphins (subfamily Delphininae). Members of the genus *Phocaena* (porpoises) usually attack small fish which live in shoals. In the Barents Sea they feed on the capelan and herring, in southern waters on the anchovy, gobies, etc. The food of the common dolphin, *Delphinus delphis* L., in the Black Sea includes the anchovy, sprat, southern haddock, sturgeon, red mullet, etc. The dolphin feeds most actively on fish (anchovies) in the summer (Kleinenberg, 1956). Considerable quantities of fish are also eaten by *Tursiops tursio* Fabr. In the Black Sea its food consists principally of the anchovy, plaice, and southern haddock. *Orca orca* Fabr., the most predatory dolphin, eats the greatest range of fishes from herring to sharks.

Seals also consume very large quantities of fishes. Thus, the tufted seal feeds mainly on fishes in the deeper water (redfish and cod). Fishes are also the main food of the species *Halichoerus gryphus* Fabr., *Histiophoca fasciata* Zim., *Phoca caspica* Gmel., and other seals.

Many fishes are also eaten by mammals which are not as closely connected with the water as are the pinnipedes and the cetaceans, such as the otter, bears (polar and grizzly), foxes, jackal, fish-eating rat, musquash, and muskrat. True, the grizzly bear only consumes fishes in its scattered habitats. Fishes are an important part of the food of the grizzly bear in Kamchatka and along the coast of the Okhotsk Sea, where during the upstream passage of the salmon this animal goes over almost entirely to feeding on fishes.

Fishes are frequently eaten by foxes and jackals, the former often making raids on fish-farms in which carp are raised. Among the insectivores the fish-eating mouse, *Neomys fodiens* Schr., eats large quantities of fish. This small animal often attacks fish which are considerably larger than itself. In some regions it can cause substantial harm to fisheries. Fishes are also an important part of the food of the musquash and muskrat, *Ondatra zibethica* L. When it penetrates into a stream where carp are overwintering, the muskrat can cause very severe damage by killing the yearlings, and also by destroying the dams and other earthworks. As consumers of the same food as fishes, certain mammals, particularly the whalebone whales, Mystacoceti, are of substantial importance. These mammals feed mainly on planktonic crustaceans. Thus, the Greenland Right Whale, *Eubalena glacialis* (Bonnaterre), feeds mostly on the crustacean *Calanus*, while the blue whale, *Balaenoptera musculus* L., feeds mostly on euphausiid krill. The grey whale, *Eschrichtius gibbosus* Erxlebn., feeds on benthic invertebrates, especially bottom amphipods.

FIG. 66. A beaver dam and the change in the water-body produced by it.

Most of the European species of whalebone whales feed to some extent on the invertebrates which also serve as the food of fishes.

There can be no doubt that the sharp reduction in the abundance of whalebone whales in the North Atlantic as a result of intensive whaling has led to a significant increase in the abundance of food for the herring.

Fig. 67. The main forms of biotic links in the sea. 1, Blue whale and herrings, both feeding on the same food; 2, sea-gulls eating fishes; 3, dolphins hunting for fishes; 4, storm-petrel diving for fishes; 5, fishes dwelling under the umbra of a medusa; 6, medusa with captured fishes; 7, squid seizing a fish; 8, humpback whale hunting for herrings; 9, *Careproctus* laying its spawn underneath the claw of a crab;

FIG. 68. For legend see page 142.

The development of the whale fishery in the antarctic puts on the agenda the problem of acclimatizing pelagic commercial fishes from the Arctic, in particular the herring, in this region because there are no mass consumers of the planktonic crustaceans (such as euphausiids) among Antarctic fishes.

Mammals are also connected with fishes as the final hosts of certain parasites, predominantly tapeworms, for which the fishes act as the intermediate hosts (see above).

Some mammals, such as the beaver, bring about substantial changes in the conditions in a river, by constructing dams and making new water-bodies, and they thereby have some influence on the fish fauna (Fig. 66). Settling in frozen lakes, as the observations of Kleinenberg have shown, the beavers, by making air holes in the ice, often improve the oxygen content of the water to such an extent that the ice melts. For certain waters of North America cases are on record of beaver dams having partitioned off a spawning river and cut the spawning grounds off from the feeding grounds (Brown, 1938). On the other hand, in the lakes which form above the beaver dams, the numbers of small non-commercial species of fishes increase, and these are the food of the trout and char, *Salvelinus*. Although the density of animals is not usually very much greater in the beaver dams than in rivers without this depth of water, the increase in the calm water increases the area which is suitable for feeding grounds for fishes (Rupp, 1955).

As may be seen from the above, the interrelationships between fishes and other animals are extremely complicated and multilateral (Figs. 67, 68). In the organization of a rational fishery these interrelationships must be taken into account, those links which have a beneficial significance for the fishery being strengthened, which will at the same time facilitate the increase in productivity of the stock of fish, and a weakening of those links which lead to a fall in the productivity of the stock of commercial fishes.

Fig. 68. The main forms of biotic links in inland water-masses. 1, Sea-eagle capturing a fish; 2, fish hawk, and 3, bear with captured fishes; 4, beavers constructing a dam, which has altered the conditions in the water-body; 5, otter with a captured fish; 6, spawn laid on a submerged plant; 7, sea-gull capturing a fish; the sea-gull's droppings fall into the water and form the source of infection of *Cyclops* with helminths; 8, fishes eating the infected *Cyclops*; 9, pike-perch hunting for small fishes; 10, merganser capturing a fish; 11, grass-snake capturing a fish; 12, heron and 13, frog with captured fishes; 14, bladderwort with fish larvae in its bladders; 15, stickleback at its nest constructed of plants; 16, ruffe and bream eating the same food; 17, female bitterling spawning into a mollusc; 18, dragonfly nymph; and 19, dytiscid larva with captured fish larvae.

PART II

FUNDAMENTAL LINKS IN THE
LIFE CYCLES OF FISHES

Part II

FUNDAMENTAL LINKS IN THE LIFE CYCLES OF FISHES

The entire life of any animal (as an individual), from birth to death, is divisible into a number of periods. The life cycle of fishes comprises the following periods:

I. Embryonic—the period of development from the moment of fertilization to changing over to external feeding. The embryo feeds at the expense of the yolk, a reserve of food which the maternal organism supplies.

This period falls into two parts:

(a) period of the egg, when development is taking place within the membrane;

(b) free-living embryo (prelarva), when development continues outside the membrane.

II. Larval period—feeding on external food; the external appearance and internal structure have not yet taken on the characteristics of the adult organism.

III. Period of the immature organism—the external appearance resembles that of the adult; gonads undeveloped; secondary sexual characteristics feebly developed or completely lacking.

IV. Period of the adult organism—which has attained to a state in which, at the appropriate time of year, it is able to reproduce itself; secondary sexual characteristics, if possessed by the species, present.

V. Period of senility—sexual function dying out; growth in length ceases or else extremely slow.

Each of these developmental periods has its adaptive significance in a specific respect, but there are features common to all species of fishes. Each developmental period has its own system of relationships with the environment, its own principal relationships, and in connection with these its own morpho-physiological peculiarities.

In the egg and embryo the principal relationships are usually in respect of respiration and protection against predators (Kryzhanovsky, 1949). There are the most varied adaptations in this respect. Feeding relationships have no

145

significance, because the embryo feeds on the yolk provided by the maternal organism. In the following period of development in connection with the change-over to external feeding the principal relationships are nutritional. In adult fishes, besides feeding relationships, such relationships as arise in respect of reproduction are of substantial importance.

Each period of development is characterized by its own adaptive specific relationships of protein growth and fat storage. In the first of these periods, up to the attainment of maturity, the main food resources which enter the fish's organism are utilized for growth. This is often a form of adaptation for protection against predators, because the larger the fish the more difficult it becomes for the predators to eat it (Vasnetsov, 1947).

In the next period of life linear growth has a subsidiary significance. The bulk of the energetic resources are used for the development of the gonads, and for the accumulation of reserve material for the support of metabolism during the fasting period while migrating, overwintering, and reproducing. Finally, during the period of senility the ratio of maintenance and growth nourishment (see page 278) is such that the growth nutrition can only support the accumulation of fats so that metabolism can continue during the period of enforced fasting.

Each of the periods of individual development falls into shorter stages (etaps). A stage is such a period in the development of a fish in which the changes and the growth taking place are very gradual, and it is not defined by any substantial qualitative changes in either the structure, function, or behaviour of the fish. Within the limits of the stage there is established a definite system of relationships with the environment which is specific for that stage (Vasnetsov, 1953).

Seasonal cyclical changes in the mode of life, physiology, and structure, which are just as characteristic of fishes as of other animals, are inseparably connected with the process of development. This seasonal cycle does not coincide with the various periods of development of the fish. In adult fishes the cycle usually comprises a series of links: wintering → migration to spawning grounds → spawning → migration to feeding grounds → feeding → migration to wintering grounds → wintering. Naturally this is a scheme which varies from one species to another; in different conditions, sometimes various links of the annual cycle may be excluded (as the wintering → wintering migration in whitefish) or new links may be included, such as the period of feeding prior to spawning in the carp in southern waters. Each successive link in the annual cycle is prepared for in the preceding one.

Thus, for example, the transition to overwintering only takes place after the completion of the period of feeding, i.e. the accumulation within the organism of a sufficient quantity of the right types of reserve materials which can support the metabolism during the overwintering period.

If, because of unfavourable feeding conditions, the fish is unable to accumulate the necessary materials for overwintering, it may not start its wintering migration. In certain cases the progressive worsening of the conditions might lead to mass mortality of the fishes, if they remain on the feeding grounds. Such occurrences are observed, for example, in the Sea of Azov in poor feeding years, when the anchovy, *Engraulis encrasicholus maeoticus* Pusanov, dies in masses as a result of the autumnal cooling.

Sometimes these cyclical periods may include more than one year, as happens in various migratory fishes. A study of the regular features of the development and cyclical changes in the structure and life of the fish enables us to approach the management of these processes to suit our needs.

Reproduction and Development of Fishes

Reproduction is the link in the life cycle of a fish which, in connection with other links, ensures the continuation of the species. The specific peculiarities of reproduction in every species are an adaptation to the particular conditions of reproduction and the development of its larvae, which provide the replenishment so essential for the preservation of the species and its abundance. The size and quality of the replenishment are determined by the quality and abundance of the spawning population, and also by the conditions under which the eggs and larvae develop. The adaptations of the fish to the conditions of its reproduction and development reflect not only the fundamental ecological factors of the embryonal period, but also the substantial features of all the other life periods. They are connected with the mode of life of the adult fish, with the character of its migrations, and other links in the life cycle (Kryzhanovsky, 1949).

The reproduction of fishes naturally possesses a number of features which are specific to aquatic animals. In the majority of fishes fertilization takes place outside the body. In contrast to terrestrial animals the sperm and eggs are in the water for some time outside the body of the parent animal.

The numbers of eggs spawned by various species of fishes varies very considerably, from a few large eggs in many sharks to three thousand million in the moon-fish, *Mola mola* L. On the whole the fecundity of fishes is much higher than that of terrestrial vertebrates. The most fecund fishes are those which have floating pelagic eggs; in second order are those which lay their spawn on plants. Fishes which protect or hide their eggs usually have a low fecundity. The fecundity of marine fishes is usually somewhat higher than that of freshwater or migratory fishes.

The number of eggs contained in the ovary of a fish is termed the individual, absolute, or total fecundity.

The individual fecundity is usually determined as follows: when the fish has been measured and weighed, the ovaries are taken out, weighed, and a subsample of 1, 5, or 10 g is taken from it (according to the size of the eggs). The eggs in the subsample are counted under a lens or by means of special apparatus. The number in the subsample is multiplied up to the weight of the ovary. If the eggs in various parts of the ovary are of different sizes, it is necessary to take several subsamples from different parts of the ovary and to calculate the average from them. If the fish has eggs of different sizes, these must be counted separately.

The relative fecundity, i.e. the number of eggs per unit weight or length of the fish, is also used as an index of fecundity.

However, the individual and relative fecundity are not characteristic of the reproductive capacity of the population, because the fecundity of the stock, or the population fecundity, depends not only on the individual fecundity, but also on the time of onset of sexual maturity, and on the periodicity and frequency of spawnings throughout the life of the individuals.

As a means of characterizing the specific fecundity, Severtsov (1941) proposed the formula:

$$\frac{1}{(1+r)^{p/js}}$$

where r is the number of eggs laid per spawning, p is the period between two successive spawnings, j is the age of onset of maturity, and s is the sex ratio.

However, this formula does not take into account a number of factors, in particular the duration of life of the individual, or, more strictly, the number of times it spawns during its life. Jogansen (1955), who modified Severtsov's formula, gave it the following form:

$$^{pj}\sqrt{r \cdot x}$$

where x is the number of spawnings during the life of the individual. Jogansen is of the opinion that, since for the majority of fishes the sex ratio is unity, this coefficient may be excluded.

Naturally both these formulae can only indicate the reproductive capacity of the species to a very first approximation. However, the fecundity, as calculated from the coefficients for three groups of fishes which differ in the value of this index, does schematically reflect the adaptations of the various species to different rates of consumption by predators. The first group (specific fecundity from 1 to 10) includes such species as the white and common sturgeons, *Stenodus leucichthys nelma* Pall., *Coregonus muksun* Pall., etc., which are adapted to a relatively low rate of predation.

The second group (specific fecundity 10–50) includes such fishes as pike, ide, carp, etc., and the third group (specific fecundity 50–210), fishes which are adapted to a considerable mortality, for example the whitefish, *Coregonus tugun* (Pall.).

In each species the individual and specific fecundity are subject to very great variation, primarily related to the variation in size of the fishes.

In the majority of fishes the number of eggs at first gradually increases with age, and then, as the individual approaches senility it usually begins to decrease. Actually the majority of our commercial fishes do not survive to an age at which the processes of senility set in; usually they are either eaten by a predator or else caught by man long before this age.

Changes in the Fecundity of Various Fishes in Relation to Length

Sturgeon *Acipenser stellatus* Pall. (acc. Derzhavin, 1922)

Length in cm	100	110	120	130	140	150	160	170	180	190	200
Number of eggs, in thousands		40	56	78	107	126	157	179	220	254	258

Salmon *Salmo salar* (L.) (acc. Berg, 1935)

Length in cm	50	60	70	80	90	100
Number of eggs, in thousands		5·9	9·4	12·2	14·0	19·4	

Carp *Cyprinus carpio* (L.) (acc. Nikolsky, 1934)

Length in cm	35	40	45	50	55	60	65	70
Number of eggs, in thousands		181	229	375	428·5	550	525	525

Pike-perch *Lucioperca lucioperca* (L.) (acc. Chugunova, 1931)

Length in cm	30	40	50	60	70	80
Number of eggs, in thousands	203	331	487	685	851	

It may be seen from the example that in all species there is an increase in the numbers of eggs with the length of the fish. Among these examples the onset of senility can only be determined in the carp, in which the number of eggs starts to decrease from a length of 60 cm.

The fecundity in a single population may undergo considerable fluctuations in relation to the supply of nourishment. A less numerous population, which therefore has a greater food supply, usually has a larger fecundity. Thus, for example, in the humpback salmon, *Oncorhynchus gorbuscha* (Walb.), in the lower reaches of the Amur, the fecundity of individuals of the same size is lower in years of poor runs than in years of good runs.

Average Fecundity of Amur Humpback Salmon (Length of Fish 44–46 cm)

Year	1928	1929	1930	1941	1948	1949	1950	1951
Number of eggs	1373	1446	1262	1447	1436	1556	1400	1505

In the North Caspian the fecundity of the roach of a particular size increases in good feeding years. Thus, in 1946 the fecundity of roach of 17·5–18·5 cm length was 38,500 eggs, while in the period 1911–31 it was only 25,400. Similar changes in the fecundity are also observed when the population is reduced through the influence of intensive fishing. Thus, under the influence of intensive fishing, and the concomitant improvement in the food supply, the fecundity of the Sakhalin herring (of length 25–26 cm) increased from 37,936 eggs in 1940 to 46,158 in 1946.

Differences occur in the fecundity of fishes of the same length in populations living under different conditions. Thus, for example, the fecundity of the pike of length 30–45 cm in the Aral Sea is 8287 eggs, and in the North Caspian 17,581; in the silver crucian carp (of length 22–24 cm) in the Amur the fecundity is 68,000 eggs, and in the lakes of the Urals it is 26,000.

Substantial differences are observed in fecundity between closely related species and even between close forms of the same species. Thus, for example, the fecundity of the Atlantic capelan, *Mallotus villosus* typ., varies from 6·2 to 13·4 thousand eggs, and that of the Pacific subspecies *Mallotus villosus socialis* Pall. from 15·3 to 39·3 thousand eggs.

Increase in the fecundity of fishes may arise from several causes. It may be due to a reduction in the reserves of yolk in the egg and the consequent reduction of the passive feeding period of the embryo, or by an increase in the density of the yolk, or, finally, by an increase in the volume of the gonad. Thus, for example, the fecundity of the Amur sturgeon *Huso dauricus* (Georgi) is greater than that of the white sturgeon *Huso huso* (L.) because of the smaller size of the eggs. In the Amur sturgeon, 1 g of ripe eggs contains 38–90 eggs, and in the white sturgeon 27–53. In the bitterling, *Rhodeus sericeus* Pall., the smaller size of the eggs is apparently due to the higher density of the yolk (Kryzhanovsky, 1949).

The individual fecundity is also increased by fractional spawning, when only part of the eggs present in the ovary together are ripe at any time. Fractional spawning is usually defined by the proportionality coefficient, which is the ratio of the number of eggs in the first portion to the total number of ripe eggs. However, this coefficient only reflects the relative size of the first portion and does not represent the phenomenon in its entirety.

Fractional spawning, and prolonged spawning periods, are mainly characteristic of tropical and subtropical species of fishes. In temperate latitudes there are only insignificant numbers of species with partial spawning, and in the Arctic they are completely absent. Often the same species, as, for example, the bream, *Abramis brama* (L.), has partial spawning in the southern part of its range, and only a single spawning in the northern part. The larger numbers of partial spawners in the tropics is explained by the fact that in the tropics there is no clear seasonal variation in the supply of plankton on which the larvae feed. This enables the larvae to find suitable food over a considerable part of the year.

Fractional spawning may not only be an adaptation to increased food supplies. It also ensures the preservation of the species under unfavourable abiotic spawning conditions—because of the death of the spawn of phytophyllic species when the spawning ground dries up through the fall in the water level in rivers (for example in carp and crucian carp, in the Amur), or through the death of pelagic eggs during storms (for example, the anchovy in the Sea of Azov). If these fishes had only a single spawning, the whole of a generation would have perished in some years; with fractional spawning only a part of it perishes.

The historical development of a fish may show a transition from single to fractional spawning or vice versa.

The occurrence of small eggs together with large ones in the ovary does not always indicate fractional spawning. In many fishes the small eggs remain in the ovary after spawning and are gradually reabsorbed. It is interesting that in certain species the number of eggs which are reabsorbed after spawning is subject to variation with age. Thus, for example, in the carp, as may be seen from the following table, the numbers of reabsorbed eggs are greater in the youngest and oldest carp than in those of middle ages.

Changes in the Proportion of Small Eggs (to the Total Number of Eggs) in Relation to the Size of Aral Carp

Length of fish in cm	35	40	45	50	55	60	65
Percentage of small eggs	24·2	21·5	16·1	15·8	12·9	34·7	

The fecundity of fishes, as that of other animals, is an adaptation which ensures the survival of the species under the conditions in which it originated and exists. Large fecundity evolves under conditions of heavy mortality, particularly when this is due to predators. Changes in individual fecundity are regulated by changes in the food supply. Faster growing individuals usually have a higher fecundity than slower growing ones of the same size. The species responds to changes in the environment by changes in its fecundity.

The notion that fecundity is a property of the species which ensures a high rate of intraspecific competition and thereby a more rapid rate of evolution, i.e. that the species with the higher fecundity have a greater biotic potential, is radically wrong. The concepts of "biotic potential" and "environmental antagonism" introduced by Chapman do not reflect any actual biological principles. Fecundity and its adaptive changes ensure the preservation of the species, and not its extermination through the survival of the most adapted individuals and divergence. As we have already said, the notion that an increase in the fecundity causes "intraspecific competition" to be more acute cannot be recognized as a principle which correctly corresponds to observations in nature. It does not lead either to the mass mortality of the numerous individuals which possess the features most typical of the species, or to a majority survival of individuals in which there has evolved a slight beneficial deviation from the typical property of the species. According to this mistaken notion, similar factors repeated from generation to generation would lead in the final account to the disappearance of individuals with the characteristic features of the original species, i.e. to the extermination of the old species, but would ensure the reproduction of individuals which deviate more and more from the original, i.e. the appearance of new forms and, finally, of a new species. Therefore, according to this notion, the greater the fecundity the more acute the "intraspecific competition," the more rapid the extermination of the old and the emergence of new species. Consequently, an increase in the fecundity of a particular species facilitates its own extermination.

In actual fact an increase, as any other change in the fecundity of an individual within the population (of course, this excludes pathological conditions), represents an adaptive response of the population to environmental changes. An increase in the fecundity ensures the preservation, and not the extermination, of the species; it ensures its relative stability both in space and in time, in the event of fairly wide fluctuations in the environmental conditions.

Fishes are adapted to reproducing under the most varied conditions. The structure and mode of life of both the adult, and the eggs, embryos, and larvae are related to the reproductive peculiarities.

The European fauna includes the following ecological groups of fishes (Kryzhanovsky, 1949), based on the features of their reproduction and development and, particularly, of the habitat in which they spawn.

Lithophils spawn on stony grounds, usually in rivers, in currents, or in oligotrophic lakes and the inshore parts of the sea, usually, though not always, in favourable respiratory conditions. This group includes sturgeons, salmon, common barbel, and others (Fig. 69).

Phytophils spawn among plants, in stagnant or slow-flowing water on vegetating or dying plants (Fig. 70). The respiratory conditions vary considerably. This group includes the carp, bream, perch, pike, many Labridae, etc.

Psammophils spawn on sand, sometimes attaching the eggs to plant roots. The eggs of psammophilic forms often become encrusted with sand. They usually develop in favourable respiratory conditions. This group includes the gudgeon, certain loaches, etc. (Fig. 71).

Pelagophils spawn in the water column. The spawn and free-living larvae develop in the water column, usually in favourable respiratory conditions. This group includes nearly all species of clupeoids (except the genera *Clupea* and *Pomolobus*), gadoids, pleuronectiids, etc.

Ostracophils spawn into the mantle cavity of molluscs and sometimes under the claws of crabs and other animals. The eggs usually develop under not particularly favourable respiratory conditions. The group includes the bitterlings, Rhodeinae, certain gudgeons, as for example, *Chilogobio, Careproctus sinensis* Gilb. et Burke (Liparidae), etc. (Fig. 72).

Of course these divisions do not include all the fishes. Apart from the exceptional viviparous species, in which the incubation period is spent either entirely or partially (for example, certain cottids) within the maternal body, there are many species of fish which occupy intermediate positions. For instance, in the smelt, *Osmerus eperlanus* L., the egg spends part or sometimes the whole of the incubation period in the attached state, and part of it free-floating. The Black Sea bream, *Vimba vimba* (L.), spawns on both

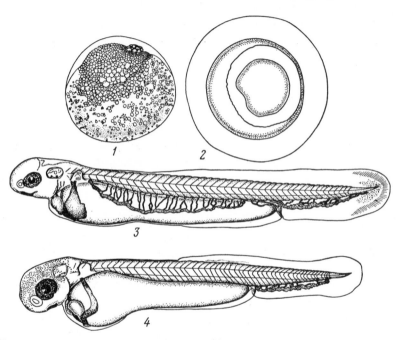

Fig. 69. Eggs and embryos of lithophil fishes (not to same scale). 1, Egg of the chum salmon, *Oncorhynchus keta* (Walb.); 2 and 3, egg and larva of the barbel *Barbus goktchaicus* Kessl.; 4, larva of the nase *Chondrostoma nasus* (L.).

plants and stones. Many such examples could be given. However, these intermediate forms are always closer to one or the other of the above ecological groups in their mode of development. Thus, the smelt is very close to the pelagophils, the *Vimba* to the lithophils, etc.

The size of the egg varies considerably from species to species. As the data presented below show, the sizes (diameters) of ripe eggs can vary from a fraction of a millimetre in some clupeoids and pleuronectiids to 80 mm or more in sharks and chimaerids.

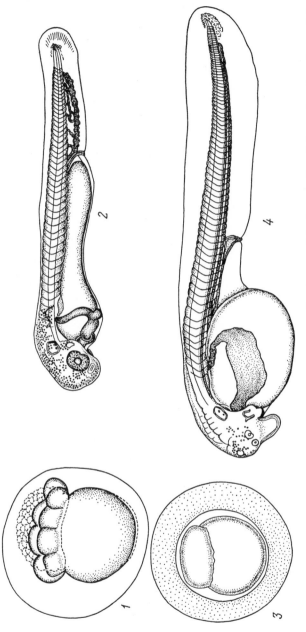

Fig. 70. Eggs and embryos of phytophil fishes (not to same scale). 1, Egg of the bream *Abramis brama* L.; 2, embryo of the bream; 3, egg of the sheat-fish *Silurus glanis* L.; 4, embryo of the sheat-fish.

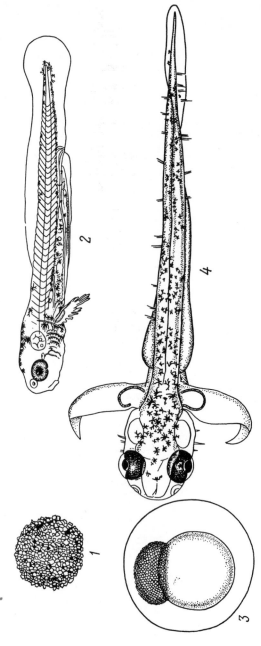

FIG. 71. Eggs and embryos of psammophil fishes (not to same scale). 1, Egg of the gudgeon *Pseudogobio rivularis* (Bas.); 2, Larva of the gudgeon; 3, egg of *Deuterophysa*; 4, larva of *Deuterophysa*.

Sizes of Ripe Eggs in Various Species of Fish

Myxine glutinosa (L.)	17–30 mm
Pristiurus melanostomus (Raf.)	65 mm (without horns)
Scyllium canicula (L.)	65 mm
Somniosus microcephalus (Bloch.)	80 mm
Acipenser ruthenus L.	1·3–2 mm
Huso dauricus (Georgi)	3·2–4 mm
Clupea harengus L.	0·9–1·5 mm
Oncorhynchus gorbuscha (Walb.)	4·5–6·5 mm
Cyprinus carpio L.	0·9–1·2 mm
Ammodytes hexapterus (Pall.)	0·7–1·0 mm
Perca fluviatilis L.	2·0–2·5 mm

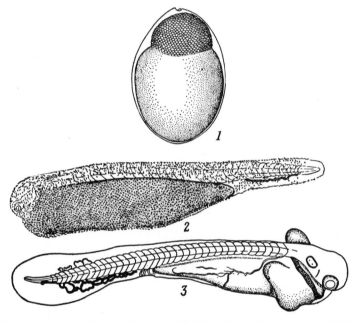

FIG. 72. An egg and embryos of ostracophil fishes (from Kryzhanovsky, 1949) (not to same scale). 1, Egg of the spiny bitterling *Acanthorhodeus asmussi* (Dyb.); 2, larva of the spiny bitterling; 3, larva of the common bitterling *Rhodeus sericeus* (Pall.).

In sharks and chimaeriids the large size of the egg enables the larva to be very large on hatching. In connection with this the small number of progeny in the shark are in a favourable position relative to the small larvae of bony fishes, for which a larva as large as that of the sharks would be very vulnerable. The larvae of bony fishes are eaten by the shark larvae. The large size of the eggs together with the protective horn-like membrane ensure a high rate of survival for young cartilaginous fishes. With their low fecundity only such an adaptation could preserve these fishes against extinction.

A fairly large egg is usual for many lithophil species. This is particularly true of the salmon. Their relatively larger size is connected with the presence of a large reserve of yolk, which is slowly used up by the embryos of these fishes under the conditions of fast-flowing rivers with low food supply and stony bottom and oligotrophic lakes, in which the planktonic organisms, which usually form the food of fish larvae in their first stages of active feeding, are either absent or scarce. The transition to external feeding in these larvae takes place when they have reached a larger size and can consume larger food organisms, and the attainment of such large size at the expense of internal food reserves naturally requires a larger reserve of yolk.

Development under more or less favourable conditions of oxygen supply is connected with the greater or lesser development of respiratory pigments in the egg, usually carotenoids—pigments of yellowish or reddish tones. The less favourable the conditions under which the egg develops, the more deeply pigmented it is. The pigmentation is usually best developed in phytophilic and lithophilic fishes. The pigment is usually weakly developed in the eggs of pleuronectiids, gadoids, many clupeoids, etc., which develop in water richly saturated with oxygen. The weak pigmentation and greater transparency of the egg makes it less noticeable to predators. The intensity of pigmentation is directly related to the conditions of oxygen supply under which the development takes place.   Thus, among the Far Eastern salmon the eggs of the humpback, *Oncorhynchus gorbuscha* (Walb.), which develop under the most favourable conditions of oxygen supply, have a very weakly developed pigmentation. The deepest pigmentation, of a crimson colour, is found in eggs of the sockeye, *O. nerka* (Walb.), which are usually buried in the ground in lakes close to where oxygen-poor spring water emerges.

In the unfertilized egg of bony fishes the whole surface layer of the plasma contains innumerable small droplets, which are enclosed in relatively large vacuoles. When fertilization occurs, these droplets shoot out under its membrane. As a result, the membrane is separated from the yolk, and it is impossible for any further penetration of the membrane by sperms to take place.

An egg which remains unfertilized in the water also, after a time, forms the separation of the droplets under the membrane. Until this separation has taken place the egg retains its ability to be fertilized (see page 177).

The specific gravity of eggs also varies. Usually the specific gravity of pelagic eggs is close to that of the water. The buoyancy of the eggs is achieved in various ways: the eggs of the cod, flatfish, and many other fish contain an oil globule, which lowers their specific gravity; the eggs of the Caspian shad develop a large perivitelline space; in the eight-barbed gudgeon, *Gobiobotia pappenheimi* Kroy., the egg membrane becomes slimy. Apart from this, buoyancy may also be achieved by the yolk absorbing water. Finally, in certain oceanic flying fishes the tendency for the eggs to sink to the bottom is hindered by small outgrowths, which increase the friction, so that the egg has time to develop before it sinks into the abyss.

In many eggs the membrane becomes sticky after fertilization, and they become attached to objects on the bottom. Sometimes this adhesiveness only lasts for part of the incubation period, and the egg later becomes released from the substrate and either concludes its development in the water column (as, for example, in certain pelagophil Amur cyprinoids), or else rolls about among the stones, as in certain lithophilic fishes which spawn in streams.

The time of onset of maturity varies considerably among different species. It is subject to considerable variation among different populations of the same species, and also varies within the limits of a single population. Usually the onset of maturity is related to the attainment of a particular size by the individual. Thus, the bream matures on reaching a length of about 27 cm, the ide at about 18 cm, and so on (Vasnetsov, 1934). Consequently, the slower the growth rate of the fish, the later the onset of its sexual maturity, and vice versa. The time of sexual maturity is thus related to the food supply, i.e. to the abundance of the food, the duration of the feeding season, and so on.

In the majority of widely distributed species, maturity usually sets in later at higher latitudes than at lower ones. Thus, for example, the roach in Finland becomes mature at an age of 5–6 years, in central Europe at 4–5 years, and in southern Europe at 3 years. The abundance of the food also exerts a direct influence upon the time of onset of maturity. Thus, for example, in aquaria *Barbus conchonius* Ham.-Buch. becomes mature in the year following hatching when fed intensively. When fed insufficiently this species matures only in its second, or even its third, year.

When populations are reduced under natural conditions, which leads to an improvement in the food supply, an acceleration of the maturation of the individuals is often observed.

Examples of fishes which mature very early are certain gobies, *Aphya*, *Crystallogobius*; toothed carps, Cyprinodontiformes; certain Scopelidae, etc.

They attain maturity even before they reach an age of one year. On the other hand, certain sturgeons, such as the white sturgeon *Huso huso* (L.), *Huso dauricus* (Georgi), mature only at an age of 15–20 years. Certain sharks also apparently mature as late as this.

Thus, the muturation of the sexual products and the development of the gonads occupies a variable length of time according to the species. There are differences not only in the time of the first spawning, but also in the length of time which passes between successive spawnings. Thus, in *Gambusia* several months pass between successive spawnings; in the majority of species the cycle of reproduction is annual, but in certain migratory species, such as the sturgeons, the cycle is biennial or more. The rate and period of development varies considerably according to the species. For convenience in the field analysis of large amounts of data on the course of maturation of the gonads, and in delimiting the separate stages of the sexual cycle, a series of scales of ripeness have been worked out for each group of fishes (for gadoids, Poulsen's scale; for pleuronectids, Heincke-Mayer's; for Caspian shad, Kiselevich's; for sturgeons, Nedoshivin's; for cyprinoids and percoids, Kulaev's and Meien's, and many others). In all these scales the specific features of the course of maturation of the gonads in each group are emphasized. However, they are all based on a universal scale, the simplest of all those which are used, which only represents the course of maturation of the gonads in general terms. This scale is as follows:

Stage I. Young individuals which have never spawned yet.

Stage II. Quiescent—gametes either have not yet started to develop or else have already been discharged; the swelling process in the cavity of the gonad is complete; gonads are of very small size; eggs not visible to the naked eye.

Stage III. Ripening—eggs visible to the naked eye; the gonad increases in weight very rapidly; testes change from transparent to pale rose colour.

Stage IV. Ripeness—gametes ripe; gonads have reached their maximum weight, but the gametes do not yet run out when light pressure is applied.

Stage V. Reproduction—gametes run out on the application of the lightest pressure to the thorax; the weight of the gonad rapidly decreases from start to finish of the spawning process.

Stage VI. Spent—gametes extruded, and cavity of gonad swollen; gonad has the appearance of an empty sac, usually with a few eggs remaining in females, or sperms in males.

This is the general scheme into which various authors have introduced variations and additions according to the characteristics of the cycle of each fish.

One of the most important symptoms of the condition of the gonads is their weight. Since the weight of the gonad is naturally closely related to the size of the fish, the influence of the body weight of the fish in analysis is eliminated by the use of a coefficient of maturity, which expresses the weight of the gonad as a percentage of the weight of the whole body or of the gutted

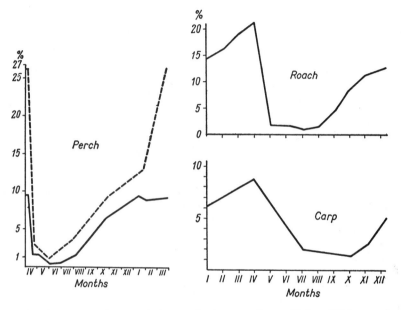

FIG. 73. The course of seasonal changes in the maturity coefficient. Right, ovaries of roach and carp; left, of perch; ovaries, broken line; testes, solid line.

weight, i.e. the weight of the body without its internal organs. From the three curves in Fig. 73, showing the course of changes in the maturity coefficient in the perch, roach, and carp, it is apparent that there are in each of these fishes specific features in the course of increase in the weight of the gonads, not to mention the time of onset of the various stages. In the roach, which like the perch has a short spawning period, the quiescent stage is longer, and the rise during winter is not so steep. The carp is distinguished from both the roach and the perch by the slope of the descending part of the curve. This is explained by the extention of the spawning period in the carp.

The dynamics of the coefficient of maturity are of a very different character in tropical fishes, which reproduce almost round the year. Spawning in these is usually partial, and the variations in the weight of the gonad (as, for example, in *Tilapia esculenta* Graham in Lake Victoria) throughout the year are comparatively small.

In the northern hemisphere the gonads of the majority of fishes attain their maximum weight in the spring months. In summer the coefficient of maturity is at its lowest value, but it starts to increase in the autumn. In fishes which spawn in the autumn and winter (the majority of salmon and burbot), the coefficient of maturity has its maximum value in the autumn.

The course of the process of maturation of the gonads also varies considerably. In cyprinoids, as we have already stated, the second stage is rather prolonged (in the roach from May to August). During this time the female gonad contains only oogonia, the male only spermatogonia. In cyprinoids at the beginning of autumn the gonads start to develop rapidly with the appearance of spermatocytes. Cyprinoids usually winter in this state. This stage corresponds to the gently rising part of the curve representing the dynamics of the coefficient of maturity. The final ripening is completed very quickly in the ten to fifteen days up to the start of spawning.

A different pattern is observed in the percoids. In the common perch the oogonia and spermatogonia very rapidly become transformed into oocytes and spermatocytes. The spermatocytes usually start to appear in June. In contrast to the Cyprinoids, spermatogenesis in the percoids mainly finishes in the autumn, and the winter is passed with spermatids already in the gonads, and even sometimes with considerable numbers of spermatozoa. The female gametes lag behind somewhat in their development. Their main increase in weight occurs just before spawning, when there appears a new generation of oogonia.

The dynamics of the coefficient of maturity naturally vary according to whether the fish spawns partially or completely.

The course of development of the gonads does not depend only on the quantity and quality of the food consumed. The development of the eggs and sperms also depends on the amount of light, the thermal regime, and a number of other factors. The stimulating action of the light apparently acts through the activation of the endocrine function of the brain, particularly the hypothalamus. The thermal regime undoubtedly acts through changes in the total metabolic rate.

The development of the gonads is connected in the majority of fishes with the formation of secondary sexual characteristics. The most frequent secondary sexual difference is that of size between the sexes. Usually the female is larger than the male, which ensures the largest fecundity of the stock. The difference in the sizes of males and females varies considerably. In some species, such as the bream, *Abramis brama* (L.), roach, *Rutilus rutilus* (L.), sturgeons, and many others, the average size of the females is only a few centimetres larger than that of the males. This difference in size is usually achieved through the earlier maturation of the males and their shorter life-span. In other species there are much greater differences in size between males and females. Dwarf males may occur. In freshwater fishes dwarf males occur in a number of salmonids (*Salmo salar* L., *S. trutta*, etc.), in which the dwarf males live together with the migratory large males (Berg, 1937; Barach, 1952; Nikolsky, 1953a) and participate in the spawning equally with them. Dwarf males occur in many deep-water fishes of the suborder Stomiatoidei (order Clupeiformes) and the suborder Ceratioidei (angler-fishes). The dwarf males of the angler-fishes parasitize the females (Fig. 44), growing on to them by means of the buccal cavity and feeding on the female's body fluids. This adaptation makes it unnecessary for the individuals of either sex to seek those of the other for the purpose of fertilization in these populations, which are dispersed in deep water.

The males are larger than the females in only a few species (certain sheat-fish, cyprinoids, etc.). This is usually the case when the male protects the offspring, so that the larger size is a protective adaptation. For example, in the common sheat-fish, *Silurus glanis* L., in the Aral Sea the average size of the males is 107·2 cm, and that of the females 98·2 cm; in *Pseudobagrus fulvidraco* Rich, which spawns into a burrow, the males average 21·4 cm and the females 17·7 cm; in the Amur gudgeon, *Pseudogobio rivularis* (Bas.), the males average 6·1 cm and the females 5·3 cm.

There are also other differences between males and females. They often differ in the length and shape of the fins (Fig. 74). Thus in the males of many cyprinoids both the paired and the unpaired fins are slightly larger than in the females; in the males of certain Lake Baikal sculpins, for example, *Cotto-comephorus*, only the thoracic fins are significantly larger; in the males of many loaches—Cobitidae—inflations appear between the rays of the thoracic fins and on the cheeks, but not in the females; in *Xiphophorus* (fam. Poecilidae) there is a long outgrowth on the caudal fin; in the males of many pleuronectids of the family Bothidae the rays of the dorsal fin are elongated, and so on.

In the majority of cases the differences between the structure of the fins in males and females is connected with the peculiarities of reproduction. Thus, for example, the dorsal fin, which is larger in the male than in the female of the grayling, *Thymallus*, and increases still further toward the time of spawning, creates a turbulence close to the spawning fish during the spawning process, and delays the dispersal of the sperm by fast currents (Brown, 1936). The larger size of the pelvic fins of the male tench (Fig. 74) also facilitates

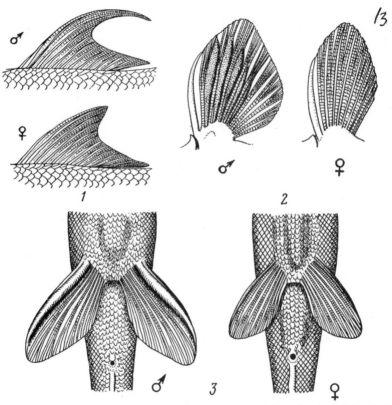

Fig. 74. Secondary sexual characters of fishes. 1, Dorsal fins of male and female *Labio dero* Hamilton; 2, thoracic fins of the male and female Tibetan loach, *Nemachilus stoliczkai* Day (from Hora and Misra, 1936 and Berg, 1948); 3, pelvic fins of the tench *Tinca tinca* (L.).

a more successful fertilization of the eggs and their attachment to plant stalks. In the females of the marine sheat-fish, *Galeichthys felis* (L.), the pelvic fins are modified to the shape of a spoon, into which the eggs fall on being spawned, and inside which they are fertilized and from which the male collects them into his mouth, where they are incubated.

Together with the secondary sexual characteristics, many fishes develop a "nuptial dress," which is particularly clearly expressed in the salmonoids. During the reproductive period the change is first of all expressed in the coloration, which becomes much brighter, and in which colours appear that were not present before. Even the skeleton of the jaws changes at the same time; particularly in the males, they become bent and large teeth appear on

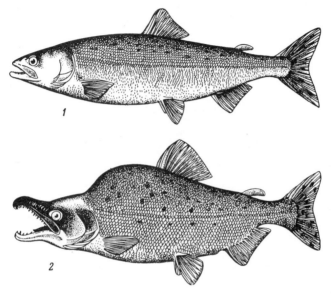

FIG. 75. Nuptial changes in the humpback salmon *Oncorhynchus gorbuscha* (Walb.). 1, The fish before the nuptial changes, silver salmon; 2, male in nuptial condition.

them (Fig. 75). In the cyprinoids the nuptial dress is expressed in the appearance of a brighter coloration and of peculiar tubercles on the horny epithelium of the head and scales of the body (Fig. 76). Very great changes occur in the coloration of many gobies. Thus, the males of *Neogobius melanostomus* (Pall.) become almost black during the spawning period.

There are several hypotheses concerning the origin of nuptial dress. There is no doubt that, in some cases, the nuptial dress bears a protective character. Thus, for example, the nuptial dress of some members of the salmon family resembles the coloration of the young of these fish living in rivers with transparent water and stony bottom, in which the pelagic marine coloration of the salmon would naturally render it more conspicuous. However, in a number of cases the nuptial dress apparently has a signalling significance.

Thus, the black stripe along the sides of the chum salmon, *Oncorhynchus keta* (Walb.), which appears at the time of spawning, possibly enables the males to orientate toward the females.

The appearance of red tones in the coloration of the nuptial dress of the salmon and the submergence of the scales in the skin are apparently connected with the increase in the respiratory function of the skin during the spawning period (Smirnov, 1959). There is no doubt that in many cases the nuptial dress is a natural stimulant which evokes the emission of the sexual products (as in the cyprinoids).

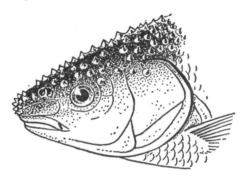

FIG. 76. Head of the Caspian kutum *Rutilus frisii kutum* Nordm. (Cyprinidae) in nuptial array.

The calendar periods of spawning have evolved as an adaptation, primarily, to the provision of the young with food. These periods are related to the seasonal and other changes in the abiotic and biotic conditions.

Usually when the young fishes are changing over to external feeding the essential planktonic and other food organisms are already developing. A delay in reproduction may lead to the larvae developing in impoverished feeding conditions. A certain coincidence of the course of development of larval fishes and of the phase of development of the nutritional plankton is often the most important factor determining the yield of a generation (herring, *Clupea harengus* L., anchovy, *Engraulis encrasicholus* L., etc.).

In the conditions of the higher latitudes with a short vegetative period, the more complete utilization of the short feeding season is often ensured by the shifting of the spawning period to the autumn, while the incubation and yolk-feeding periods continue into the spring (many salmon). The transition of the larvae to external feeding thus occurs at the beginning of the vegetative period, and the food is exploited most thoroughly in the short vegetative period. As a rule, the longer the time in which the larvae are provided with food during their first stages of external feeding, the more protracted is the spawning period. This is most clearly seen in tropical, partial-spawning species.

The time of spawning also has a protective significance in ensuring that the eggs and larvae develop at a time when predators either have not yet appeared or else are relatively inactive. Thus, for example, in the Volga delta, the pike, roach, perch, and other early-spawning fishes spawn at a time when spawn-eating fishes are practically absent from the rivers. In certain river pelagophil fishes, such as the grass-carp *Ctenopharyngodon idella* Val. and *Aristichthys nobilis* (Rich.), and *Hypophthalmichthys molitrix* Val., spawning takes place in rising water, which becomes more turbid, and pelagic eggs carried in the water column are less conspicuous to predators. The American atherinid, *Leuresthes tenuis* (Ayres), spawns at the edge of the water on the spring tide. Development takes place in the damp sand out of the water and lasts until the following spring tide, when the spawning ground is flooded again and the hatching larvae enter the water. In this way the larvae are well protected against predators living in the water. *Galaxias attenuatus* Ienyns also spawns similarly on the spring tide. The eggs of this fish remain among the cast-up weeds and also develop out of the water until the following spring tide.

European fishes can be divided into the following groups according to the season in which they spawn: (1) spring spawners—shad, pike, perch, roach, smelt, and many others; (2) summer spawners—anchovy, rudd, carp, tench, many gobies, etc.; (3) autumn-winter spawners—many salmon, whitefish, burbot, navaga, etc.

This division is to some extent subjective. Often the same species will spawn at different times of the year in different regions according to the conditions. Thus, for example, the capelan, *Mallotus villosus* (Müller), spawns at Finmark and western Murman from March to May, and at eastern Murman in June to July, and in the eastern part of the Barents Sea in August-September.

There is also a variation in the part of the day during which fishes spawn. Many fishes spawn at night (salmon, burbot, anchovy, and several others) usually in not very great depths. This gives the spawning fish some protection against predators which orientate visually. In some species (such as many anchovies) which have a short incubation period, spawning takes place in the evening, and the larvae, which are less vulnerable to predators than the eggs, hatch in the morning. The diurnal spawning period undoubtedly has other adaptive features, which have not yet been properly investigated.

The duration of the spawning period also varies considerably in different species. The roach and perch, for example, may have a short spawning period of one morning. Many tropical fishes, such as the Apogonidae, which are characterized by their oral protection of the eggs (Fig. 77), spawn all their eggs in the course of one hour. On the other hand, even in fishes which do not have a clearly marked partial spawning, such as the bream, the spawning of one individual may take place in several sessions over the course of several

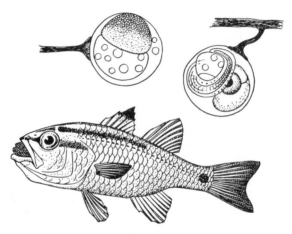

Fig. 77. A male *Apogon semilineatus* Schlegel (Perciformes) with spawn in its buccal cavity; above, separate eggs in various stages of development.

days. Thus, even in those bream populations in which the spawning is not partial, the females remain on the spawning ground in considerable numbers for 10 days each, and in masses for up to 5 days. The same is also true of the carp, but their spawning is even more spread out, and the females remain on the spawning grounds for an even longer time than the bream. In fishes with a well-marked partial spawning (in which the eggs ripen in separate portions), the total duration of the spawning period is, of course, longer.

The males usually remain longer on the spawning grounds than do the females, and participate in the spawning with several females in turn. This has been observed for salmon, many cyprinoids, percoids, and other fishes.

While the course of development of the gonads is to a significant extent determined by the food supply and depends on the course of metabolism, the moment of commencement of actual spawning is usually a reaction to some "natural stimulus," some signal, which frequently has a complex character. Thus, in many fishes the stimulus for the start of spawning is a particular water temperature (for spring-spawners, a rising temperature, for autumn-spawners, falling temperature). However, the temperature only stimulates egg-laying in the presence of male individuals.

The usual stimulus for spawning in lithophil, phytophil, and ostracophil fishes is the presence of the spawning substrate—stones, plants, molluscs. Often the rising water-level acts as a stimulus for the start of spawning. According to observations of Indian ichthyologists (Hora, 1945, etc.) in certain Indian cyprinoids the stimulus for the start of spawning, in addition to the rising water-level, is a particular phase of the moon. The mechanism of the action of "natural stimuli" for spawning has not yet been studied sufficiently, although there is no doubt that it includes a neuro-humeral reaction.

A substantial part is played by the so-called sterohormones, i.e. substances which are secreted into the water by the ripe males and which evoke in the females of egg-laying fishes the appearance of a state of readiness to spawn, and in the females of viviparous fishes readiness to be fertilized. The main steroid hormone is copulin. This hormone, when introduced into the water, stimulates the appearance of the nuptial dress in the females of a number of species, and in the bitterling the growth of the ovipositor. The mode of action of the copulin is unknown. Some believe that it is absorbed into the blood through the gills and stimulates the hormonal activity of the female organism, and others that the reaction to copulin is directly through chemoreceptors (Puchkov, 1954; Kirshenblat, 1952).

The sex ratio varies considerably from species to species, but in the majority of species it is close to one. It differs from one population to another of the same species, and may vary from year to year in the same population. For example, in the common perch, *Perca fluviatilis* L., the sex ratio varies in different lakes from 1:1 to 1:9, with a predominance of females. Apparently, in the common perch under poor feeding conditions, there appear a large proportion of stunted females, which form the food of the faster growing individuals of the same species.

Both the time and the place of spawning are adaptations which ensure the most favourable conditions for the development of the eggs and larvae. In many sea fishes the eggs develop while floating in the water column. Lithophil fishes either attach their eggs to stones or bury them in the ground. In the sturgeons, for example, the eggs are attached to stones among the deposits transported from ravines (Aliavdina, 1951), while the salmon buries its eggs in the ground, constructing a special nest, the spawning redd, for this purpose. Phytophil fishes attach their eggs to plants or else construct a special nest for them out of plants. Sometimes, as has been stated, the eggs are laid inside other animals—molluscs, crabs. Shells, claws, and other hard remains of animals may be used as the spawning substrate. For example, certain gobies and blennies lay their eggs into empty mollusc shells. Finally, a number of species incubate their eggs about their body (Fig. 78).

However, with all the great variety of conditions for the reproduction of fishes they have a very substantial specificity for each species, or even form. Thus, for example, all the salmon of the genus *Oncorhynchus* bury their spawn among the shingle, but in each species the conditions for development are specific. The humpback, *O. gorbuscha* (Walb.), buries its eggs in midstream in coarse shingle, so that the eggs develop in a fast current under the most favourable oxygen conditions, but subjected to great mechanical influences. In connection with this, as has already been stated, the egg of the humpback is least richly pigmented with carotenoid respiratory pigments, but by comparison with other Far Eastern salmon the egg membrane is tougher. The keta or chum salmon, *O. keta* (Walb.), usually constructs its nests closer to the shore in quieter water; the spawn is buried among rather finer shingle; it develops under less favourable respiratory conditions, but is less subjected to mechanical action. It is interesting that the autumn form of the chum salmon usually constructs its nests at the outlets of underground waters, because of which the spawn is less subjected to freezing in severe winters than that of the summer form. The summer form of the chum spawns in places where there are no outlets for underground waters. In the chum the egg membrane is less tough than in the humpback, but the carotenoid pigmentation is better developed. The sima salmon, *O. masu* Brev., rises to the head waters of small rivers, but spawns near the shore in quiescent parts. The egg of this species is even more deeply pigmented than that of the chum, but in the toughness of its membrane it occupies an intermediate position between the chum and the humpback, being somewhat closer to the latter. Similar narrow differences also exist among species belonging to the other ecological groups. The roach, *Rutilus rutilus caspicus* Jak., spawns in almost the same parts of the Volga delta as the bream, *Abramis brama bergi* Grieb., but earlier than the latter. The egg of the roach develops at significantly lower temperatures ($+7.0–16°C$), and is usually attached to last year's dead weeds. The bream spawns later and naturally at higher temperatures ($1+5–23°C$), attaching its eggs to already vegetating weeds.

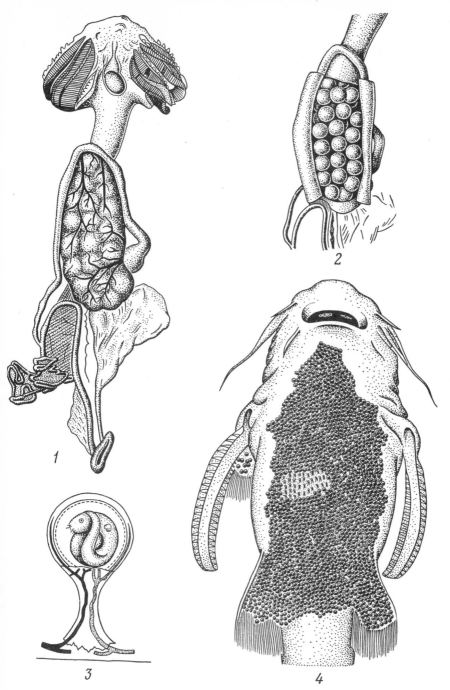

FIG. 78. Protection of spawn in sheat-fishes. 1 and 2, Intestinal incubation of the eggs in *Tachysurus barbus* Lacep; 3 and 4, incubation of the eggs on the abdomen in *Platy-stachus cotylephorus* Bloch.

Substantial differences also exist among the spawning conditions for pelagophil species, such as the sprat, *Sprattus sprattus* (L.), which spawns in regions of lower salinity (such as fjords, into which rivers flow, or in estuarine regions) with a fairly large amplitude of salinity, while flying fishes spawn in stable salinity of about 34–35°/$_{oo}$ and at a temperature of about +26–27°C (Bruun, 1935). In connection with the need to ensure the buoyancy of the egg at various water densities the size of the sprat egg varies considerably from one region to another. Thus, in the North Sea, where the salinity is higher, the size of the sprat egg varies between 0·82 and 1·23 mm, and in the Baltic, between 1·23 and 1·68 mm, i.e. in the denser water the ratio of the surface area of the egg to its volume is smaller (Rass, 1953).

The character of the approach of the fish to its spawning ground and the course of its spawning process also have an adaptive significance. Usually in the majority of fishes the males approach the spawning ground first, and participate with several females in turn in the spawning. The females, having spawned, either leave the spawning ground and commence to feed (bream, roach, and many others), or, as happens in the salmon, they remain to protect their nest. As Table 9 (compiled from the data of A. I. Smirnov) shows, in

TABLE 9

Number of Portions and Volume of Sperm in Various Species of Far Eastern Salmon

	Species			
Amount of sperm and number of portions	*Humpback*	*Spring chum*	*Sockeye*	*Chinook*
Largest volume of one portion, in cu mm	21·7	17·9	8·5	46·0
Largest number of portions of sperm obtained from one male	6	11	8	14
Maximum total amount of sperm obtained from one male, cu mm	68·8	133·6	41·8	192·8

Far Eastern salmon a single male may produce up to fourteen lots of sperm.

In the majority of species the largest broods are obtained from fishes of middle age. Young and very old individuals give less viable offspring. Thus, in the carp *Cyprinus carpio* L., according to Martyshev, the largest broods are those produced by fishes of age 8+; younger and older individuals produce less viable young (Table 10).

There are differences also in the amount of fat contained in the eggs of fishes of different ages. Thus, in the North Caspian roach the largest amount of fat is contained in the eggs of fishes of ages 4–5+. The reserve of fat is smaller in the eggs of younger and older individuals (data of J. I. Cheprakova).

TABLE 10

Index of Numbers of Offspring of Carp of Various Ages

Characteristic of offspring	Age of fish			
	17 +	8 +	4 +	3 +
Average diameter of eggs in mm	1·64	1·71	1·39	1·26
Length of larvae on hatching in mm	6·18	6·41	5·05	4·80
Weight of yearlings in autumn in g	25·04	34·5	32·08	No data

The first to approach the spawning grounds are usually the largest females, which produce the most viable eggs. Their eggs are fertilized by the first portions of the sperm, which are the most viable. If there are very many females, the males expend a significant proportion of their sperm in fertilizing their eggs. Thus there is insufficient sperm to fertilize the later spawning females, which are younger and smaller, and there is a large amount of loss in fertilization. When there are fewer old females the success of fertilization of the eggs of the younger females is higher. Thus the young and predominantly first-time spawners form a reserve, so to speak, for ensuring the increase of the generation in a reduced stock.

In the majority of fishes the eggs are fertilized in the water. The sperms acquire mobility on entering the water and, penetrating through the micropyle of the egg, fertilize it. The sperm of different species preserve their mobility in the water for various periods. In fishes which spawn in a current, in which the sperms may make contact with the eggs for a very short period, the sperms move in the water for a shorter time than those of species which spawn in stagnant water. Thus, in the humpback and chum salmon, which spawn in fast currents (rate of flow 0·5–1·0 m/sec), the sperms are mobile in the water for only 10–15 sec. In the Russian sturgeon which spawn in slower currents (about 0·2 m/sec), the sperms retain their mobility for about 230–290 sec. In the Volga shad, *Caspialosa volgensis* Berg., only 10% of the sperm placed in water retained their mobility after 10 minutes, and only individual sperms were still mobile after 30 minutes (Stroganov, 1938). The addition of ovarian fluids to the water activates the movements of the sperms, an adaptation which ensures that their movements increase as they approach the egg.

In species of fishes which spawn in stagnant water, the opportunity for the sperms and eggs to contact each other is considerably longer than in running water, and the viability of the sperm is correspondingly much greater. Thus, for example, the sperm of the oceanic herring, *Clupea harengus pallasii* Val., retains the ability to fertilize for more than a day (Kryzhanovsky, 1956).

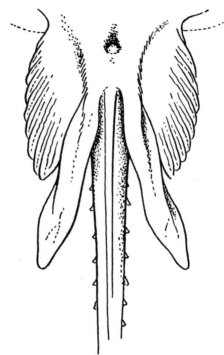

Fig. 79. Pterygopods (copulatory organ) of the skate (from Kyle and Ehrenbaum, 1927).

In the majority of fishes fertilization is external, but in a number of species, both egg-laying and those in which the eggs develop inside the maternal body, internal fertilization takes place, in connection with which they have often evolved special copulatory organs. In their simplest form, the copulatory organs are represented by anal papillae, as in the lamprey (Cyclostomes), and also in a number of fishes—cottids, gobies, and certain others (Brown, 1957).

In the female shark and skate internal fertilization occurs, in both egg-laying and viviparous species. In connection with this they possess a special copulatory apparatus, the pterygopods (Fig. 79), which are the modified extreme internal rays of the pelvic fins. These rays increase in size, appearing as a massive outgrowth on each pelvic fin, with a groove on the internal edge of each. When pairing, the male places both these outgrowths together and introduces them into the females' cloaca. It is interesting that the earliest fossil sharks apparently did not possess the copulatory organ and fertilization in them must have been external. The recent polar shark *Somniosus microcephalus* Bloch., also lacks the pterygopods, but this is undoubtedly a secondary evolution.

There are also many viviparous species among the bony fishes. In the order Cyprinodontiformes, which is very rich in species, a significant proportion of the species produce living offspring. In these fishes the modified rays of the anal fin (usually the third and fourth) form a very complexly constructed copulatory organ, the gonopod. It is interesting that in the viviparous cyprinodonts this organ has acquired mobility and can turn forward and backward.

The gonopods of *Horaichthys setnai* Kulkarni (Cyprinodontiformes) are very complex (Fig. 80). Their function is to suspend the spermatophores up to the genital aperture of the female. In fishes of the order Phallostethiformes the copulatory apparatus develops on the pharynx and consists of the elongated first pair of ribs and parts of the thoracic and pelvic girdles. Fishes in several other groups also possess copulatory organs.

Normal, nonpathological hermaphroditism is very rare in fishes. It is only known definitely in representatives of the sea-perches, Serranidae and the Sparidae. In some species of the genus *Serranus* even self-fertilization is possible; in other genera of the Serranidae and Sparidae the male and female gonads develop in turn, and self-fertilization is impossible.

In some individuals of *Chrysophrys aurata* (L.), a hermaphrodite species, the testes ripen first, and the ovaries later, in others the gonads ripen in the reverse order. Because of this there are always both "males" and "females" present at the spawning times, although each individual participates in turn as both a male and a female, but self-fertilization does not take place.

The actual course of the spawning process varies considerably in different fishes. In a number of fishes the egg-laying is preceded by the construction of a special nest. Many sheat-fishes of the families Bagridae and Loricariidae lay their eggs into a burrow which they dig out specially for this purpose, and which the male then protects (Fig. 81). Something like a spawning colony develops. Various types of nests are constructed out of weeds by such fishes as the common sheat-fish, *Silurus glanis* L., the mudfish, *Amia calva* L., certain Labridae, and sticklebacks, Gasterosteidae. A complex floating nest is con-

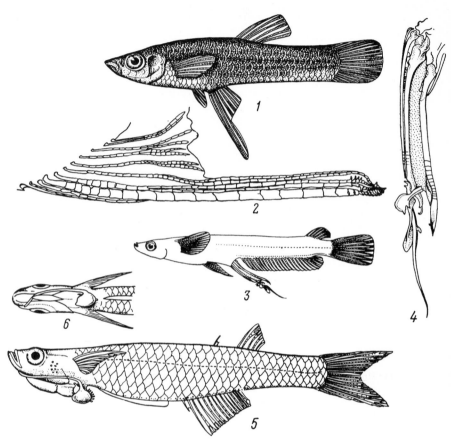

Fig. 80. Copulatory organs of various fishes (not to same scale). 1, and 2, Male *Gambusia* and its gonopodium (from Lindberg, 1934); 3 and 4, male of *Horaichthys setnai* and its gonopodium (from Kulkarni, 1940); 5 and 6, male of *Neostethus amaricola* (Vill. et Man.) and its priapium (from Berg, 1955).

structed out of weeds by *Gymnarchus nilotichus* Cuv. Certain labyrinthici, such as *Macropodus*, *Betta*, etc., form a nest out of air bubbles. The nest is usually the work of a single male, but in some species, such as the gouramis, the females also participate in its construction (Kulkarni, 1943).

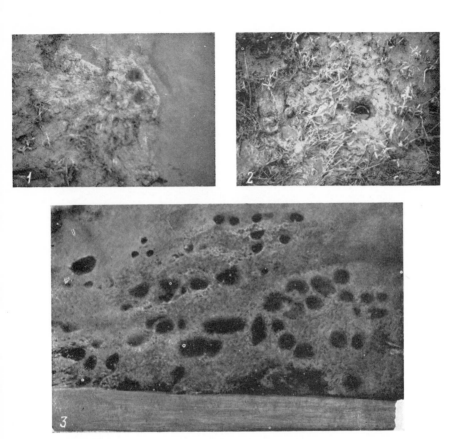

FIG. 81. Nesting burrows in the ground. 1 and 2, Catfishes, fam. Bagridae; 3, sheat-fish, fam. Loricariidae.

[*To face page* 176

Both monogamy and polygamy occur among fishes. Thus, among the salmon family, in the humpback, several males (up to ten) usually spawn together with one female, which is apparently connected with spawning in a fast current, in which a large part of the sperm is carried away downstream and perishes. In *Oncorhynchus masu* Brev. usually only one ripe male spawns together with a female. (In this species, dwarf freshwater males frequently participate in the spawning together with the large ones.) In the sticklebacks, on the other hand, one male spawns with several females, chasing them in turn into the nest which he constructs. In the wrasse, *Crenilabrus ocellatus* Forsk., there are two groups of males, large and small. The large male constructs a nest out of *Cladophora*, in which the eggs are laid and fertilized by both the large and the small males, after which the small males are chased away while the large males remain at the nest to protect the spawn.

Fighting over females takes place, for example, among the male salmon, and also in certain sheat-fish and labyrinthodonts. In the salmon and certain labyrinthici this fighting sometimes results in the death of one of the contestants.

Competition between males over females, the so-called sexual selection, is an adaptation which preserves the species by sifting out the weaker males.

When a sperm has penetrated through the egg membrane, as noted above, droplets in the plasma rapidly spread out beneath the membrane, which separates from the yolk, and further penetration of sperm under the membrane becomes impossible (Kryzhanovsky, 1953).

The secretion of the droplets under the membrane increases its toughness. In unfertilized eggs of the sturgeons, salmon, whitefish, and other species which are adapted to spawning in a current, the droplets shoot out under the egg membrane in the course of a few minutes, and the eggs lose their capacity to be fertilized. The fluid which these droplets contain causes the sperms to aggregate.

In some species in nature, parthenogenetic development occurs, which usually has a different course from the normal and, as a rule, does not lead to the formation of normal larvae.

In the salmon, the unfertilized eggs which happen to get into the burrows along with the fertilized eggs do not die, but proceed with a peculiar form of development. This parthenogenetic development lasts for a long time, until the fertilized eggs hatch. If the unfertilized eggs were unable to develop, but died and decomposed in the nests, this would lead to the death of all the eggs. The occurrence of such a peculiar adaptation ensures the preservation of the fertilized eggs (Nikolsky and Soin, 1954).

In the Baltic herring, *Clupea harengus membras* L., and the Pacific herring, *Clupea harengus pallasi* Val., parthenogenetic development sometimes leads to a free-living larva (Kryzhanovsky, 1956). Parthenogenesis also occurs in several other species, but normal development in parthenogenesis is unknown among fishes. In gynogenesis, i.e. when the sperm penetrates the egg, but the nuclei of the sperm and the egg cell do not fuse, in some species development proceeds normally, but the offspring consists of females only. This pheno-menon has been observed in the silver crucian carp, *Carassius auratus gibelio* (Bloch.), and in the viviparous *Molienisia formosa* (Girard). In the silver crucian carp in East Asia the populations contain both males and females, which ensures normal fertilization of the eggs. In Central Asia, Western Siberia, and Europe males are very rare in the populations of the silver crucian carp, and they are even completely absent from some of the popula-tions. In such populations gynogenesis results from fertilization by the males of other species of fish. The adaptive significance of this phenomenon apparently lies in the fact that it ensures the reproduction of the population even if only a single female remains, i.e. in extremely unfavourable condi-tions (Golovinskaia and Romashov, 1947).

Care of the young is expressed in very many fishes, belonging to various orders. As was stated above, many species construct a nest out of plants, stones, or even out of air bubbles. Many labyrinthici lay their eggs in a nest of floating foam; in this nest the eggs are guarded by the male. It is interesting that the air bubbles out of which the nest is constructed are en-closed in a film from the mouth of the fish, which is tougher than water. Because of this film the bubbles do not burst.

Very complicated nests are constructed by the sticklebacks (*Gasterosteus* and *Pungitius*). In these fishes the male constructs a completely spherical nest out of fragments of weeds, and into this the females lay their eggs, which are afterwards guarded by the male.

In many orders of fishes there are representatives which incubate their eggs about their own bodies while they develop after fertilization. Oral incubation of the eggs is also fairly widely distributed. This adaptation has been evolved convergently in a number of groups, for example the sheat-fishes and percomorphs (see above).

In the American marine sheat-fish, *Galeichthys felis* (L.), the male incu-bates up to fifty eggs in his mouth. During the incubation period the male apparently does not feed at all. It is of interest that in the females of several of the sheat-fishes, the males of which incubate orally, a peculiar change takes place in the structure of the pelvic fins (see above). When the male has collected the spawn into its mouth, the female eats the remaining eggs.

In species of *Tilapia* the eggs are incubated orally by the female. The females of some species can collect more than 100 eggs into their mouths. Apparently to improve the aeration of the eggs, the female moves them about inside the buccal cavity, and this continues until they hatch. The incubation period in some species, may last 10 to 15 days, according to aquarium observations. During this time the female hardly feeds at all. For some time after hatching the larvae hide in their mother's mouth at the slightest danger. The small sea-fishes of the genera *Apogon* and *Chelidodipterus* also incubate their eggs orally, both the males and females of *Apogon* participating.

The eggs gathered in the mouth form a compact mass, because they are fastened to each other by thin horn-shaped threadlike outgrowths from each egg (Fig. 77). The buccal cavity is sometimes so full of eggs that it remains half open. The evolution of such a peculiar adaptation as "oral gestation" in fishes is due not only to the need for greater protection of the eggs from danger, but also to the fact that the eggs in the buccal cavity are constantly washed by a current of fresh water passing through to the gills.

Some fishes incubate the eggs not in the mouth but on the body. Thus, in the sheat-fish *Aspredo* the spawn is incubated on the ventral side of the body. A curious adaptation for incubating the eggs is found among the pipefishes, Syngnathiformes. The male of the pipefish has an egg-pouch on the ventral side of the body, formed by two folds of skin on the sides of the body. These folds bend over on to the belly and enclose the eggs. In the sea-horse and pipefish the adaptation to incubation of the eggs is carried even further—the edges of the egg-pouch, when it is full of eggs (the eggs are usually laid there by several females), fuse completely, while the internal walls of the chamber become densely covered by blood vessels, which apparently supply the eggs with the essential oxygen.

In a number of fishes the whole or a part of the incubation period is passed inside the maternal body. In a number of sharks and skates there have evolved several special adaptations connected with viviparity. Thus, in the nurse-hound *Mustelus mustelus* (L.), and several other species, there are organs with a similar function to that of the placenta in mammals; in the skate *Pteroplatea* the walls of a peculiar "uterus" have outgrowths which grow into the oral cavities of the embryos and secrete into it a peculiar oily fluid, i.e. there is a form of nutrition which resembles the milk feeding of mammals.

In a representative of the family Cichlidae, *Symphysodon discus* Heckel, which inhabits the Rio Negro and Amazon basins, the larvae, after absorbing the yolk-sac, are nourished for some time by the mucus secreted by the epidermal glands of the parents. Both male and female parent fishes secrete the mucus. When the mucus of one parent has all been consumed, it swims to the other parent, to which the larvae all transfer. This method of feeding proceeds from an age of four days up to five weeks.

In the majority of both cartilaginous and bony fishes with intra-uterine development, ovoviviparity occurs, in which the egg develops inside the maternal body but does not feed at its expense. Such a method of incubation of the eggs differs but little in principle from the "oral gestation" of certain sheat-fishes and cichlids, or the incubation inside the intestine in *Tachysurus* (Fig. 78 [1,2]). In some fish, like certain species of *Cottidae* (*Myoxocephalus scorpius* L., etc.), part of the incubation period is intra-uterine, and part is spent in the water, often under the protection of the parents.

The adaptive significance of viviparity and ovoviviparity in fishes is primarily the fact that the intra-uterine development ensures a far greater degree of protection against predators and a more stable abiotic environment. Besides this, in viviparous forms the embryos receive supplementary nourishment at the expense of the maternal body fluids. All this ensures the greater survival of the young and enables the viviparous and ovoviviparous fishes to have a lower fecundity.

Fishes which develop in the external environment are usually subjected to a much more intensive predatory activity and to greater variability of the abiotic conditions. This leads to the fact that, with the exception of a few species which protect their young, the mortality of eggs and larvae of egg-laying fishes is much greater than in viviparous and ovoviviparous ones, and as a compensation for the higher mortality they have a greater fecundity. The development of fishes proceeds in the closest relationships with the environment and it is natural that in every ecological group there are specific features in their development which are determined by the specific features of the environment in which they develop.

Development is both a gradual and a discontinuous process, which, as stated above, falls into separate qualitatively specific stages. Sharp changes in the structure, physiology, and mode of life are brought about in very short intervals of time; usually nearly all the systems of organs are modified simultaneously. Every species is adapted to developing under a particular range of conditions. Changes in the environment beyond the limits to which the species is adapted leads to the disruption of the development and to the death of the developing organism. These adaptive limits do not remain constant throughout the course of the development, but are subjected to definite changes. Thus, for example, in the stage in which the pigment appears in the eyes of the embryo, the egg of the humpback salmon easily withstands considerable shaking and blows, but in the period of swelling it dies even if only lightly shaken. During the course of development the demand for oxygen varies, and so on.

As soon as the egg is fertilized, the process of development of the embryo commences at once. As stated above, the duration of the incubation period is extremely variable between species; from 12 hours in *Danio rerio* (Ham. Buch.) and many other tropical fishes, to 100 days or more in certain salmon and other fishes in high latitudes. The duration of the incubation period varies in a single species in relation to changes in various environmental factors, particularly the temperature. It has been established for a number of species that the number of degree-days, used for the development of the eggs under conditions close to the optimal, remains more or less constant for a given species. Thus, for the trout it equals 410 at various temperatures:

Temperature	Duration of Incubation Period	Number of degree-days
$+2°C$	205 days	$2 \times 205 = 410$
$+5°C$	82 days	$5 \times 82 = 410$
$+10°C$	41 days	$10 \times 41 = 410$

Of course, it does not at all follow from these data that it would be possible to keep a trout egg at $20.5°C$ and that it would then develop in 20 days. This rule, as we stated above, only holds for conditions which are close to the optimal. It is well known that in sea-water, the freezing temperature of which is below zero, many eggs, particularly those of the navaga, polar cod, certain flatfish, and others often develop at negative temperatures. Reibisch (1902) called the minimum temperature at which the development of the egg of a particular species could proceed the "threshold." For the cod this theoretically calculated threshold is $3.6°C$, for the navaga $2.3°C$, for the plaice $2.4°C$, and for the flounder $1.8°C$. It has been established that the change in the duration of the incubation period for one degree change in temperature is greater at lower temperatures than at higher ones.

Light also exerts a great influence on the development. For a number of fishes an increase in the amount of illumination produces a significant acceleration in the development of the egg. Thus, the egg of the plaice takes 1½ days longer to develop in the dark than in light (Johansen and Krogh, 1914). An acceleration of the rate of development in light and a slowing down in the dark has also been observed for the American herring-shad and for the sturgeon.

A contrasting situation is observed in the case of fishes whose eggs, under natural conditions, develop in the dark. Thus, in the trout, whose eggs develop in the ground, the development takes 4–5 days longer when the egg is illuminated than in the dark (Willer und Schnigenberg, 1927). Excessive illumination of the eggs and embryos of the salmon causes a disruption of their metabolic processes and death. In connection with this factor, the larvae of these fishes have evolved a negative reaction to light, and they hide from it. Hiding from the light is also apparently connected with protection against predators.

Changes in the conditions within the range to which the species is adapted evoke corresponding adaptive morpho-ecological changes in the developing embryo. Thus, a reduction during the period of segmentation of the embryo of temperature, or an increase in the salinity of the water in which the development is taking place, causes an increase in the number of vertebrae in the caudal part of the body, which is related to a change in the motorization and represents an adaptive response to changes in the density of the water. Conversely, an increase in temperature or a reduction in the salinity causes the reverse effect—a decrease in the number of caudal segments. This has been established for a number of species—herring, salmon, and *Fundulus*.

As the egg develops, its environment changes, and the resistance of the egg membrane also changes considerably (Table 11).

TABLE 11

Changes in the Resistance of the Egg Membrane of Chum and Humpback Salmon During Their Development

Species	Before fertilization	2 hours after fertilization	Late morula	Heart starting to pulsate	5 days before hatching	Just before hatching
Chum	100 g	700 g	3·5–4 kg	4–5 kg	2–3 kg	200 g
Humpback	200 g	900 g	5·5–6 kg	8–9 kg	4–5 kg	300–500 g

Note: The load on the eggs is given in g and kg.

The more resistant egg of the humpback develops under a covering of coarse stones, usually in midstream, where there are more frequent movements of the ground. The eggs are most resistant towards the midwinter, when it often happens that ice settles on the bed and the pressure on the eggs increases (Nikolsky and Soin, 1954).

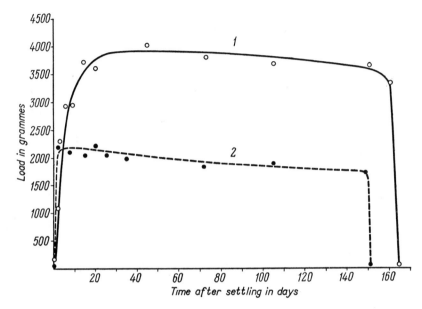

FIG. 82. Changes in the resistance of the egg membranes of salmonids (from the data of Zotin). 1, *Salmo salar m. lacustris* L.; 2, *Coregonus lavaretus swirensis* Pravdin.

The resistance of the egg membrane is also variable, and changes as the egg develops in various species of sturgeons (Fig. 83) (Zotin, 1953). The most resistant is the egg of the white sturgeon, which usually develops in midstream and in spawning grounds which are high upstream; slightly less resistant is the egg of the Russian sturgeon, which spawns further downstream, and the least resistant of all is that of the sevruga-sturgeon, whose spawning grounds are the lowest of all downstream.

The emergence of the embryo is facilitated by the dissolution of the egg membrane, which takes place through the action of a hatching enzyme secreted by hatching glands on the head of the embryo. These glands only start to secrete the enzyme when the embryo is inside the egg membrane; if it is removed from the membrane, the enzyme is not secreted (Zotin, 1954).

The further development after emergence from the égg membrane is just as much an adaptive process as the development within the membrane. As may be seen from the example of the roach, *Rutilus rutilus caspicus* Jak., as one stage of development gives way to the next (Fig. 84), not only the shape of the body changes, but also the character of the sense organs, the mode of movement, the feeding behaviour, etc. (Vasnetsov, 1948, 1953a); i.e. the

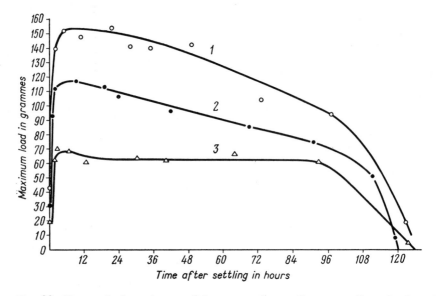

FIG. 83. Changes in the resistance of the egg membrane of sturgeons (from the data of Zotin). 1, Beluga (white sturgeon); 2, Russian sturgeon; 3, sevruga.

conditions of life change in correlation with the structure and mode of life of the developing organism. Naturally, the particular features of the development of the representatives of each ecological group of fishes are related to the specific features of their structure and physiology.

As we have stated, the predominant relationships in larval fishes are usually in respect of respiration, and we find the greatest variety of adaptations to respiration.

The larval respiratory organs are most feebly represented among pelagophil fishes (Fig. 5), where development takes place in favourable oxygen conditions (clupeoids, anchovies, etc.).

The larval respiratory organs are better developed in phytophils. They are represented by a network of blood-vessels on the yolk-sac, and on the

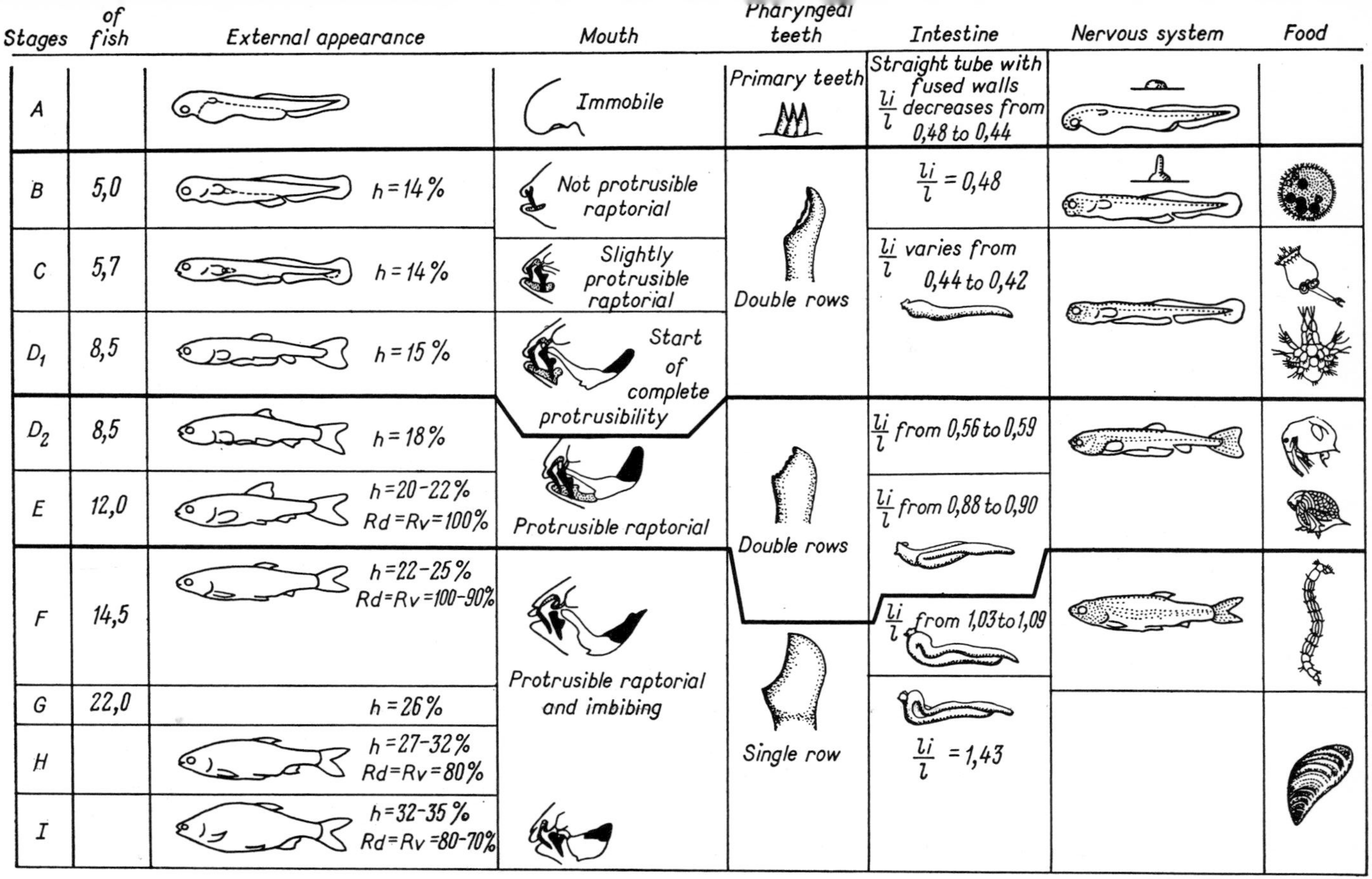

Stages of fish	External appearance	Mouth	Pharyngeal teeth	Intestine	Nervous system	Food
A		Immobile	Primary teeth	Straight tube with fused walls $\frac{Li}{l}$ decreases from 0,48 to 0,44		
B 5,0	h = 14%	Not protrusible raptorial		$\frac{Li}{l} = 0,48$		
C 5,7	h = 14%	Slightly protrusible raptorial	Double rows	$\frac{Li}{l}$ varies from 0,44 to 0,42		
D₁ 8,5	h = 15%	Start of complete protrusibility				
D₂ 8,5	h = 18%			$\frac{Li}{l}$ from 0,56 to 0,59		
E 12,0	h = 20–22% Rd = Rv = 100%	Protrusible raptorial	Double rows	$\frac{Li}{l}$ from 0,88 to 0,90		
F 14,5	h = 22–25% Rd = Rv = 100–90%			$\frac{Li}{l}$ from 1,03 to 1,09		
G 22,0	h = 26%	Protrusible raptorial and imbibing	Single row	$\frac{Li}{l} = 1,43$		
H	h = 27–32% Rd = Rv = 80%					
I	h = 32–35% Rd = Rv = 80–70%					

Fig. 84. Growth changes in the body form, various organs, and the feeding behaviour of the Caspian roach *Rutilus rutilus caspicus* Jak. (from the data of Vasnetsov).

fin-folds, and sometimes also on the gill-covers (Fig. 70). The larval respiratory organs are also usually fairly well developed in lithophils, especially in those which develop like the salmon in the ground. There is, therefore, a close correlation between the development of the larval respiratory network of blood-vessels and the respiratory conditions. In fish embryos which develop in less favourable oxygen conditions—phytophils, lithophils, ostracophils—the elements of the blood are formed long before they hatch from the egg, and much earlier than in the embryos of pelagophil fishes which develop in a high oxygen saturation. Eggs and larvae which develop in nests do so under the least favourable oxygen conditions. These have particularly well-developed larval respiratory organs (dipneusts, gymnarchs, sheat-fish, marine catfish, etc.). Many fishes which develop under unfavourable respiratory conditions possess special external larval gills. Larval gills are possessed by the African and South American representatives of the dipneusts— *Polypterus, Gymnarchus niloticus* Val., the common loach, *Misgurnus fossilis* L., and a number of other species (Fig. 18); when the definitive adult gills develop, the larval ones are reduced (see page 43).

The newly hatched larva possesses special adaptations to enable it to keep in the most favourable region: in a particular layer of the water (pelagic fishes), in the inshore zone (littoral fishes), and so on. Larvae and young fishes which lead a pelagic life often possess various outgrowths which increase their resistance to water movements and which enable them to soar in the water column (see above). In phytophil fish (carp, bream, etc.), whose eggs develop attached to plants in the inshore zone, the larvae often possess "cement organs," by means of which the larvae attach themselves to plants and other objects in the water, thus enabling the larvae to keep to the surface layer of the water, which is richest in oxygen.

In certain ostracophil fishes, such as the common bitterling, *Rhodeus sericeus* (Pall.), special outgrowths of the yolk-sac develop, by means of which the larva holds itself between the gill-plates of the mollusc. This function is also performed by the epidermal scales which develop on the body of the larval spiny bitterling, *Acanthorhodeus asmussi* (Dyb.). The fundamental function of these scales is to enable the larva to crawl about between the gills.

In psammophil fishes the larvae usually keep to their substrate by means of the enlarged pectoral fins, which in some Far Eastern gudgeons even form something like a peculiar type of sucker (Fig. 71).

Enormous fecundity in fishes is related to enormous mortalities, which mainly occur during the egg and larval stages. The percentage of fishes which survive to maturity is extremely small. For the sturgeon, it is about 0·01 %, for the autumn chum salmon in the Amur 0·13–0·58 %, for the Atlantic salmon 0·125 %, and for the bream 0·006–0·022 % (Cherfas, 1956).

In connection with the fact that the conditions under which fishes develop are subjected to very great fluctuations, it is natural that the mortality of each generation varies from year to year, i.e. there are very great fluctuations in the yield of successive generations. These fluctuations may be of very different magnitudes for different species. Thus, in the oceanic herring, *Clupea harengus* L., and the cod, *Gadus morrhua* L., the yield of a year-class (according to the proportion which reach maturity) may vary by 60–90 times, whereas in the sturgeons, flatfish, and certain others the variation in separate year-classes is not more than ten times.

The factors which cause the fluctuations in year-class strength, i.e. the survival of the eggs and larvae to maturity, may be very variable. In the Far Eastern salmons of the genus *Oncorhynchus* an unsuccessful year-class very often results from the death of the eggs due to the redds freezing up in cold winters with little snow. In the herring, anchovy, cod, and various fishes a "critical stage" in nutrition occurs when the larva transfers from yolk- to external feeding (Hjort, 1914; Rounsefell, 1930; Kryzhanovsky, 1956; Pavlovskaia, 1955). At this stage it is not the absolute amount of food in the sea which is of primary significance, but its presence in sufficient concentrations in the places in which the larvae are concentrated, i.e. in such quantities that the energy expended in capturing it is compensated for by the calorific content of the food. For fishes such as the plaice, the strength of a year-class is apparently determined to a significant extent by the food supply at the time when the larva is changing over from plankton to benthos feeding. In many freshwater pelagophil fishes the greatest and most variable mortality occurs at the time the larvae are approaching the inshore zone.

A knowledge of the factors which determine the yield is of considerable importance both for forecasting the success of a year-class, and for working-out methods of controlling it.

The Size, Growth, and Age of Fishes

The growth of a fish results from the consumption of food, its assimilation, and the construction from it of the organism's body (Vasnetsov, 1947, 1953b). The growth process is specific for each species of fish, as for any other organism. Growth is a specific adaptive property, ensured by the unity of the species and its environment. Slow growth and small size of individuals enables several populations of fishes to exist on comparatively restricted food supplies. But at the same time, small size (as, for example, that of the anchovy, gambusia, gobies, and many other fishes) is connected with an increased rate of consumption by predators, and there should, therefore, be some compensatory increase in the reproductive capacity of the population. Fast growth and large size ensures that the fish will have some protection against predators, but this is only possible in the presence of an abundant food supply and it limits the abundance of the population (sturgeons, sharks, sheat-fish, and many others). In order to explain the correlations between the growth of a species and the environment, it is essential to establish the principles of growth which determine the correlations, both in the individual and historically (Vasnetsov, 1953b).

Fishes vary considerably in size and in their life span.

The smallest fish we know of, and possibly even the smallest vertebrate, is a goby, *Pandaka pygmaea* Herre, which only reaches 7·5–11·5 mm in length. Another goby, *Mistichthys lusonensis* (Smith), is also very small, reaching a length of only 12–14 mm. Both these fishes inhabit Philippine waters. Slightly larger are the European gobies, *Aphya* and *Crystallogobius*, and also many representatives of the order Cyprinodontiformes, which inhabit tropical fresh waters.

On the other hand, there are such gigantic fishes as the polar shark, *Cetorhinus maximus* (Gunn.), which attains to a length of 15 m, and even possibly more. Some fossil sharks were undoubtedly of larger size.

The largest fish of fresh waters is the white sturgeon, *Huso huso* L., which attains to a weight of 1000 kg; the South American *Arapaima gigas* (Cuv.) weighs up to 160 kg and the common sheat-fish, *Silurus glanis* L., up to 200 kg.

The life span of various fishes is also very variable. Some representatives of the families Gobiidae and Scopelidae live at most one year, while the white sturgeon lives to a hundred years or more.

The maximum age and size are specific for every species (Table 12). Some species have a short life, while the limiting age of others is 25–30 years.

Within the limits of the species, there are variations among the different forms in both the maximum and the average size and age of individuals in the population, in relation to the environmental conditions (Table 13).

The natural life span of a fish is closely connected with the course of its metabolism. In very many species a complete mortality as a result of exhaustion occurs after the first spawning. This is true of the far eastern salmons of the genus *Oncorhynchus*, and also of the common eel, *Anguilla anguilla* L. In the common salmon, *Salmo salar* L., an average of up to 87·5 % die after

TABLE 12

Normal Limiting Sizes and Ages of Various Species of Fishes

Species	Location	Limiting length, cm.	Limiting age, years
Anchovy, *Engraulis encrasicholus maeoticus* Pusanov	Sea of Azov	13	3
Sprat, *Sprattus sprattus balticus* (Schn.)	Baltic	16	6
Roach, *Rutilus rutilus caspicus* Jak.	North Caspian	35	10
Bream, *Abramis brama bergi* Grieb.	Aral Sea	45	15
Silver crucian carp, *Carassius auratus gibelio* (Bloch)	Amur	40	12
Carp, *Cyprinus carpio haematopterus* Temm. Schl.	Amur	90	16
Oceanic herring, *Clupea harengus harengus* L.	Norwegian and North Seas	37	23
Cod, *Gadus morhua morhua* L.	Barents Sea	169	25
Sturgeon, *Acipenser stellatus* Pall.	Kura	214	31

TABLE 13

The Size and Age of Various Forms of the Herring *Clupea harengus* L.

Form of herring	Average		Maximum	
	length, cm	age, years	length, cm	age, years
Norwegian	28–31	6–7	37	22
Iceland	31–33	9–13	38	25
Sakhalin	27–31	4–6	35	15–17
Channel	26–27	3–5	31	12
White Sea, Egorievsk	14–15	2–4	20	10
White Sea, Ivanovsk	24–25	5–6	32	13
Baltic (salaka) from Bay of Riga: spring	14–16	3–4	20	10
autumn	17–19	4–5	26	12

their first spawning. More of the males die after their first spawning than females. This higher mortality of males than of females after first time spawning has an adaptive significance, because the preservation of large females is more important for the reproduction of the species than the preservation of large males.

The post-spawning mortality of the Far Eastern salmons also has a beneficial effect for the species, because the organic matter of the dead fish in the rivers enables the development of the nutritional fauna on which the young salmon feed. According to the data of Krokhin (1954), the amount of phosphates in the water of Lake Dalnie increases by 10–20 mg/l as a result of the deaths of many red or sockeye salmon, *Oncorhynchus nerka* (Walb.). In certain rivers the young autumn chum salmon feed directly on their parents' corpses, preserved in the water since the autumn owing to the low temperature. An attempt to feed young salmon in fish-farms on the flesh of their parents gave positive results (Smirnov, 1954a).

In many fishes ageing is correlated with morphological changes. Thus, for example, in old individuals of the cod, *Gadus morhua* L., the lower jaw becomes hook-shaped, which hinders feeding and thus leads to starvation.

A characteristic feature of the growth of fishes (as in all animals with an inconstant body temperature) is its periodicity. In certain seasons of the year the fish grows rapidly, in others it grows more slowly. This inequality in the growth rate throughout the year is well reflected in various bones of the skeleton and the scales. The periods of slow growth are imprinted on the skeleton in the form of rings or stripes, which are pale in reflected light (Fig. 85). These stripes consist of small flattened cells and they appear dark in direct light. Conversely, the periods of faster growth are characterized on the scales and skeleton by wide fields or rings, which are dark in reflected light and pale in direct light (Fig. 86).

The first to state that the rings on scales and bones of fishes correspond to periods of retarded and accelerated growth and that the age of the fish could be read from these rings was the Dutch naturalist van Leeuwenhoek (1684). All the same, the practical evaluation of this method, which has enormous practical value, began much later and is, substantially, an achievement of the last fifty years.

Russian investigators have played a significant part in the development of the method of determining the ages of fish. The papers of Soldatov on the study of the age-composition of the sturgeons of the Amur from the bones, the investigations of Arnold, Chugunov, Suvorov, Monastyrsky, Chugunova, and others contributed much to the theoretical solution of the problem, and also to the direct application of the method in the solution of practical problems.

The great importance of the determination of the age of fishes in the solution of biological problems of fisheries has led to the accumulation of a large amount of information in this field, and there are many investigations which are interesting from a technical point of view (a review of the methods of determining the age and growth rate of fishes is given by Chugunova, 1959).

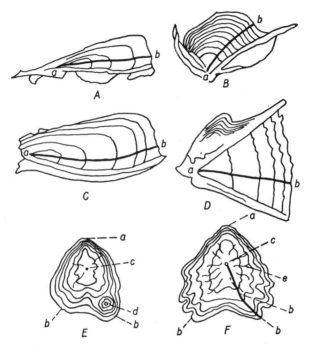

FIG. 85. A, Cleithrum of a roach; B, cleithrum of a bream; C, cleithrum of a sturgeon; D, opercular bone of a perch: line of measurement—*ab* (from Chugunov); E, transverse section of a ray of the sevruga sturgeon; F, section of the ray of Russian sturgeon: (a) dorsal part, (b) lateral blade, (c) centre, (d) supplementary centre, (e) radial fissure, (f) line of measurement of the section.

In the majority of fishes the age is determined from the scales. Scales are simply collected. They are easily torn out and in many fishes—nearly all salmonids, clupeoids, cyprinoids, gadoids, and others—enable the age to be determined fairly certainly. The scales to be used for determining the age of a fish are usually taken from just below the base of the first dorsal fin, and placed between sheets of unsized paper; information concerning the fish from which each scale was taken (length, weight, sex, place of capture, gear,

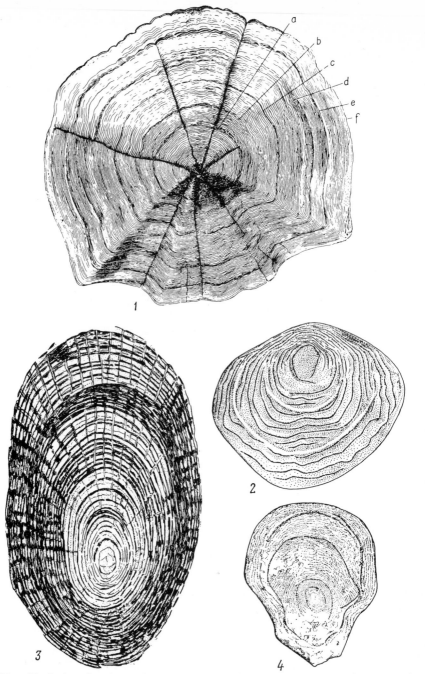

FIG. 86. Scales of various fishes showing annual rings (not to same scale). 1, Roach; 2, freshwater smelt; 3, cod; 4, salmon.

etc.) is written down on the same sheet. For determining the age the scale, after washing in ammoniacal solution, is placed between two glass slides and examined with either a lens or a microscope, depending on its size. Delicate scales, such as those of the cod, are sometimes better examined in glycerine-gelatine. It is not recommended to place scales for age determination in canada balsam, because they become so transparent that the age rings cannot be defined.

In the perches, burbot, and certain other fishes the flat bones such as the gill covers and the cleithrum are useful in age determination. The annual rings are often no less easy to see on the bones than on the scales. The most trustworthy age determinations are those made by using both the scales and the bones of the same fish, which serve as a useful control. The method of preparing the bones for age determination is very simple: the bone is cleaned of flesh and fat and then dried. It is impossible to determine the age from the bones of rotten fish or fish which have lain in formalin, because such bones usually become discoloured.

In gadoids and pleuronectids the age is frequently determined from the otoliths or earstones (Fig. 85), which are removed from the skull by dissection of the labyrinths. The otoliths have to be freed from fat, and in some cases polished up, to improve their transparency. In sturgeons, sheat-fishes, and certain sharks (*Acanthias*) the age is determined from the fin rays; in the shark, those of the unpaired and in the sturgeons and sheat-fish, those of the paired fins. In the shark the rings are visible even just after cleaning the rays; in the sturgeons and sheat-fish it is necessary to prepare a transverse section of this ray, which is polished up to transparency, and then stuck to a slide with canada balsam, in which state it can be used for the age determination (Fig. 85). A special machine, which consists of two parallel discs rotated by an electric motor, has been developed for the preparation of the sections. By regulating the distance between the discs, sections of any thickness can be prepared.

Since the annual marks are produced as the result of changes in the growth rate, the problem naturally arises as to whether "annual rings" could not possibly be formed several times in the year, not only as the result of the cessation of feeding in the winter, but also as the result of fasting, for instance, during the spawning period, or of changing from one type of food to another and more nourishing one, and so on. The fundamental method of showing the correlation between the number of rings and the age is to study the scales of fishes of known ages, or else of fishes which have lived for a known length of time since the examination of an earlier sample of scales from them. As has been shown by the study of fishes which have lived for a known number of years in ponds or aquaria, and also of fishes which had been marked previously in the open water (cod, roach), the numbers of rings on the scales and of layers on the bones usually corresponds to the number of years through which the fish has lived. True, there do occur on scales and bones supplementary rings, the appearance of which is often regular and is connected with some particular event in the life of the fish. Thus, for example, in some fishes (dace, roach, etc.) inside the first annual ring there occurs a so-called fry or larval ring, which is connected with the event of the larva changing over from planktonic to benthic food.

The scales of many fishes show spawning rings and marks, which are the result of the cessation of feeding and exhaustion during the spawning period. For example, in the Caspian shad at the time of spawning the scales begin to break down, which leads to the formation of a definite type of mark (Zamakhaev, 1940) (Fig. 87). The scales of the salmon also bear clear spawning marks in the form of a ring, though of a somewhat different character from the annual rings. The spawning rings in *Salmo salar* L. are usually more clearly marked in the male than in the female.

In the Caspian roach the study of the scales of fish which have been recaptured after being marked has established (Chugunova, 1940) the existence of another three types of supplementary rings besides the larval and the spawning rings—type 1, appearing when the growth of the fish is retarded accidentally; type 2, forming in the event of a change in the character of the growth of the scale; and type 3, forming along the line of a tear in the ring due to accidental injury.

Naturally, there arises the question of whether the occurrence of supplementary rings on the scales, bones, and otoliths of fishes does not make the whole method of the determination of age from annual rings fallacious, and how to differentiate between the annual and supplementary rings. Much work has been done on this problem. In particular, Petrov and Petrushevsky (1929) attempted to macerate the scales of the carp and to divide them into separate sheets, each corresponding to a particular year of life (Fig. 88). Vinge (1915) measured the widths of the separate sclerites on the scales of the cod and plotted these values on a graph. From the number of maxima, which corresponded to the size of the widest sclerites, he obtained the number of annual rings; the supplementary rings, although they gave some change in the size of the sclerites, were less significant than the annual ones.

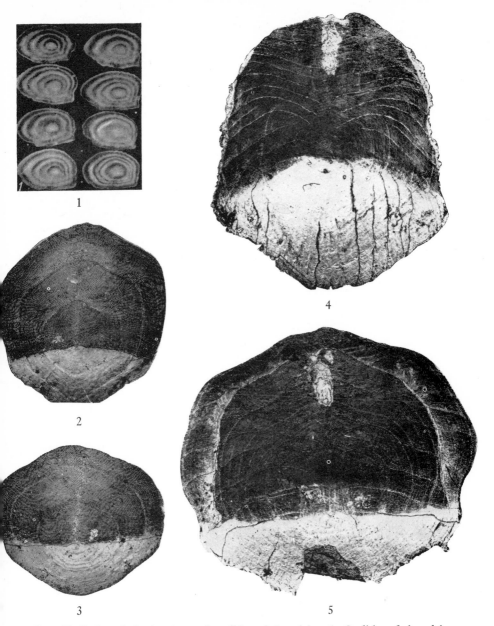

Fig. 87. Scales of the herring and otoliths of the plaice. 1, Otoliths of the plaice *Pleuronectes platessa* (from Alward, 1932); 2 and 3, scales of the White Sea herring *Clupea harengus maris albi*; 4, scale of the Caspian shad *Caspialosa kessleri*, with its edges fraying at the time of spawning; 5, scale of the Caspian shad showing regeneration of the frayed edge.

[*To face page* 194

Usually several of the methods are used, e.g. the bones of the gill covers in addition to the scales of a number of fishes, for the verification of the age determination.

Besides studying the rings on the scales and bones it is essential to study the mode of life of the fish in order to explain the regular features in its growth, which could be reflected in the growth of the scales. A knowledge of the events in the life of a fish, which could be reflected in the growth of the scales, would enable one, when such rings are present on the scales, to

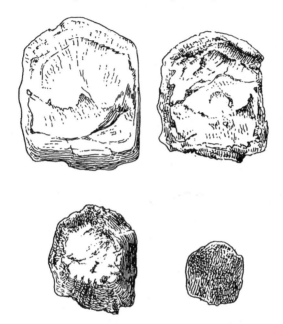

FIG. 88. A scale of a three-year old carp, treated with chloral hydrate and separated into lamellae which correspond to the separate years of its age (from Petrov and Petrushevsky, 1929).

approach them with care and to assess their nature more easily. Recognition of the larval ring is most difficult. Usually, in order to avoid confusing the larval and the first annual rings, a few samples of the larvae of the species in question are taken in the autumn, and the analysis of their size makes it clear which is the larval and which the first annual ring. On the whole, the additional rings and marks of all types are usually less clearly expressed than the annual ones, and with some experience they can usually be recognized without difficulty.

We have discussed cases in which there may be more zones on the scales and bones than the number of years of life, but it is also possible for there to be fewer rings and marks than the age of the fish. This problem is particularly important when determining the age from the scales. A regenerated scale has fewer rings than a normal one. In addition, in certain fishes, such as the eel, the scales may not develop until the third or fourth years of life, and naturally the number of annual rings on the scales will definitely be fewer than the number of years of life, and of marks on the bones.

As may be seen from the above, the calculated deviation from the norm does not in any way reduce the value of the method of determining the age of a fish from its scales or bones. In using the method it is essential to make a detailed analysis of the nature of the rings, an individual approach to each object studied, and particularly an assessment of the specific features of the ecology of the fish.

The time at which the annual rings are laid down is very important for the study of the age of the fish. If the annual ring is the direct result of the retardation of the growth during the winter, the time of appearance of the ring should apparently fall in the spring. But it is well known that in fishes of different ages the period when the annual rings are laid down occurs in different seasons. Thus, for example, in immature individuals of the pike-perch, *Lucioperca lucioperca* L., in the Sea of Azov, the annual ring is laid down in the spring, but in older fishes it is laid down in the second half of the year (Chugunova, 1931). In young individuals of the bream, *Abramis brama bergi* Grieb., in the Aral Sea the start of a new year's growth also falls in the spring, but in older fishes it falls in the autumn (Konstantinova, 1958).

It would be incorrect to regard the formation of the annual rings as a direct consequence of a retardation of the metabolism and of the growth of the fish only as a result of a disturbance of feeding or of an unfavourable change of temperature. The time at which the rings are laid down is the result of simultaneous processes, both internal and external, the result of an adaptive reconstruction of the course of metabolism within the fish's body. There often takes place in mature fishes a process of accumulation of reserve materials without linear growth occurring, and then, when a certain state of satiation is reached, the process of fat accumulation either ceases or slows down, and protein growth becomes more intensive. In connection with this the deposition of the annual ring in mature fishes is displaced to the end of the year. In immature fish most of the food supply is used in protein growth.

The fact that the annual rings are not formed directly under the influence of the temperature is supported by the presence of annual marks on the scales and bones of fishes in the equatorial and tropical zones. Among equatorial marine fishes, for example, annual rings are laid down on the scales of a number of clupeoids. Among freshwater fishes we may mention the characinid *Curimatius elegans* Steind. in Brazil and Paraguay, in which the Brazilian investigators Azevedo, Dias, and Vieira (1938) also observed the presence of annual rings on the scales.

The designation of the separate age groups presents a considerable problem. There is a lack of uniformity in this respect among the literature. The following terminology is accepted at present:

Age group	Number of rings	Designation
Less than one year old	None	0+
One year old (yearling)	One	1
Less than two years old	One	1+
Two years old	Two	2
Less than three years old	Two	2+
Three years old	Three	3

The plus sign signifies the start of the following year's growth.

The presence of annual marks on the bones of fishes would enable the growth of the fish in previous years to be calculated if there was a proportional relationship between the growth of the scales and bones of the fish and its body. However, to make such calculations possible it is first necessary to establish the nature of the relationship between the growth of the body of the fish and that of its bones and scales.

The Norwegian scientist Einar Lea (1910) assumed that the length of the scale and that of the fish increased in direct proportion to each other, i.e. that the proportionality was of a linear character, and could, therefore, be represented by a simple equation. On the basis of his investigations on the herring, Lea proposed the following formula:

$$L_n = \frac{V_n}{V} \cdot L$$

where L is the measured length of the fish, V that of the scale from the centre to the edge, along the mid-line, L_n is the calculated length of the fish at age n years, V_n is the distance between the annual ring and the centre of the scale at age n years. The relationship calculated by Lea is well illustrated by the drawing in Fig. 89, in which there is a series of similar triangles, the proportional sides of which represent the size of the fish and that of the scale for a given year. Using this relationship, Lea constructed a special apparatus for the calculation of the growth rate of a fish. This apparatus was later considerably improved by Monastrysky (1924) (Fig. 90), who suggested projecting the scale directly on to the board by means of a camera lucida, and placing a slide at a point on a centimetre scale which corresponds to the length of the fish when captured. This slide is connected with the base line *FO.* by a thread, which passes through the edge of the scale, the centre of

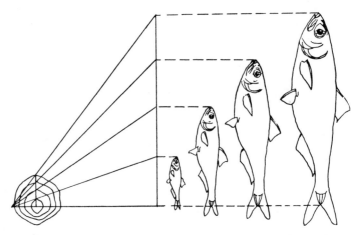

FIG. 89. The correlation between the rate of growth of a fish and that of its scales (the principle of a direct proportionality, formulated by Einar Lea).

which coincides with an upright of a right-angle formed by the side of a triangle passing through the zero on the centimetre scale against which the length of the fish is placed, and a line joining the centre of the scale and the line *FO.* Moving the slide so that the thread coincides with the annual rings gives the length of the fish at the age corresponding to the rings. Lea's method is at present used by many ichthyologists, because it gives quite satisfactory results for comparative purposes. However, in order to compare the growth rate so obtained, it is necessary to use fishes of the same age.

In 1920 the English investigator Rosa Lee proposed certain improvements in Einar Lea's method, on the basis of the accumulated data on the subject. According to Rosa Lee, it is only the increment in the length of the fish and in the size of the scale that are proportional to each other, and not their actual sizes. The main factor which disturbs the proportionality between the length of the fish and that of the scale is the fact that the scale is not laid down at the birth of the fish, but somewhat later, when the fish has already attained a certain length. Rosa Lee therefore proposed to introduce into Einar Lea's formula the additional length a, corresponding to the length of the fish at the moment the scale began to be laid down.

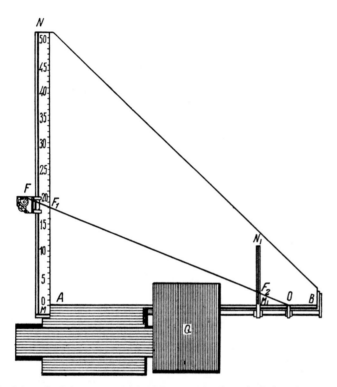

FIG. 90. A board of the type used by Monastyrsky for calculating the growth rate by Einar Lea's method (from Monastyrsky, 1924).

With Rosa Lee's correction the formula takes on the following appearance:

$$L_n = \frac{V_n}{V}(L-a)+a.$$

Subsequent investigations, and particularly those of Monastyrsky (1926, 1930), showed that for certain fishes the relationship between the growth of the scales and bones and that of the body has a curvilinear character, that is, it cannot be expressed by an equation of the first order. As a result of his detailed investigations over many years, Monastyrsky came to the conclusion that the increase in the logarithm of the length of the scale was proportional to the increase in the logarithm of the body length (Fig. 91). The equation which expresses this relationship is as follows:

$$\lg Y = \lg k + n \lg X$$

where Y is the length of the fish, X the corresponding length of the scale, $\lg k$ the intercept of the straight line on the axis of the ordinate, and n the slope.

Monastyrsky also constructed a very simple apparatus for the calculation of the growth rate by the method of logarithmic scales (Fig. 92).

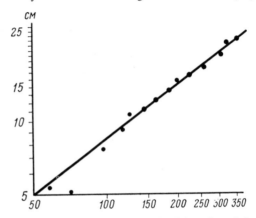

FIG. 91. The correlation between the growth of a fish scale and that of the fish (roach from Lake Bisserov), plotted on logarithmic scales. Abscissa, measurement of scale; ordinate, length of fish (from Monastyrsky, 1930).

Further investigation by Vovk (1955) showed that there is a specific characteristic in the nature of the curve relating the growth of the fish to that of its scales (Fig. 93). In using this to reconstruct the growth of a fish from its scales it is first necessary to compile a special scale (Fig. 94) based upon direct measurements of the scales and fish, from which the growth of the fish is very easily calculated.*

The growth rate of fishes can also be expressed in terms of the relative growth rate formula (Schmalhausen, 1935) or the growth characteristic (Vasnetsov, 1934, etc.).

The growth characteristic formula used by Vasnetsov is as follows:

$$\frac{\lg L_2 - \lg L_1}{0.4343 \, (t_2 - t_1)} \cdot L_1$$

*For a method of determining the growth of fishes see Chugunova (1959).

in which 0·4343 is the modulus for transforming natural to common logarithms, L_1 and L_2 are the lengths of the fish at ages 1 and 2 years, t_1 and t_2 are the increments in the corresponding years.

Analysis of the characteristics of the growth enables one to determine both the general and the specific principles of the growth of individual species

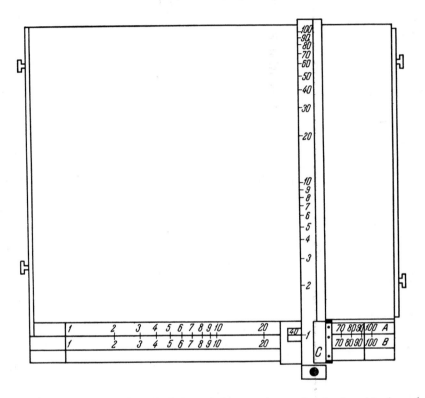

FIG. 92. A board for the calculation of the growth rate by the logarithmic scales method. A, Logarithmic ruler; B, slide of logarithmic ruler; C, vertical slide.

and of intraspecific groups. Each of the life periods of a fish is characterized by a particular character of growth. Thus, the period of most rapid linear growth usually occurs before the onset of maturity. This is an important adaptation which ensures that the fish escapes the influence of predators. Small fish are much more easily available to predators than large ones. During the period prior to the attainment of maturity the growth of the fish

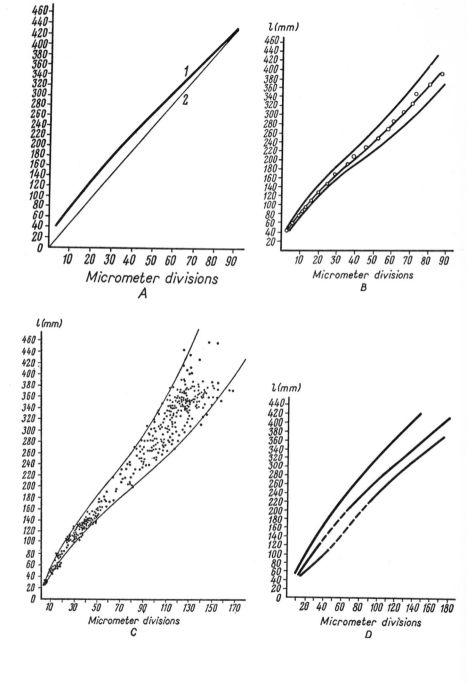

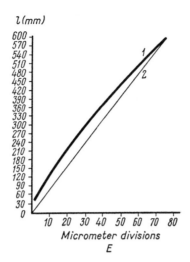

Fɪɢ. 93. Curves correlating the growth of fishes and their scales in various species (from Vovk, 1955). A, *Coregonus autumnalis* (Pallas) in Ob Bay; B, ide; C, bream (male); D, *Pelecus cultratus* (Linné) in the Rybinsk Reservoir (upper curve—posterior radius; middle—anterior radius; lower—lateral radius); E, pike-perch *Lucioperca lucioperca* (Linné) in the Rybinsk Reservoir: 1, empirical curve, 2, straight line according to Lea's method.

is most closely related to the food supply, and is therefore subject to the greatest fluctuations. Thus, for example, in the bream in different waters the growth characteristic prior to the attainment of maturity varies from 0·97 to 7·22, i.e. in a ratio of eight times, but in mature bream it only varies from 0·90 to 4·0, a ratio of 4 times.

After the attainment of maturity the main part of the food consumed by the fish is used not for linear growth but for the ripening of the gonads and the accumulation of fat for overwintering. The ratio of maintenance and growth food changes in the direction of an increase in the relative amount of maintenance food. During the period of old age linear growth practically ceases; the value of the growth characteristic is sharply reduced; most of the food is used for maintenance and only occasionally for fat accumulation, particularly in overwintering fishes.

Growth, like every characteristic of life, has its specific character in different groups of fishes. In cyprinoids, whitefish, and many other fishes it is more variable before the attainment of maturity. In this period its variations are most closely related to the food supply. In the Percidae and the Esocidae the growth rate varies little before maturity, which is perhaps due to the fact that when their food supply is low they consume their own young. The character of linear growth is also specific in those fish which have an interruption in their feeding in connection with overwintering and migration, which is related to the need to accumulate fat reserves and, therefore, to a retardation of the linear growth.

FIG. 94. Scale for the calculation of the growth rate of fishes (from Vovk, 1955).

Changes in the growth of fishes before the attainment of maturity, related to changes in the food supply, may be determined by various factors. Each species of fish has its own temperature optimum, at which the rates of metabolism and growth are most rapid. Naturally, therefore, deviations in either direction from the temperature optimum will affect the growth rate of the immature fish.

As the following table shows, in years when the temperature was lower than the average in Kandalaksk Bay, the growth rate of the smelt (*Osmerus eperlanus* [L.]) in the bay was slower:

Increment*	Years				
	1924	1925	1926	1927	1928
t_1	4·3	4·5	3·9	4·5	4·2
t_2		8·3	7·0	8·2	6·3
t_3			5·3	6·9	6·3
t_4				4·5	4·0
t_5					2·7
Deviation of temperature from annual average	+0·13	+0·34	−0·72	+0·68	−0·44

The temperature not only affects the character of the growth of fishes. In a number of cases the temperature acts as a "signal factor." A reduction of the temperature below a certain level leads to a cessation of protein growth and the commencement of the fat accumulation processes. This was noted for young carp by Kirpichnikov (1958) and also holds for a number of other species. In this case the reorganization of the metabolism in relation to the change in temperature is an adaptive reaction, which ensures the necessary preparation of the organism for overwintering.

In many species of fish, such as the bream, etc., before the attainment of maturity all the basic food intake is used for protein growth, which ensures a protection against predators and the preservation of the stock of fish. In connection with this, practically no fat is accumulated by young fish, and these feed throughout the year (see below). Even some fishes of adult ages such as many gadoids (*Boreogadus saida* Lepech., *Eleginus navaga* L.), and also the pike (*Esox lucius* L.) also sometimes behave in this way. In these fishes a reduction in the rate of linear growth is connected primarily with the period of ripening of the gonads and spawning, and depends less upon the temperature.

We have already stated that the variability of the growth of fishes belonging to the same species may be very great. Fish cultivators know very well how to accelerate the growth of fishes through correct nourishment (Movchan, 1948).

The biomass of benthos, in the case of benthophagic species, or of plankton in the case of planktophagic ones, naturally affects the growth of fishes. Thus, for example, the carp, living under more or less similar conditions where the only difference is in the biomass of the benthos and the quality

*The letter t is used to signify the calculated increments; for example, t_1 means the growth in the first year; $t_2 = L_2 - L_1$ (where L is the length of the fish) means the growth in the second year, and so on.

and availability of the food, varies considerably in its growth rate. The variation in the growth increment is greatest in the first years of life. This is very
graphically seen in the data given in Table 14 on the growth rates of carp
from the lakes of Central Asia, which vary in their benthos biomasses.

The growth of the fish is affected not only by the quantity, but also by the
quality and size of the food objects. Experiments on the effect of different
types of foods on the growth of the carp, as might have been expected,
showed that the foods with the greatest calorific content usually give the
most rapid growth. The growth of fishes is also influenced by the presence of

TABLE 14

Relationship Between Growth Rate of the Carp and the Value of the Benthos Biomass
in Certain Lakes

| Lake | Length of Fish | | | | Benthos biomass |
	L_1	L_2	L_3	L_4	in g/m²
Ildzhik	6·9	12·6	17·0	—	0·26
Karakul	8·0	14·2	18·1	20·0	1·43
Djoldibai	8·6	14·7	18·2	23·2	1·83
Aral Sea	12·6	21·5	29·3	36·0	18·0

vitamins in the food. The growth is most retarded if vitamin B is missing
from the diet. Vitamins A and D are stored in the fat, and even their prolonged absence from the diet does not produce any noticeable change in
growth, because any deficit in these vitamins in the food is supplemented
at the expense of the reserves stored in the fats of the fish's body.

Changes in the quality and quantity of food consumed by the fish very
quickly affect the growth rate. Thus, in the salmon, the change in the food
on passing from the river to the sea is immediately reflected in the growth
rate. Plaice, transplanted from parts of the sea with a low benthos biomass
into a region of high biomass, very quickly overtake in growth the fishes of
the same species left in the original habitat (Fig. 95).

When the feeding conditions are impoverished there occurs not only a
reduction of the total growth rate of the fishes of a population, but also an
increase in the variability of growth, which leads to the existence of individuals of very different sizes but in the same age group. Some of the individuals,
those of largest size, have already entered the next stage of development,

while the smallest ones have been retarded in their development. Such a divergence in the growth of fishes of the same ages under impoverished feeding conditions is an important adaptation which enables a wider range of foods to be used by the population. The small individuals consume some organisms, the larger ones consume others. When the feeding conditions improve the growth of the fishes evens itself out, and all the fishes begin to eat the same food. This phenomenon has been studied most clearly by Poliakov (1958a) using yearling carp (Fig. 96).

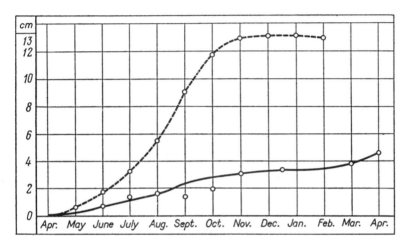

FIG. 95. Growth of the plaice *Pleuronectes platessa* L. in the nursery grounds (Horns Reef ground) (solid line) and in the acclimatization area (Dogger Bank) (broken line).

The seasonal periodicity of growth varies considerably not only for different life periods of a single species, but also for different species. Thus, in arctic fishes the most intensive growth usually occurs during the winter, when these fishes, such as the whitefish, feed most intensively. In some arctic whitefishes it has been established that two "annual" rings are formed each year, i.e. during one year the growth of the fish is retarded and accelerated twice.

The growth of fishes in temperate latitudes is also closely related to the mode of life. Thus, in the oceanic herring *Clupea harengus* L. the most rapid linear growth falls in the season March–July (Fig. 97), when the herring feeds most intensively (Hjort, 1914).

In the Aral Sea bream the period of linear growth occurs either in the summer months in immature fishes, or in the autumn in mature fishes.

The dynamics of the fat content and condition are closely related to the linear growth of a fish. As already stated, the course of the changes in condition and fat content varies considerably from one species to another. In such fishes as the sturgeons, salmons, and the majority of cyprinoids, there is a clear seasonal dynamics in the condition. In others [pike (*Esox lucius* L.), cichlids (Cichlidae), and many others] the fat content and the condition change very little throughout the year, which is related to the fact that there are only short intervals between feeding.

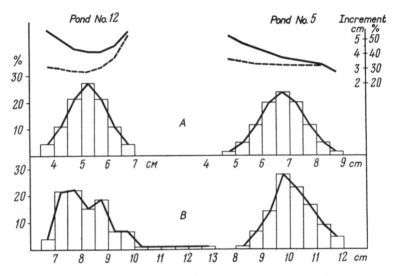

Fig. 96. Growth increments of various size-groups and changes in the length-composition of yearling carp in ponds with poor (No. 12) and good (No. 5) feeding conditions. A, At start of rearing (July 30); B, autumn sample. Broken line, total growth; solid line, relative growth.

For the purpose of comparing the condition of a species the ratio of the length to the weight of the fish is usually used. The larger this ratio, the better the condition of the fish is said to be. Naturally, the value of this condition factor calculated in this way is highly dependent upon the exterior of the fish. In high-bodied fishes with a broad back the ratio of the weight to the length is greater than in elongated ones.

The usual mode of expression of the value of the condition is the mathematical equation proposed by Fulton (1902):

$$Q = \frac{w \cdot 100}{l^3}$$

where w is the weight of the fish, l its length, and Q the condition coefficient. The cube of the length is taken because the growth in weight is proportional to the growth in volume.

By using Fulton's condition coefficient it is possible to define the seasonal changes in the condition of fishes in relation to the age and sex of the fish, and differences between the condition of the same species in different waters, which might also serve as an index of the productivity of the water-mass. Unfortunately, if the whole body weight is used in calculating the condition coefficient, it is impossible to exclude the effect of the gonads, which may form up to 15 % of the body weight of a fish, and also the weight of the gut

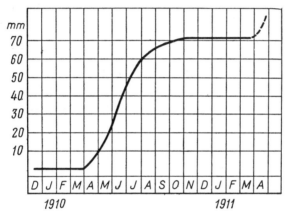

Fig. 97. Growth rate of the ocean herring from December, 1909, to April, 1911 (from Hjort, 1914).

contents, which in many fishes reaches a considerable weight (up to 30 or more per cent of the body weight). The weight of the gonad and the intestinal contents might often alter the value of the condition coefficient and mask the true dynamics of the condition of the fish. In order to exclude the effect of the weight of the gonads and intestinal contents, Clark (1928) suggested calculating the coefficient from the body weight of fishes without the internal organs. The use of this method does exclude the effect of the weight of the gonads and ingested food, but when the internal organs and the intestines are removed so also is the internal fat, the amount of which is subjected to equally great changes and is to a significant extent connected with the condition of the fish. It is therefore better to use both coefficients together, i.e. to calculate a coefficient from both the whole fish and the fish without its internal organs.

Naturally this coefficient gives only a first approximation to the actual condition of the fish, but for a comparative analysis and for valuation purposes it is quite suitable, and can also be used for practical purposes (Table 15).

TABLE 15

Seasonal Changes in the Condition Coefficient (Fulton's) in Various Species of Fish

Name of fish	Month	I	II	III	IV	V	VI	VII	VIII	IX	X	XI	XII
Aral Sea Bream		—	—	—	—	2·24	2·25	2·28	2·25	2·30	2·35	2·42	—
Pike in Farkhadsk reservoir		1·00	1·00	0·95	0·80	0·93	—	0·99	0·77	0·82	0·83	0·96	0·83
Pike in Volga delta	F	1·00	1·00	1·02	1·05	0·95	0·90	0·90	—	—	0·91	1·09	—
	M	1·04	1·01	1·91	0·90	0·92	0·90	0·94	—	—	1·03	1·04	—
Perch in Volga delta	F	2·57	2·16	2·55	2·51	2·35	2·05	2·18	—	—	2·38	2·73	—
	M	2·46	2·10	2·39	2·15	2·07	2·04	2·21	—	—	2·41	2·56	—

Variations also occur from one year to the next in the condition of a single species in relation to the nutritional conditions. Thus, in the Azov Sea anchovy the condition coefficient on September 1st in various years had the following values:

Condition Coefficient of Large Anchovies on September 1st (Salnikov, 1957)

Years	1950	1951	1952	1953
Coefficient of condition	0·91	0·84	0·90	0·78

Sometimes a sharp reduction in the condition coefficient is associated with a mass mortality of fishes.

An equally important coefficient of the fish's living condition is its fat content, not only from the purely quantitative aspect but its composition as well, particularly the ratios of saturated and unsaturated fatty acids. Those fats which consist principally of unsaturated fatty acids are deposited for daily expenditure, while fats with a predominance of saturated acids are deposited to form a reserve against the overwintering or migrating period.

The most accurate method for determining the fat content is a chemical analysis, but under field conditions it is often necessary to use a simplified technique.

If the fat accumulates in large amounts in the interior of the fish during the feeding period, it is comparatively easy to remove it. For the determination of the fat content of such a fish as the bream, the weight of the "internal" fat is expressed as a percentage of the total weight of the fish. Changes in this coefficient of the fat content reflect the changes in the total fat content of the fish quite well. Hjort (1914) proposed a scale of units of fat content for the herring, which could only be determined by dissecting the fish. Using Hjort's scale, it is only possible to obtain a first approximation of the fat content of the herring, but this is often close enough for a preliminary orientation.

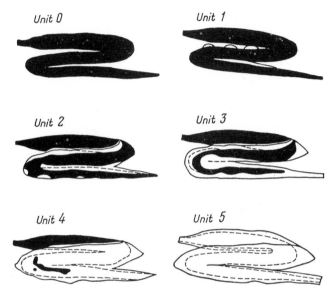

FIG. 98. Units of the fat content scale for the roach (from Prozorovskaia, 1952).

There have been several assessments of the fat content of fishes on various scales of units. The most detailed of these was made by Prozorovskaia (1952), who proposed the following scale of fat content for the Caspian roach. Scale of fat content:

Unit 0—No fat present on intestines. Sometimes the intestines are covered by a thin white connective film. Threadlike extensions of this film may be seen between the loops of the intestine (Fig. 98).

Unit 1—Thin cordlike strips of fat distributed between the second and third segments of the intestine. Sometimes there is a very narrow interrupted strip of fat along the upper edge of the second segment of the intestine.

Unit 2—A rather narrow strip of fairly dense fat between the second and third segments of the intestine. Along the upper edge of the second segment there is a narrow continuous strip of fat. Somewhere along the lower edge of the third segment there can be seen some separate portions of fat.

Unit 3—A wide strip of fat in the middle between the second and third segments of the intestine. This strip widens in the loop between the second and third segments. Wide strips of fat along the upper edge of the second and the lower edge of the third segments. In the first bend of the intestine, counting from the anterior end, there is a triangular growth of fat. Anal end of the intestine, in the overwhelming majority of cases, covered with a thin layer of fat.

Unit 4—Intestine almost completely covered by fat except for small gaps through which the intestine may be seen. These gaps are usually on the second loop of the intestine and on the third segment. Fatty outgrowths on both loops very large.

Unit 5—Intestine completely covered by a thick layer of fat. No gaps at all. Large fatty outgrowths on both loops.

With small modifications this scale is suitable for use with many cyprinoids and other groups of fish.

Tester (1940) suggested assessing the fat content of a fish by its density. On the basis of the herring he worked out a method which enabled him to determine the dynamics of the fat content of a fish with sufficient practical accuracy. This method, which is also suitable for use in the field, consists of finding the weight of the fish in air and in water. To avoid the possibility of inclusion of air-bubbles it is necessary to determine the density of the gutted fish, making sure that no bubbles are trapped in the buccal and gill cavities.

Average Fat Content in the Body of Various Commercial Fishes

Russian sturgeon	8·0	Atlantic salmon	11·0
Sevruga-sturgeon	11·0	Chum salmon	10·0
Baltic herring	4·5	Stenodus	18·0
Whitefish	1·5	Haddock	0·2
Smelt	3·0	Navaga	0·6
Anchovy	23·0	Mullet	1·5
Roach	2·5	Mackerel	8·0
Bream	5.5	Gobies	1·2
Carp	1·5	Pike-perch	0·5
Sheat-fish	4·0	Perch	0·7
Pike	0·5	Halibut	5·0
River eel	22·0	Plaice	2·0
Cod	0·3		

Both the condition and the fat content of fishes is subject to great variations. As the table shows the percentage of fat in the body of various commercial fishes may vary from 0·2 % (haddock) to 23 % (anchovy).

The fat content also changes in relation to the age and sex of the fish. Thus, for example, in the Black Sea shad the percentage of fat changes with age: from 12 % in small fishes (300–1000 fish per 16 kg—a commercial measure) to 20 % in large (about 150 per 16 kg). The same is also true for many other species. In the bream in the North Caspian at three years old the fat comprises 4·85 % of the body weight, and at seven years 8·2 %.

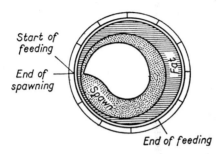

FIG. 99. Scheme of the correlation between the ovaries and fat in the herring through-out the year.

There are also very large seasonal variations in the fat content, and these are closely related to the feeding and reproductive periods of the fish. Figure 99 shows a scheme relating the size of the gonad and the fat in the body of the oceanic herring throughout the year. The size of the gonads and the amount of fat both increase together at first; when feeding ceases the amount of fat rapidly decreases, but the growth of the gonads continues.

The differences in the fat content of closely related species are closely connected with the peculiarities of their modes of life. Thus, for example, the length of the migration course, and the speed of the current which the fish has to overcome in its spawning migration up river, are directly proportional to its fat content (see Table 16).

Such a pattern is observed, for example, in the Caspian shads. In the blackback, *Caspialosa kessleri* Grimm, which swims well up the Volga, the fat content at the estuary before the start of the spawning migration is 16·2 %, in the Volga shad, *Caspialosa volgensis* (Berg), which only reaches the lower part of the river, it is 8·7 %, and in the Caspian shad, *Caspialosa caspia* (Eichw.) it is 7·4 %.

TABLE 16

Connection between the Fat Content and the Type of Migration Course
in the Lampreys

Species	River	Length of course along river, km	Average maximum velocity of current, m/sec	Fat content %
Lampetra japonica	Amur	About 1200	1·2–1·8	33·1
Caspiomyzon wagneri	Kura	About 600	1·5–1·8	31·2
Caspiomyzon wagneri	Volga	About 1000	0·80–1·0	28·8
Lampetra fluviatilis	Neva	70–80	1·2–1·5	16·1

TABLE 17

Seasonal Dynamics of the Fat Content of the Bream in the Central Part of the Aral Sea,
as per cent of the Dry Weight

State of fish	Month	Females		Number of fish	Males		Number of fish
		Fat	Moisture		Fat	Moisture	
Muscular tissue							
Spawning	April	6·2	74·0	3	4·3	74·2	1
Spawning	May	9·8	78·5	3	6·4	72·6	4
Spawning	June	8·3	72·1	4	5·6	70·9	3
After spawning	June	3·3	77·2	2	1·4	76·4	3
After spawning	July	—	—	—	2·4	78·0	1
Feeding	July	7·5	73·3	4	—	—	—
Feeding	August	8·9	72·0	6	9·4	69·4	2
Feeding	September	9·8	71·6	10	9·0	71·4	6
Feeding	October	10·9	69·9	9	8·7	71·5	9
Feeding	November	13·5	62·0	1	8·9	64·1	5
Intestines							
Spawning	April	9·8	56·2	2	19·2	67·4	1
Spawning	May	9·4	64·9	3	31·8	61·2	4
Spawning	June	35·6	—	2	27·7	63·0	4
Spawning	July	18·6	68·3	2	—	—	—
After spawning	June	10·1	74·4	2	—	—	—
Feeding	July	38·3	48·8	3	—	—	—
Feeding	August	62·9	33·6	5	52·7	40·1	1
Feeding	September	48·4	38·3	5	64·8	30·3	6
Feeding	November	—	—	—	48·4	—	4

There is also a direct correlation in single species between the fat content and the length of the migration course. Thus, the autumn chum salmon in the Amur, *Oncorhynchus keta autumnalis* Berg, which passes up this river to beyond Khabarovsk, has a fat content in the estuary of 11·3 % (females), while the summer chum, which even goes as far as Komsomolsk, has only 8·0 %. A similar pattern is also observed in many other fishes. See Table 16.

As has already been stated, overwintering fishes, i.e., those that cease to feed and lower their level of metabolism at a certain season of the year, also accumulate in their bodies a large amount of fat, which is slowly expended during the overwintering period. Table 17 shows that the difference between the spring (after the overwintering) and the autumn (before) fat contents is very large.

In young individuals, which, in contrast to the adults, do not cease to feed in the winter, there is not usually such a sharp seasonal fluctuation in the fat content. See Table 18.

TABLE 18

Seasonal Dynamics of Fat Content of Mature and Immature Roach in a German Lake as per cent of Dry Weight of Fish (from von Westphallen, 1956)

| | Fish | | | | Fish | |
Month	Adult	Young	Month	Adult	Young
I	5·18	2·95	VII	5·10	4·02
II	5·00	3·57	VIII	6·53	6·17
III	5·00	—	IX	6·00	4·67
IV	4·44	1·23	X	6·31	2·78
V	2·89	—	XI	6·70	2·89
VI	3·97	2·75	XII	—	—

The range of variation in the amount of fat laid down in the different organs of the fish depends on the organ.

In percoids (pike-perch, perch), pikes, and whitefishes the amount of fat on the internal organs is variable. As Fig. 100 shows, the maximum fat content of a fish about 20 cm long occurs in August–September. The greatest seasonal changes in the fat content occur in the internal organs, changes in the flesh being rather smaller (Morawa, 1956). A similar pattern is also observed in the whitefish, *Coregonus albula* (L.) (see Fig. 101).

It is interesting that in starvation, as Makarova observed, the last organ to suffer from a loss of fat is the gonad. This important adaptation ensures that

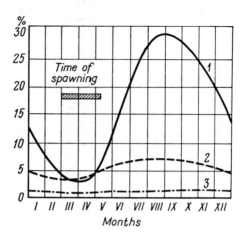

FIG. 100. Seasonal dynamics of the fat deposition in the common perch (from Morawa, 1956). 1, Body cavity; 2, head; 3, flesh.

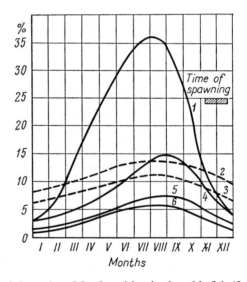

FIG. 101. Seasonal dynamics of fat-deposition in the whitefish (from Morawa, 1956). 1, Body cavity; 2, vertebral column; 3, head; 4, belly; 5, back; 6, tail.

the future offspring has food during its yolk-feeding stage even if the parent fish encounters extremely unfavourable feeding conditions.

In different groups of fishes and cyclostomes there are differences in the distribution of the fat among the various organs. In the sharks and gadoids the fat accumulates mainly in the liver; in gadoids and percoids the flesh contains little fat. In cyclostomes and eels, on the other hand, the flesh is the main site of fat accumulation. In the majority of fishes the larger part of the fat is stored around the intestines. However, hardly any fat is deposited on the intestines in gadoids.

What adaptive significance there could be in such differences in the fat deposition is unknown at present.

The age composition of the stock, the relative strengths of the different age groups, and the maximum life span are, within certain limits, a species characteristic, a species adaptive property.

Fishes with a short life cycle, with a population which consist of only a few age groups, such as the anchovy, *Engraulis encrasicholus* L., the sprat, *Sprattus sprattus* L., the gambusia, *Gambusia affinis* Gir., members of the genus *Gobio* and related genera, are adapted to living under the conditions of a very high and variable mortality. Their population dynamics are of such a character (early maturity, annual spawning, etc.) as to ensure a rapid replacement of the stock. The populations of such species can be very greatly reduced, as in certain American cyprinodontids, the populations of some of which may fall to a few thousand individuals in drought years (Miller, 1943), but thanks to the high reproductive capacity the population can increase by a thousand times in the following year, if conditions are favourable.

On the other hand, there are some species of fishes (sheat-fish, sturgeons, large sharks, and some others) in which the populations contain several decades of age groups. The time of onset of maturity of fishes with this type of stock dynamics (late maturation of a population consisting of many age groups) is usually late, and in contrast to the first type, the recruitment each year is only a small percentage of the whole population.

Fishes belonging to species which form populations containing many age groups and with late maturity are adapted to living under conditions of a relatively stable food supply and negligible annual fluctuations in the mortality of mature individuals and comparatively slight effect of predators on older fishes. If a substantial part of the population should die, its replacement is slow.

Monastyrsky (1953), analysing the structure of the mature part of the stock, the spawning population, distinguishes three types of structure.

The first type of spawning population (P) consists entirely of recruits (K), i.e. of first-time spawners. Fishes which are spawning for the second time, i.e. the residue (D), do not occur in such populations. A spawning population of this first type may include fishes of one or of several ages. In the first case (humpback salmon) the fishes all mature at the same age, while in the second type (chum) they mature at various ages. Simultaneous maturation of the whole of a generation is characteristic of species with relatively stable spawning conditions, so that there is a relatively stable recruitment. If there were a combination of simultaneous maturation and years of poor recruitment, the entire population could be wiped out. Populations in which maturity sets in at various ages are maintained even under conditions in which two or three year-classes are unsuccessful.

Spawning populations of the second type consist of both the recruits and the residue, i.e. the second-time spawners. But the numbers of the latter are smaller than those of the recruits. Such populations are typical of the salmon, *Salmo salar* L., the Caspian shads, *Caspialosa*, and many others.

The third type of spawning population also consists of recruits and residue. But in contrast to the second type the residue is more numerous than the recruits. This type includes the majority of the sturgeons, bream, carp, cod, and many other fishes with long life spans and several spawnings in the course of their lives. These three types of spawning populations may be formulated as follows:

     1st type of population $D=0$, $K=P$

     2nd type of population $D>0$, $K>D$, $K+D=P$

     3rd type of population $D>0$, $K<D$, $K+D=P$

where D is the residue, K the recruitment, and P the total spawning population.

Naturally, the separation of these three types of spawning populations is to some extent subjective, and it is possible for any one population to be of the second type in some years, and of the third in others, depending on the ratio between recruitment and residue. On the whole, however, the three types do reflect a definite characteristic of the relationship between the population and its environment.

The population structure may vary within the species but between stocks in different areas. As was stated above for the herring, in various local stocks the life span, time of onset of maturity, and the average age may differ considerably, reflecting the specific conditions of the environment for each of the stocks.

We have observed even greater differences in the structure of populations in the smelt, *Osmerus eperlanus* (L.). The population structure of the resident form, the European smelt *O. eperlanus spirinchus* Pall., is extremely different from that of the migratory smelt (Table 19).

TABLE 19

Population Structure of Migratory and Resident Forms of the Smelt

Population	0+	1+	2+	3+	4+	5+	6+	7+	8+
Migratory smelt of the R. Enisei	—	—	—	0·3	7·7	20·0	43·0	22·5	5·5
Migratory smelt of the R. Onega	0·04	0·4	18·65	63·61	12·72	4·37	0·21	—	—
Pskov—Chudsk smelt	90·0	10·0	—	—	—	—	—	—	—
European smelt of Rybinsk reservoir	—	55·0	39·0	6·0	—	—	—	—	—
Lake Zhizhetsk smelt	—	68·1	31·9	—	—	—	—	—	—

In the lake smelt the spawning population is commonly of the first type; in the migratory form it is of the second type.

Significant changes in the population structure may occur within a single stock or local form as an adaptive reaction to changes in the environmental conditions. For example, in the North Caspian bream the percentage recruitment of fishes of various ages varies considerably (Table 20).

TABLE 20

Size of Recruitment in Percentage of Total Numbers of Fish in Every Age Group (on the Basis of Counts of Spawning Marks on Scales of North Caspian Bream) (from Data of K. L. Zemskaia)

Years	3	Age groups 4	5	6	7	8	Catch in hundred thousand kilos
1942	100	87	64	40	0	0	486
1943	100	80	68	61	45	0	632
1944	100	46	24	25	13	0	834
1945	100	85	56	29	25	15	877
1946	100	80	52	14	0	0	898
1947	100	68	25	6	0	0	615
1948	100	88	59	22	19	14	648
1949	100	85	65	30	24	15	833
1950	100	84	68	0	0	0	748
1951	100	84	49	8	0	0	510
1952	100	83	58	25	0	0	335

Naturally, the variations in the proportions of the age groups forming stocks of fishes depend to a great extent on the success of the separate generations.

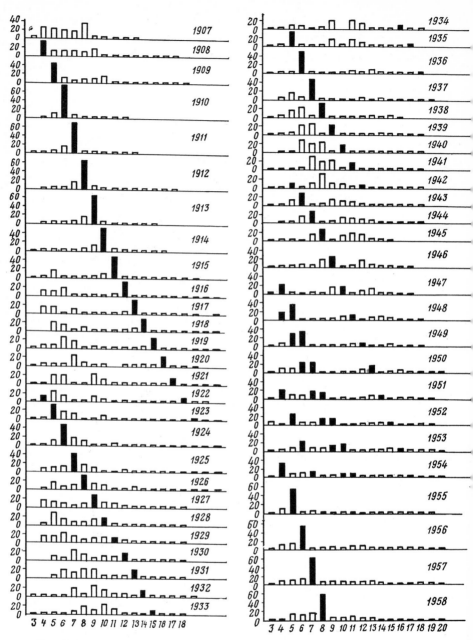

Fig. 102. Age composition of the spawning stocks of the Norwegian herring; black columns, strong year-classes.

In some species there are very great fluctuations in the annual recruitment, and there is a corresponding variation in the proportions of the age groups in the stock. Thus, for example, as the data on the variations in the age composition of the catches of Norwegian herring show (Fig. 102), strong year-classes can bring about very great changes in the proportions of the age groups on entering into the fishery.

On the other hand, in some fishes there is hardly any variation in the age composition of the stock due to fluctuations in year-classes, i.e. every year-class is of about the same strength. An example of this is the tiger flathead *Neoplatycephalus*, which is an important commercial species on the east coast of Australia. Its age composition is subject to fluctuation, but this is due to an increase in the fishing intensity.

In the practical analysis of the age composition of stocks, we usually deal with the age composition of the catches, caught of course by means of filtering gear, which allows only the younger, smaller fishes to escape through the meshes of the cod-end of the seine or trawl. From the maximum size of fish released by the meshes of the commercial gear, we may believe that with practical accuracy the right-hand side of the length (and age) distribution of the catch corresponds to the actual proportions of the sizes and age groups in the stock.

In order to obtain the actual size and age composition of the population it is necessary to use gear of a type that will capture all the size and age groups in their natural proportions. The curves in Fig. 103 are an example of such a size distribution.

As stated above, an important factor which affects the age composition of a stock of fish is the success of the separate year-classes. It depends, as we have seen, upon several factors. The success of a year-class varies in relation to various factors. As Fig. 104 shows, for the roach in the North Caspian the most successful year-class was that of 1931 (Monastyrsky, 1940). This successful year-class was reflected in the catches; in 1933 there was a significantly high percentage of 2-year olds, and of 3-year olds in 1934 (Fig. 105). The successful year-classes, naturally, affect not only the proportions of the age groups in the commercial catches, but the sizes of these catches as well. The dynamics of the age composition depend not only on the size of the recruitment, but also on the amount of reduction. The factors which cause an unequal reduction of the various age groups may be extremely variable—including the influence of predators and epizootics which cause the mortality of adults or young fishes. Finally, changes in the age composition may be due to the mortality of separate generations as a result of unfavourable changes in the abiotic conditions, which may lead to the death of separate age groups during the overwintering period.

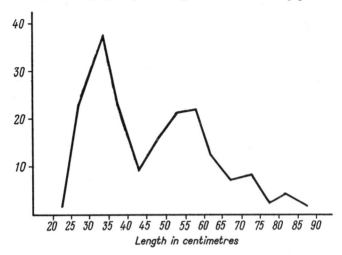

FIG. 103. Length-frequency distribution of a population of the Tibetan loach *Nemachilus stoliczkai* Steindachner (from Nikolsky, 1938).

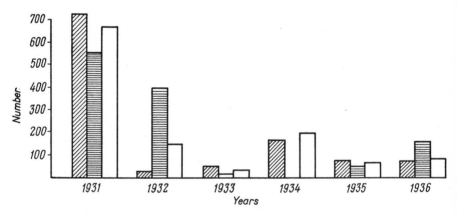

FIG. 104. Average catch (numbers) of young roach per hour's trawling in the North Caspian. Inclined hatching, Volga region; horizontal hatching, Ural-Embensk region; plain, average for North Caspian (from Monastyrsky, 1940).

Another powerful factor which affects the age composition of the stock is the rate of fishing. If the fishery selects the older individuals, an intensification of the fishery could lead to the rejuvenation of the population. Thus, for

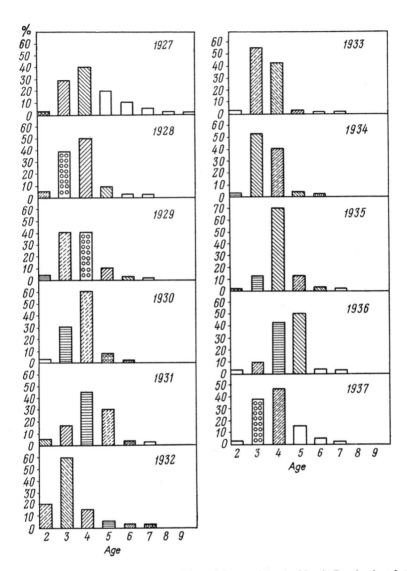

FIG. 105. Changes in the age composition of the roach in the North Caspian in relation to the strength of the separate year-classes (from Monastyrsky, 1940).

example, the take of bream in the Aral Sea by coarse-meshed nets led to a significant decrease in the average size and age of the fish in the catches.

If the fishery, by decimating the population, should lead to an improvement in its food supply, this could result in an acceleration of the growth and

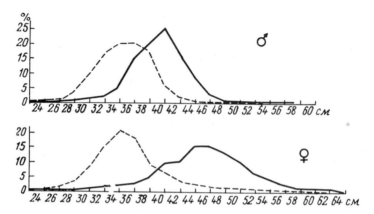

FIG. 106. Changes in the length composition of catches of the plaice *Pleuronectes platessa* (L.). Solid line, 1907; broken line, 1935 (from Milinsky, 1938).

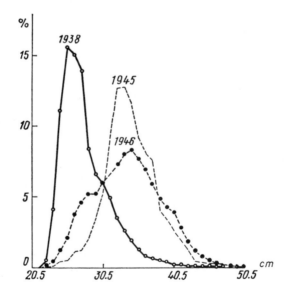

FIG. 107. Changes in the length composition of the North Sea plaice as a result of the reduction in the fishing intensity during the Second World War (from Margetts and Holt, 1945).

maturation of the fishes and through this a younger age composition in the spawning population. This phenomenon took place in the North Sea herring (Nikolsky and Belianina, 1959), and also in the plaice of the Barents and North Seas (Fig. 106). On the other hand, a pause in the fishery might lead to an increase in the percentage of older individuals in the population, as happened in the same North Sea plaice populations during the years of the Second World War (Fig. 107).

Population Dynamics of Fishes

The size of the total stock does not remain constant from one year to another; it varies, sometimes very greatly.

The fluctuations in the size of the stock of fish are usually assessed on the basis of changes in the size of the catches, both the actual catch of a given species or population, or the "catch per unit effort." The catch per unit effort can be expressed as the catch per hour of trawling, the catch per net with stake nets, per voyage of a commercial vessel, per set of a purse seine, per box of hooks, etc.

This coefficient is often used in the study of migrations, and particularly in the study of stock dynamics.

Fluctuations in the size of the total stock of fish bear a different character for each species, and may be due to the most varied direct causes. Both the frequency of the fluctuations and their amplitude are variable.

Thus, for example, the size of the catches of Pacific halibut, *Hippoglossus hippoglossus stenolepis* Schmidt, for the period 1925–47 varied by more than twice (Thompson, 1950), and the catches of the Pacific sardine, *Sardinops sagax melanosticta* Schl., from 1937 to 1957 in Russian waters ranged from nil to 100 million kg.

It is well known that there is a 2-year periodicity in the catches of most stocks of the humpback salmon, while in the Atlantic salmon, *Salmo salar* L., the periodicity is usually one of 10–11 years (Berg, 1935).

As was stated above, the population structure (age composition, proportion of recruits to residue in the mature stage, the age composition of the first-time spawners, the fecundity) is a property of the species within fairly wide limits. The whole type of the population dynamics is also a specific adaptive property. "The population dynamics are a sort of focus, which reflect all the characteristics of a given species, they are the resultant of its entire ecology: reproduction, feeding, mortality, as determined by the adaptations of the species" (Severtsov, 1941; Vasnetsov, 1953).

The total maximum size of the stock of fish is generally limited by the food supply. "It is only possible for fishes to exist in such numbers as are able to find nourishment" (Baer, 1854). However, the fluctuations in the size of the stock are not only determined by the food supply. For example, the catastrophic reduction in the size of the stocks of Far Eastern salmon in some regions is related to mass mortality in the egg stage, as a result of freezing of the grounds in dry winters with little snowfalls. The success of year-classes of the Pacific herring, *Clupea harengus pallasi* Val., is often strongly affected by ice crushing the spawn. Fluctuations in the year-classes, i.e. in the recruitment, are reflected in the provision of food for the population. If the food supply does not vary when a strong year-class appears, the food resources of the population as a whole are impoverished, but if the year-class is a poor one, the food resources, on the contrary, are improved. In connection with this, species of plants and animals have evolved the adaptive property of responding to changes in the food supply by changes in their rate of reproduction, i.e. by self-regulation of the size of the stock.

A fairly general method of varying the size of the population in fishes is as follows. Improving food supplies cause an increase in the growth rate. With this is connected an earlier onset of maturity, and frequently, as in the Far Eastern salmons, an increase in the fecundity of younger fishes at the same size. In this way, replacement of the stock is faster when the feeding conditions are better. The qualitative changes in the structure of the population are mutually related to the size of the stock. Thus, in the Amur autumn chum salmon the average size of the fish and the catch, the number of age groups in the stock, the average age of maturation are directly related to the strength of the spawning stock (Table 21).

TABLE 21

Changes in the Size of the Stock of the Amur Autumn Chum Salmon and the Structure of its Population (from I. B. Birman, 1953)

Years	Average length of fish in cm	Average annual catch in per cent of perennial mean	2+	3+	4+	5+	6+	7+
1923–28	74·6	84	8·2	65·1	23·7	3·0	—	—
1928–35	69·8	121	4·3	57·1	31·8	5·7	1·0	0·1
1937–41	64·2	118	1·1	61·8	27·8	8·6	0·6	0·1
1946–49	67·0	56	15·3	75·1	9·5	0·1	—	—

In some species of fishes an improvement in the food supply may not cause an increase in the growth rate (as in some populations of the oceanic herring) and an acceleration in the maturation associated with this. Maturation sets in at the same age, but the better-fed individuals have a higher fecundity.

Among a number of groups of fishes, the Percidae, Gadidae, Centrarchidae, and others, the larger individuals, when their food supplies are depleted, feed on the smaller ones of the same species. In this way the species can maintain itself if the food supply is low. In the navaga, *Eleginus navaga* (L.), its own young can form a high proportion of its food in years of good recruitment. According to Chang Hsiao-wey, during the spawning period of the Japanese mackerel *Pneumatophorus japonicus* Houtt. in the Yellow Sea, its own spawn forms a large part of its food. In years in which the size of the spawning stock is small the spawn scarcely figures in its food.

In some species of fishes their own young annually form part of their food. This particularly applies to certain populations of the common perch *Perca fluviatilis* L. in a number of West Siberian lakes, in which up to 80 % of the food of the larger individuals consists of their own young. In large individuals of the Lake Balkhash perch *Perca schrenki* Kessl., its own young may similarly form 70–80 % of its food. This adaptation enables the larger fish to feed on their own young when there is no other suitable food; only its young are able to feed directly on the plankton. Naturally, this consumption of their own young is not a conscious act, but the mass-occurrence of the young fishes, particularly when other food is not available, renders them more vulnerable as food for the larger fishes.

There have, therefore, been established the following adaptations to self-regulation of abundance in the event of an increase in the food-supply: (Nikolsky, 1953b):

1. Acceleration of the growth rate, earlier onset of maturity, an abbreviation in the length-range of the first-time spawners, an increase in the fecundity of individuals of the same size.

2. An increase in the fat-content; increase in the fecundity.

3. A reduction in the consumption of its own young.

4. A reduction in larval mortality at the time of changing over to active feeding (see page 187).

5. An increase in the number fertilized of the eggs laid by younger females, which come to the spawning grounds late.

6. A reduction in the range of sizes of eggs laid simultaneously (yolk supply) and in the range of sizes of fish of the same age in the stock.

The converse is observed when the food supply is reduced:

1. A retardation of growth, later onset of maturity, an extension in the size range of the first-time spawners, a reduction in the fecundity of fishes of the same size.

2. A reduction in the fat content and fecundity of fishes of the same size.

3. An increase in the consumption of the young of the same species.

4. A reduction in larval survival during the first stages of active feeding.

5. A decrease in the numbers of fertilized eggs in younger females.

6. An increase in the size range of the eggs and an increase in the amplitude of variability of the size of fishes of the same age.

Naturally, of course, all these adaptations to regulation of the population abundance can only give results under particular conditions. Often, as a result of unfavourable conditions for development and with an increase in the fecundity of the population, we may have a low recruitment, and, conversely, with low fecundity of the population and favourable conditions we may have a high recruitment.

Thus, the dynamics of the abundance and biomass of the population are the result of the interaction of the environment and the specific adaptive properties of the population.

The character of the fluctuations in the size of the stock and the catches depends not only on the character of the influences, but to no less an extent on the character of the responses of the population, as determined by its adaptive properties and in particular its structure.

Changes in the size of a population are the result of changes in the relationship between recruitment and decline.

It has long been known that the size of catches varies from year to year and that for many fishes it has been possible to establish some periodicity in the catches. The first to investigate this problem in detail were the Norwegian investigators Helland Hansen and Nansen (1909), who observed that the periodicity in the fluctuations of the catches of cod was correlated with the temperature of the Gulf Stream. Later it was established by Derzhavin (1922), Jensen (1927), Berg (1935), and others, that for many commercial species the catches give a maximum every 9–11 years. Such a periodicity in the maximum catches was established for fishes of the most varied modes of life—sturgeons, herring, salmon, cod, etc. But it has been established for the salmon that the periods of maximum catches do not always coincide all over the whole range of distribution. Thus, by comparison with Norway, the maximum and minimum catches of salmon often occur a year later in

Russian waters, but the periodicity of the maximum catches is the same in Canada and the U.S.S.R., and the difference in the time of onset of a maximum in the catches is rarely more than a year. Usually the maximum and minimum coincide over the whole area of distribution of a commercial species. Thus, 1928 gave minimal catches of salmon in all the fishery regions.

These examples of periodical fluctuations in catches are related to general climatic causes; the mode of influence of the latter may vary considerably, being expressed through changes in the food supply, or the spawning or overwintering conditions, etc. However, in the majority of cases fluctuations in the size of the stock bear a non-periodical character and are determined by local causes.

The number of eggs laid and fertilized depends on the number of spawners which reach the spawning grounds, and on their fecundity; the number of fertilized eggs is also of considerable importance. It is unknown for any species that 100 % of the eggs laid should survive to maturity. The percentage of individuals which survive to maturity in various species of fishes (this is the coefficient of the fishing returns) is extremely variable as the data given on page 187 shows. It varies considerably from year to year for the same species.

The curve of mortality is specific in its general features for every species, although at present, admittedly, we only know that part of this curve which relates to the mature part of the stock, and from this we estimate the proportions of the age groups in the catches by filtering nets. As may be seen from the data given above, in fishes, as in other animals, the greatest mortalities occur in the immature individuals. In many fishes the main part of the mortality usually occurs in the egg stage; thus, in the chum salmon *Oncorhynchus keta* Walb. in the river Iski the mortality of the eggs amounts to 90 %; the same is often observed in the bream *Abramis brama* L. in the Volga delta when there is a change of wind direction and the eggs get caught up in the oxygen-depleted "reed-water" which is blown out of the reed-beds.

In very many fishes (herrings, anchovy, etc.) the greatest mortalities occur at the time the larvae transfer from passive (yolk) to active feeding. In many pelagophil fishes of the Amur the main mortality due to predators occurs at the time the larvae are changing over from living in the open water to the coastal zone.

Predators are a significant cause of the decline in many species of fishes, and only in comparatively few (anchovies, herring, etc.) does the main predatory mortality fall on the mature individuals of the population.

In present times fishing by mankind exerts a substantial influence on the mature part of the stocks of many species of fishes. In its influence on the population of a species of fish and in the adaptive responses evoked in the population, fishing is similar to the action of predators, which eat principally the adult part of the stock. Differences in population structure allow the take to vary in size without destroying the reproductive capacity of the stock. A short life cycle and early maturation allow the removal of a larger percentage of the stock annually than later maturation and populations which contain many age groups. Thus, for example, the humpback salmon, the entire population of which matures in its second year, tolerates with a good year-class the taking of over 60 % of all the spawning population. The chum salmon, the populations of which have a more complex structure and later maturation, tolerates a correspondingly lower percentage of removal (about 50 %) of the mature stock (Neave, 1953). In order to forecast the size of the possible catch, it is usual to use the data on the strength of the recruitment, the analysis of age compositions and growth rate of the fishes.

If the growth rate of the fish is high, maturity sets in early, the catch per unit effort and the total catch remain relatively stable, and also if the food resources (assessed before the feeding season starts) are more or less stable, the plan of the fishery may be established at the previous year's level.

If the growth rate of the fish is high, maturation sets in early, and there is an abundant food supply, but the catches still fall, it is essential to reduce the amount of fishing in order to improve the reproductive capacity of the stock.

If the growth rate is retarded, the maturation sets in late, the age composition of the first-time spawners is extended, the food supply is largely consumed, the total catch is stable, and the catch per unit effort increases, an increase in the total catch is permissible.

Naturally this method of prognosis is only applicable to fishes in which the growth of the individuals is restricted by the food supply, because then the growth rate varies as the abundance of the fish varies.

If the growth rate of a fish does not vary from year to year (certain stocks of oceanic herring), the fundamental criteria for the prognosis of possible catches are the larval recruitment in different years, the age structure of the population, and the catch per unit effort.

The Migrations of Fishes

The migrations of fishes, as those of other animals, are usually an active, though sometimes passive, mass movement from one habitat to another.

Fishes migrate to the places where they find the conditions they require at the particular phase of their life history which sets in toward the end of the migration.

The migrations, like other properties of the species, have some adaptive significance, ensuring the favourable conditions for the existence and reproduction of the species. The migration is a link in the life cycle which is inseparably connected to both the preceding and the following links.

The cycle of migrations usually consists of the following:

1. Spawning migration—i.e. the movement of fishes from the feeding or overwintering grounds to the spawning grounds.

2. Feeding migrations—a movement away from the spawning or overwintering grounds to the feeding grounds.

3. Wintering migrations—a movement away from the spawning or feeding grounds to the overwintering grounds.

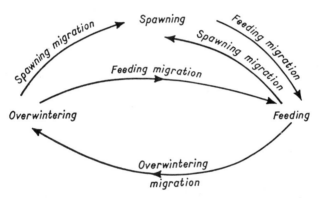

FIG. 108. A scheme of the migration cycle of various fishes.

The migratory cycle of fishes, and also of other animals, may be represented schematically as in Fig. 108.

Comparatively few species of fishes live constantly in the same place without performing any regular, longer or shorter migration. Such "settled" species include the gobies, and many coral fishes of the family Pomacentridae, Siganidae, Apogonidae, and others. For the majority of fishes the migration is an essential link in the annual life cycle.

The migration is not expressed identically in all species. In some, such as many whitefishes, the spawning and feeding migrations are performed, but not the overwintering one. In others, the spawning grounds of which coincide with their feeding grounds, such as many gudgeons, there is only an over-wintering migration, which is related to a movement into deeper water at the end of the feeding season.

In some species the migrations are performed only by the adult fishes which have attained maturity, while the young, on descending from the spawning to the feeding grounds, live there and do not perform any significant movements, as happens, for example, in many of the salmon family. In other species the young make migrations that are just as protracted as those of the adults. We observe this, for example, in the shad *Caspialosa brashnikovi* (Borodin), in which both the adults and young pass from the overwintering grounds out of the Southern Caspian into the Northern Caspian, in which the spawning and feeding grounds of this fish are distributed.

The first type of migration cycle, which is a property of the salmons and many other species, takes place in cases when the spawning and feeding grounds are in different places, but the wintering and feeding grounds coincide.

The second type of migration cycle is characteristic of those species in which the spawning and feeding grounds coincide.

Since the migration is a link in the life cycle which is inseparably connected to both the preceding and the following links, it is natural that the fish starts to migrate when it has reached a certain condition, i.e. when it is prepared for it.

Thus in the majority of fishes the start of the spawning migration is usually related to the attainment of a definite stage of maturity and the appearance of a definite hormonal activity in the endocrine glands. The reactions of the fish to its external environment are altered, i.e. there appears a new natural stimulus, which acts as a signal for the start of the migration.

In the majority of fishes the start of the wintering migration is connected with the attainment of a definite condition and fat content, which would ensure the successful overwintering of the fish. The Aral Sea bream preparing for overwintering has a condition coefficient of about 3·0 and a high fat content in the flesh. The Azov anchovy preparing for its overwintering migration has a condition coefficient averaging 1·00 (Lebedev, 1940). Preparedness for the migration does not mean that the fish will immediately start to migrate. The migration begins only under particular conditions. Underfed bream or anchovy will not start their wintering migration even if there is a sharp fall in temperature. But for bream or anchovies which are prepared for the winter a sharp fall in temperature acts as a natural stimulus or signal for the start of the wintering migration. Thus according to Shuleman (1959), the anchovy containing 14 % of fat does not start to migrate however far the temperature falls. With a fat content of 14–17 % a drop in temperature of 9–14°C is necessary for the start of the migration, and the course is extended and not simultaneous. With a fat content of 22 % the anchovy starts to migrate with any drop in temperature, and the course is simultaneous.

The start of the migration thus depends on both the state of the fish itself and the environmental changes. The time at which the migration starts evolves as an adaptation which ensures favourable conditions for both the fish (in the case of the wintering and feeding migrations) and for the future offspring (in the case of the spawning migrations).

The spawning, feeding, and wintering migrations are mutually related; they are prepared for during the preceding links in the life cycle, and themselves ensure the further life of the fish. As already stated, the transition into the migratory state is always related to a definite condition of the fish, its state of nourishment, fat content, the development of its gonads, etc.

Apart from those migrations which are a link in the life cycle, many fishes perform mass movements in various biological conditions, and which most frequently bear a protective character. Examples of such movements are the movements away from the coastal zone during stormy weather, the movements of fishes away from lakes and bays when the water level in the rivers falls, etc.

The majority of fishes perform migrations actively moving in the direction in which their migration course lies, and they therefore expend on the migration the energy which they accumulated in their bodies. But besides their active migrations, many fishes also perform passive ones, in which the fish, or more often its pelagic spawn, is passively transported over considerable distances. In this case the fish does not expend any energy in migrating, because this is brought about by the movement of the water-masses, the currents. In many cases part of the migration course is performed passively, and part actively, as happens, for example, in the larvae of the common eel in their migration from the coast of Central America to the coast of Europe. This movement is at first performed passively together with the water of the Atlantic current, but on approaching the coast the elvers start to migrate actively to the rivers.

What are the factors which have led to the evolution of such a complex biological phenomenon as migrations in the various groups of fishes? There is no doubt that the migration is an adaptation which ensures the existence of the species. Supposing, for instance, that the salmon which enters a particular river to spawn had remained on its nursery grounds instead of moving to the sea to feed—there is no doubt that the food resources of the river would very quickly be exhausted, and the population would become reduced. Naturally, females, which expend a greater amount of energy on the development of the eggs and are usually, in migratory fishes, of larger size than the males, require more nourishing food than the males, both to ensure their own existence and for the development of the eggs. They can only obtain this nourishment in the sea. In nature we observe that in many fishes the males or part of the males always live in the rivers, while the females lead a migratory mode of life. This phenomenon has been recorded for salmon, barbels, and certain other fishes.

Naturally there arises the question, why have the migratory fishes, which find more favourable feeding conditions in the sea, not migrated completely to the sea (as happened with a number of species which now live in the sea but originated in the fresh water), instead of preserving their spawning grounds in fresh water.

The majority of marine fishes which lay demersal eggs protect them (Kryzhanovsky, 1949). If they did not do so the eggs would very soon be completely eaten by predators. Therefore, if they transferred their spawning grounds into the sea, migratory fishes would have to protect their spawn, as it would otherwise all be eaten. Nearly all migratory fishes (except for lampreys and herrings) as large animals which have a considerable hunting area, perform considerable feeding migrations, would starve if they protected their spawn through a protracted incubation period; they would then die of starvation before the end of the incubation period, leaving the eggs unprotected. Eggs developing without active protection in the river are subjected to far less danger than in the sea. It would apparently be impossible to bury the spawn in the sea-bed, as the salmon does in the rivers, because of the unfavourable oxygen conditions in the bottom at great depths, and the constant movement of stones in the coastal zone.

Thus, the transference to a marine nursery ground enables the species to increase its abundance significantly at the expense of the enormous food resources in the sea, while reproduction in the rivers ensures a greater survival of the larvae (Vasnetsov, 1953). However, the stock abundance is restricted by the size of the spawning ground. As Kuznetsov (1928) stated, as the concentration of the nests on the spawning redds of the salmon increases (beyond one nest per 2 m²), the percentage mortality of the eggs in the nests increases, which thus restricts the size of the population. The area of river-bed which is suitable for spawning is restricted, and is often quite small.

Therefore, a basic factor in the evolution of the migration cycle of migratory, primarily fresh-water, fishes is the insufficient food supply in the rivers.

For primarily marine fishes, which lead a migratory life, the origin of the migration cycle is also explained in a similar way: since the conditions for the development of the eggs are more favourable in the rivers than in the sea, so the fish is adapted to spawning in flowing water. It would be impossible for such marine fishes as the herring, which feeds predominantly on plankton, to transfer completely to living in the rivers because of the scarcity of plankton in the rivers, although the migratory primarily marine fishes are usually of smaller size than the primarily freshwater ones. Such primarily marine fishes as the ling, which feed mostly on fish, discovered sufficient food in the rivers and were able to transfer completely to living in flowing water, but they are not very abundant.

In marine and freshwater fishes the cause of origin of the migration cycle is the same as in migratory species, because none of the stocks of migrating fishes could find sufficient food in the region of their spawning grounds, and they would have to either restrict their abundance or widen their feeding area. The latter circumstance leads to the initiation of migrations from the spawning to the feeding grounds and vice versa.

Naturally, migrations, like any other adaptive property of the species, have developed in the process of evolution. Among fishes, as also among the majority of other animals, we have examples of species in which the spawning, feeding, and overwintering grounds all coincide, species in which they are only partially separated, and finally species in which the spawning, feeding, and overwintering grounds are separated by very great distances, sometimes several thousands of kilometres.

The fact that the migration is an adaptation toward increasing the abundance of a species is well illustrated by the fact that among closely related forms of the same species the migratory form is considerably more abundant than the form which lives constantly in one place. An example of this is the shad, *Caspialosa brashnikovi* (Borodin), in the Caspian Sea, of which the type that performs considerable migrations from the South to the North Caspian is considerably the more abundant form. We may also observe a similar pattern in the oceanic herring, *Clupea harengus* L.; the most abundant forms are the Norwegian and Sakhalin-Hokkaido herrings, which perform the longest migrations, ensuring the largest feeding areas for them (Svetovidov, 1953a).

Although the factors which initiate the migration cycle are, as we have seen, the same for the majority of species, the circumstances under which they originate may vary greatly. In many fishes (salmon, whitefish) the change to a migratory mode of life was made easy because of the dilution of the sea which occurred in the northern hemisphere in the interglacial epochs, when enormous masses of melt-water significantly lowered the salinity of the adjacent parts of the sea. The fact that the majority of migratory species of fishes are tied to temperate and high latitudes in the northern hemisphere is possibly related to this dilution of the sea, which took place at the end of the Tertiary period and in Quaternary times (Zenkevich, 1933).

However, the existence of migratory fishes in the subtropical, tropical, and equatorial zones indicates that the dilution of the sea is not the only cause for the initiation of the migratory mode of life. The transference of marine or freshwater fishes to the migratory mode of life could have evolved in the relatively stable flow conditions of the rivers into which the fish entered to spawn.

The length and character of the migration course which the fish performs is most closely related to the structure and condition of the migrating fish. The larger, stronger, and fatter fish is able to cover the greater distances and to swim for a long time against a fast current. This principle is observed both for different species, and for different forms of the same species. Among the Caspian shads the largest and fattest is the beshenka or black-back, *Caspialosa kessleri* Grimm, which performs the longest migrations upstream, while the least well-nourished is the large-eyed shad or puzanok, which does not enter the rivers at all (Table 22).

The same is also observed in the various forms of a single species. Thus, for example, the autumn chum salmon, *Oncorhynchus keta autumnalis*, has males which average 75 cm in length and females 72 cm, while their fat content in the estuary of the Amur is about 10–11 %. It rises up the Amur for more than 1500 km. The summer form is of smaller size (the males average 61 cm in length, the females 58 cm) and also a lower fat content. They have 8–9 % fat content in the flesh and rise for 400–500 km up river. The fact that fishes usually return to spawn in the river in which they themselves were spawned is to a significant extent explained by the fact that their biological coefficients of fat content, and condition, enable them to reach their spawning grounds successfully, compensating for the energy expenditure which is essential for them to reach the spawning grounds.

In performing their migrations, sometimes over many thousands of kilometres, fishes successfully locate their course to the estuaries of their spawning rivers, or from the spawning to the feeding grounds, by means of their sense organs. Apparently, in very many cases fishes moving in the sea orientate themselves against the current. This, for example, occurs in the cod and herring in the eastern part of the North Atlantic, where in their spawning migrations they swim against the flow of the Atlantic current. The chum, which passes up the Amur to spawn, orientate themselves against the Amur current when they enter the Sea of Okhotsk.

TABLE 22

Percentage Fat Content in the Flesh, and Length of Migration up the Volga, of Various Species of Caspian Shads

Name of fish	Per cent fat content	Maximal length of course up river, in km
Blackback, *Caspialosa kessleri* Grimm	16·0	1000
Volga shad, *Caspialosa volgensis* Berg	8·71	c. 500
Caspian shad, *Caspialosa caspia* (Eichw.)	7·48	c. 100
Large-eyed shad, *Caspialosa saposhnikovi* (Grimm)	5·61	0

However, we still do not know how the fish finds its migration course in the open sea. All the theories concerning this are only of a very preliminary character.

There is no doubt that many fishes orientate themselves to the coastline and the bottom relief in their migrations. In vertical migrations the light undoubtedly plays a considerable role in orientation.

Nearly all fishes migrate in shoals. Usually the migrating shoal consists of fishes of similar size and biological condition. The migrating shoal has no permanent leader; the foremost fishes in the shoal soon fall back and are replaced at the front by others. This has been confirmed in experiments on small shoals of cod, saithe, and herring, carried out by Radakov at the Murmansk Biological Station.

The migrating shoal of fish usually has a definite shape, which ensures the most favourable hydrodynamical conditions for movement (Shuleikin, 1953).

The adaptive significance of the shoal (see page 87) consists not only of ensuring the most favourable condition for movement, but also of making orientation easier during the migration. The size of the migrating shoal is so variable from species to species, that it is undoubtedly related to the need for ensuring the most favourable conditions for migration.

The basic general data on the character of fish migrations, their courses and periods, have been and are being obtained by means of direct observations of the migrating fishes and the animals which pursue them (whales, seals, birds), and also by analysis of the size and composition of the commercial catches.

The analysis of commercial catches—their total size, species, and size composition—combined with the analysis of catches by research vessels, is the most important method of investigating the pattern of migrations.

An increase in either the total catch or the catch per unit effort indicates the approach of fish to a particular place; conversely, a fall in the catches usually indicates the departure of fish from the fishing ground. However, it should be borne in mind that a fall in catches might be related not only to a decline in the numbers of fishes on the fishing grounds, but also to a change in the behaviour of the fishes; for example, feeding fishes are often less easy to capture by means of enmeshing gear than migrating fishes. A change in the catches might also be caused by a change in conditions: illumination, waves, atmospheric pressure, etc. All these factors must be taken into account when using the data of commercial catches in studying the migrations of fishes.

A fundamental method of studying the migrations of fishes is by marking them. This makes it possible to establish the migration paths of actual individuals of a given species, or of shoals in a population, and in many cases to determine the speed at which the fishes move. A study of the recaptured marked fishes also permits the solution of a number of other problems: an approximate assessment of what percentage of the whole population are captured, a more accurate study of the growth rate, etc.

Various types of marks are used (Figs. 109, 110), which are attached either to the gill covers (like the Gilbert mark (Fig. 109), or at the base of the dorsal fin, like the Petersen mark (Fig. 110[1]), which consists of two ebonite or celluloid discs connected with a wire. The Petersen disc is used in marking flatfishes. For marking cod in the North Atlantic the Lea hydrostatic tag is at present widely used (Fig. 110[4]); this consists of a hermetically sealed celluloid cylinder, inside which are printed instructions for the finder. The marks are attached either by means of special pincers (the Gilbert mark), or by means of an awl or a needle.

An internal metallic mark (Fig. 110) is often used, mainly for marking herrings. These marks are prepared in the form of a strip. They are introduced into the body cavity of the fish by means of a "marking gun." The

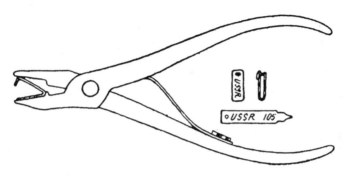

FIG. 109. The Gilbert tag and pliers used for applying it.

metallic internal marks are found by special electromagnets in fish-meal factories, where the fishes are reduced for fish meal and oil. The electromagnets or other detecting devices are usually placed on the transporter belts at the factories (Karavaev, 1958).

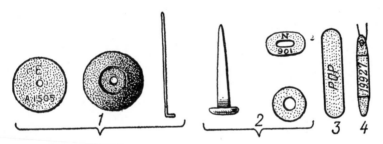

FIG. 110. Various types of tags (from left to right). 1, Petersen tag; 2, tag for salmon; 3, internal tag for clupeoids; 4, the Lea hydrostatic tag.

All these and many other types of marks bear a number, and are used for the marking of individual fishes. For deep-water fishes (redfish, *Sebastes*, etc.) which die when brought to the surface, Kotthaus used marking by means of a numbered fish hook which breaks off. The fish, seizing the baited hook, breaks it off and is thus marked.

Even modern methods of marking are far from perfect, and do not ensure a complete return of the marks from all the recaptured fishes. Many of the fish lose their marks, and the marks often go unnoticed by the fishermen. Besides, the marking affects the behaviour of the fish, while the recapture of marked fish often gives distorted data on the speed of migration and the route followed.

However, despite these deficiencies, individual marking does provide important data and explains several aspects of the mode of life of the fish. When marking is undertaken on a massive scale, it is essential to work out improved methods of marking.

Besides the individual marking, group marking is also widely used. Group marking is usually used to study the movements of groups of fishes over a short time. Group marking is performed either by painting or branding the fishes, or by cutting part of the fins or part of the gill cover, husking part of the lateral scuta in sturgeons, marking with radioactive isotopes, and so on. "Biological marking" is also used, in which the fish or shoal is repeatedly recognized by some biological symptom, physiological condition, the presence of specific parasites, and so on.

Hydroacoustic instruments are very important for the study of migrations and the distribution of fishes. It is now possible to discover fish concentrations, and to observe their movements by this means. Combining the hydroacoustic observations with the catches (or often without the catch), it is possible to establish the type of "trace" recorded by a species.

A knowledge of the periods of migration, the migration course of the fish, and the factors which govern the migrations, is of considerable practical value. At the time of migration the majority of fishes form more or less considerable shoals—consequently it becomes easier and economically more advantageous to catch them. As already stated, migrating fishes are usually easier to capture with enmeshing gear (floating and stake nets) than fishes which are not moving or are wintering.

During their migrations many fishes often concentrate in enormous masses in a comparatively small area, such as the mouth of a river, which makes them easily available to fishing gear. At the moment when they start their overwintering or spawning migrations fishes are usually in better condition and have a high fat content, i.e. they are commercially more valuable, which makes their capture, particularly at this time, far more profitable.

A knowledge of the factors which govern the migrations would enable the period and course of the migrations to be forecast, as well as the areas in which the commercial fishes concentrate. This would ensure the greatest effectiveness of the fishing, and a smaller loss of time spent in awaiting the approach of the fish to the fishing grounds. For preparing forecasts of the migrations, or so-called short-time forecasts, it is necessary to have information on the biological condition of the fishes (state of nourishment, fat content, state of the gonads, rate of feeding) and the rate at which these are changing. On the basis of these data, and also of data on the food supply and the conditions for feeding or overwintering, it is possible to forecast the time at which the fish will reach a state of readiness to migrate. A knowledge of the forecast of the hydrometeorological conditions makes it possible to establish the time of appearance of the particular "signal" (a drop or rise in temperature, a particular light intensity, etc.) which serves as the natural stimulus, evoking in the fish which is "prepared" for migration a response in the form of the migration. At first the forecast can only be fairly general, but it is later improved upon.

In the majority of fishery regions in the U.S.S.R. there is a special service for fishery surveys, making short-time forecasts and guiding the fishing vessels toward the concentrations of fish. The problem of fishery surveys includes reviewing the data on distribution of fishes obtained by the fishing vessels with the aim of perfecting the forecasts (Marty, 1948). The fishery survey work is carried out in close contact with the weather forecasting service, which provides the necessary hydrometeorological data.

Spawning Migrations

The spawning migration is a movement away from the overwintering or feeding grounds to the spawning ground. It has evolved as an adaptation for ensuring the most favourable conditions for the development of the eggs and larvae, and especially for the protection of the early stages from predators (Vasnetsov, 1953b).

Many migratory fishes and cyclostomes feed in the sea, but enter the rivers to spawn, performing an anadromous migration. Anadromous migrations are performed by lampreys, sturgeons, salmon, some shads, cyprinoids, etc. Some migratory fishes feed in the rivers, but pass out into the sea to spawn, performing a catadromous migration like the eel, etc.

The migration may be against the current, or contranatant, or else with the current, or denatant. In some fishes a part of the spawning migration is contranatant, and part denatant.

Marine fishes also perform spawning migrations, many of them making quite long journeys to their spawning grounds, sometimes up to a thousand or more kilometres. Some marine fishes, which usually live in deep water rise to spawn in the upper layers of the water, while others, conversely, swim down to greater depths from the surface waters.

The time of year at which the fish performs its spawning migration usually immediately precedes the time of spawning. Only in a comparatively small group of fishes (some sturgeons, salmon and cyprinoids) does the spawning migration turn into the overwintering one: the fish approaches the region of its spawning grounds, where it winters, and spawns in the following year. Thus, different species of migratory fishes start their passage up-river at different times of the year, depending primarily on the time of spawning and on whether the fish will spawn in the same year or whether it will winter in the river and spawn in the following year.

In many fishes, such as certain sturgeons, the Atlantic salmon, *Salmo salar* L., etc., there are winter and spring races, which differ in the time of their approach to the rivers. Thus, the salmon which enters the rivers of the White Sea is represented by two forms: one enters the rivers in the autumn, when its gonads are feebly developed, and spawns in the following year; the other group enters the rivers in the summer, with its gonads well developed, and spawns in the same year.

The formation in fishes of intraspecific groups which differ in the time when they enter the rivers, in the length of their migration course along the rivers, and in the location and sometimes the nature of the spawning grounds, is an important adaptation which ensures that the fish makes the most use of those parts of the river that are suitable for its spawning grounds. If the spawning ground is distributed high up-river and the fish cannot reach it in a single season, such rivers are usually entered by the winter form, which covers a large part of the course as a wintering migration, wintering in the river and spawning in the following year. If the spawning ground is not far from the sea, the river is mainly used by the spring form, which spawns in the same year. Thus, the Pechora, in which the main spawning ground is high up-river, is used mainly by the large winter-spring salmon, while the rivers of the Kola peninsula, where the distances to the spawning grounds are comparatively short, are entered predominantly by the spring form of the salmon (Berg, 1937, 1953; Gerbilsky, 1953; Nikolsky, 1953a, etc.).

As already stated, the time of onset of the spawning migrations varies greatly from species to species. Many whitefishes start their spawning migrations in the autumn, the majority of cyprinoids in the spring. There is also a great deal of variation in the distance up-river to which the fish rise. The length of the migrations up-river varies from a few to several thousand kilometres. The lampreys vary in the distances to which they rise: the Neva lamprey, *Lampetra fluviatilis* (L.), does not swim very far up-river, the Caspian lamprey, *Caspiomyzon wagneri* (Kessl.), on the other hand, rises up the Volga as far as the Kuibyshev dam, and even sometimes beyond the mouth of the Kama. The sturgeons may swim for several thousands of kilometres up-river, until they reach a part where the bottom is stony, where they spawn. But the same sturgeons in the rivers Sephidrud and Terek do not rise as much as a hundred kilometres from the mouths. Migratory salmon also rise high up-river: for example, the sockeye *Oncorhynchus nerka* Walb. rises for more than 3600 km up the Yukon, and travels, as the marking of fish has established, at a speed of 30–40 km per day, while the chum in the Amur travels at a speed of 50 km per day. The Far Eastern salmon and many other migratory fishes overcome numerous obstacles in their paths: waterfalls, rapids, etc. The European salmon also rises well up-river: it almost reaches the source of the Pechora. Some shads enter rivers to spawn; for example, the blackback, *Caspialosa kessleri* Grimm rises up the Volga almost as far as the mouth of the Kama; the Volga shad does not swim as far as this.

There are not as many migratory fish among the cyprinoids. In European waters they include the Black Sea roach *Rutilus frisii* Nordm., the Aral barbel *Barbus brachycephalus* Kessl., the dace *Leuciscus brandti* Dyb., and a few others. *Rutilus frisii* used to enter the Dnieper, in which it would rise to above the Dnieprovsk barrier. Its Caspian subspecies used to rise up the Kura as far as Mingechaur. The barbel *Barbus capito* Guld. enters the Kura and rises up it as far as Aragva; the Aral Sea barbel swims up the Amu-Daria for more than a thousand kilometres and reaches the mouth of the Piandzhe.

The up-river swim of fishes demands an enormous expenditure of energy. The faster the current in the river, the greater the difficulty in overcoming it. It is therefore natural that the movement of the fish is directly connected with the course of flood waters. In the sea the flood waters, by increasing the influence of the fresh water at the mouths of rivers, facilitate the orientation of the fish to the river mouth. In the river itself, the floods, which increase the current, make it more difficult for the fish to swim. In connection with this, many fishes enter the rivers at the end of the flood season (Far Eastern salmon, Aral Sea barbel, etc.) (Figs. 111, 112).

The majority of fishes, while migrating up-river, usually either cease to feed, or else feed less intensively than in the sea, while the enormous energy expenditure naturally requires the utilization of the nutritional substances accumulated during the feeding period in the sea. This is the reason why the majority of migratory fishes are so exhausted at the end of their migrations.

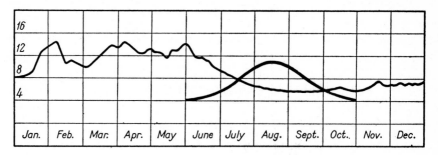

FIG. 111. The progress of the chinook salmon *Oncorhynchus tschawytscha* (Walb.) in the Klamath River, and changes in the Water level (from Snyder, 1931).

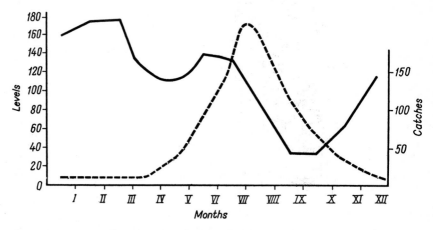

FIG. 112. The progress of the Aral barbel *Barbus brachycephalus* Kessl. (broken line) and changes in the water level in the Syr-Daria River at Kazalinsk (solid line).

The white salmon, *Stenodus leucichthys* (Güld.), before it enters the Volga, has a fat content of 21 % (at Astrakhan); whereas at the spawning ground (Upha) the fat content has fallen to 2 %. The Aral Sea barbel at its feeding grounds in the sea has a fat content of up to 15 % on its internal organs, while on its spawning grounds the quantity of fat has fallen to 1–2 %. Descending individuals have absolutely no fat on their internal organs.

The percentage fat content in the body of the chum salmon changes in the following manner in relation to the distance which it has swum up the Amur:

Distance from the sea in km	0	221	407	570	729	1193
Percentage fat in males	9·19	9·14	8·26	5·72	4·47	3·39
Percentage fat in females	11·28	10·85	7·70	6·58	5·90	3·04

In connection with the change in osmo–regulation and the cessation of feeding in the rivers, very great changes take place in the size of the intestinal tract of migrating fishes. This is particularly well expressed among the salmon family. The intestine of *Oncorhynchus tschawytscha* Walb. (Fig. 113),

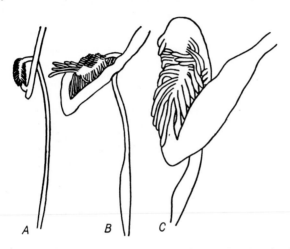

Fig. 113. Changes in the intestine of the chinook salmon as it enters the river. *A*, On the spawning grounds; *B*, at the start of the migration; *C*, at the river mouths (from Scheuring, 1929).

in its spawning grounds, has the shape of a thin thread with very feebly developed pyloric caecae. Changes also occur in the activity of the intestinal enzymes, which in the salmon lose their ability to split proteins.

The amount of energy expended by migrating fishes in order to reach their spawning grounds is very great. Thus, in the male chum salmon the energy expended per kilogram live weight equals 25,810 cal, and in the female 28,390 cal. In connection with the transition from the sea to fresh water, the osmotic pressure of migrating fishes changes, and, consequently, so does the freezing temperature of the blood. In the chinook salmon the freezing point of the blood in the sea is $-0·762°$, in the dilute water outside the estuaries it is $-0·737°$, and at the spawning grounds it is $-0·628°$

(Greene, 1904). The fact that the osmotic pressure of the fishes' blood is closely related to the salinity of the water, and changes as the salinity changes, is confirmed by observations on the Caspian shad *Caspialosa caspia* (Table 23).

TABLE 23

Changes in the Salinity (Freezing Point) of the Water and the Freezing Point of the Blood of the Shad *Caspialosa caspia*

	Open sea	Outside estuary	Estuary	River	Spawning grounds
Water	−0·121	−0·040	−0·018	−0·015	−0·000
Blood	−0·792	−0·747	−0·731	−0·697	−0·666

When they leave the sea-water there is a change in the vitamin content of the flesh of migratory fishes. Thus, according to Wald (1938), the vitamins $A–A_1$, which are present in the eye tissues of migratory fishes in the sea, become altered to the form A_2 when the fish leaves the sea for the fresh water.

As the foregoing shows, the changes which the migrating fish undergoes during its spawning migration are very profound. The organism of the fish undergoes an adaptive reconstruction on passing from one set of environmental conditions to another, from life in still waters to overcoming the movement of flowing water.

Examples of catadromous migrations, in which the river serves as the feeding ground while the sea serves as the spawning ground, are much more unusual among migratory fishes. The most complex catadromous spawning migrations are those of the American, and especially of the European, eels. When it reaches maturity (in its 9th–12th year of life, and sometimes even later), the European eel starts to move downstream, out of the rivers in which it was feeding and growing, and into the sea. The passage of the eel downstream is rarely observed, because it usually takes place at night. In the sea the eel swims from the European to the Central American coast, where it spawns at great depths. Like other migratory fishes, the eel, during the course of its journey from its feeding grounds in the European rivers to its spawning grounds at the American coast, undergoes very profound changes, which, unfortunately, have not yet been sufficiently well studied. Before it enters the sea, the eye of the eel becomes enlarged, sometimes becoming four times as large as the eye of freshwater eels. At the same time its face becomes sharper and its coloration changes—the back becomes darker, while the belly changes from yellow to a silvery colour. The eel starts its migration in a well-fed condition, but during the course of its migration, as a result of the enormous amount of energy expended, it becomes very thin. The migrating eel does not feed, and its alimentary canal degenerates considerably. When the eel passes out of the rivers into the sea the osmotic pressure of its blood rises. Also the size of its swim-bladder decreases. The stimulus for the start of the spawning migration is apparently the ripening of the gonads, which starts in the rivers. In the rivers the eggs of the eel have a diameter of 0·03–0·09 mm in December; in the following September it is 0·1 mm, in October 0·16 mm, and in November from 0·18 to 0·23 mm, i.e. a slow process of ripening takes place.

The causes of the origin of such a complex course of migrations as the eel's have not yet been finally explained. The adherents of the Wegener hypothesis of continental drift explain the migration course of the eel on the grounds that in the Mesozoic the eel spawned in inland lakes which were then distributed in those places in which the present spawning grounds are found. Then, as the continents drifted apart, the migration course lengthened and finally attained its present dimensions. According to Ekman (1932), the eel travels in the direction of increasing salinity and temperature. The spawning grounds of the eel are in the warmest parts of the deep areas. Schmidt (1947) suggests that the present-day migrations of the eel are the result of the cooling which took place during the Ice Age. According to Schmidt, at that time, and also in the Tertiary period, because of the higher temperatures in the deep waters, the spawning grounds of the eel were distributed along the European coast; as the Ice Age set in, the warmer waters and the spawning grounds of the eel, which were adjacent to them, became displaced westward to occupy their present position, which coincides with the spawning grounds of the American eel. Thus, the present-day spawning grounds of the eel are very far distant from the feeding grounds; in connection with this the time of development of the eel has become greatly extended, so that it lasts considerably longer than that of the American eel, the spawning grounds of which are considerably nearer the mouths of the rivers in which the eel feeds.

Vasnetsov (1953b) suggests that the occurrence of the spawning grounds of the eel in the halistatic zone of the Central Atlantic is connected with the fact that in this place there are the fewest predators on the eggs and larvae.

Lebedev (1959) suggests that, in its migration from the rivers to the spawning grounds, the eel follows currents flowing in the deep water. Migrating with a following current enables the eel to cover enormous distances without feeding, at the expense of those resources which it accumulated in its body.

Catadromous spawning migrations, although considerably shorter than those of the eel, are also performed by certain members of the families Galaxiidae and Gobiidae. They usually pass from the lower reaches of the rivers to the adjacent shallow parts of the sea.

Many fishes do not perform significant movements from the oceans and seas to the fresh waters of the upper and middle reaches of rivers. They usually feed without passing beyond the limits of the dilute zone and the estuaries, and move into the lower and middle reaches of the rivers to spawn. Such fishes are classified as fluvial anadromous ("semi-migratory") fishes. They include many whitefishes, cyprinoids (like the roach), and a number of others. The changes in these fishes in relation to adaptation for migration are not as profound as those in fully migratory fishes.

Naturally the migratory and semi-migratory groups are not sharply delimited. There are fishes (barbels, *Coregonus muksun*, *Stenodus leucichthys nelma*), which could equally well be placed in either group. Vladimirov (1957) calls them pseudo-migratory fish. Often the same species leads a semi-migratory mode of life in certain waters, and in others a stationary one. Thus, the roach in the North Caspian leads a semi-migratory life, while in the North Volga it is stationary. In the Aral Sea the carp is represented by both a semi-migratory form and a stationary one.

Considerable spawning migrations are performed not only by migratory fishes, but by marine and freshwater ones as well.

In many marine fishes the length of the spawning migration is also very considerable. For example, the Atlantic cod, at the end of its feeding, performs a spawning migration from the east part of the Barents Sea to the Lofoten Islands. The oceanic herring, which feeds along the western coast of Spitzbergen, approaches the north-west coast of Norway to spawn. The Japanese mackerel, *Pneumatophorus japonicus* Houtt., which winters to the north of Taiwan, goes to the Yellow Sea to spawn along the coasts of Yentai (Chiefoo), Korea, and southern Primorie.

The spawning migrations of the plaice are rather different. The plaice, *Pleuronectes platessa* L., usually spawns at some considerable depth and away from the coast. Thus, in the North Sea the plaice spawns mainly in the deep gully opposite the entry to the English Channel. Plaice come to this area both from the English coast and from the Channel itself. In Russian waters the plaice spawning grounds are at even greater depths than in the North Sea, though they are not particularly far from the shore (the Teribersk and Kildin Banks). The migrations of some Far Eastern flatfishes are very different. Here the flatfishes winter at great depths, and approach the coastal zone to spawn.

The spawning migrations of freshwater fishes are also different. Many of them leave the lakes to spawn in the rivers. Thus, for example, the white fish *Coregonus lavaretus* L., lives in Lake Ladoga, but enters the rivers to spawn. Some fishes move from the open parts of a lake to the shore zone to spawn among the weeds and in marshy places. Thus, the pike, *Esox lucius* L., spawns on the flood plains when the rivers are flooded. The African lungfish, *Protopterus*, also moves inshore from the open parts of the lakes to spawn among the weeds.

In contrast to the migratory fishes, marine and fresh-water fishes usually feed during their spawning migrations, though less intensively than during their feeding season. In both marine and freshwater fishes the changes which are connected with the preparation for migration (increasing fat content and condition, changes in the condition of the blood, and so on), also take place, though they are usually less profound than in migratory fishes.

Many marine and some freshwater fishes perform vertical spawning migrations, rising from the deep layers to the surface. Thus, many deep-water fishes of the order Scopeliformes rise to spawn in the upper layers, where their eggs develop and often their larvae live feeding on the phytoplankton. Among freshwater fishes the clearest example of a vertical spawning migration is that of the Lake Baikal Comephoridae. These viviparous fishes rise from the great depths in Lake Baikal at which they feed into the surface layers of the water in order to give birth to their larvae.

FEEDING MIGRATIONS

The feeding migration consists of a movement away from the spawning or overwintering grounds to the feeding grounds. In many fishes the feeding migration even begins in the egg stage. The transport of the pelagic eggs and free embryos from the places where they were spawned to the feeding grounds is a passive feeding migration. Passive feeding migrations are found in migratory, marine, and freshwater fishes.

An example of a passive feeding migration is the transport of the eggs and larvae of the migratory shad and the Aral Sea barbel from the spawning grounds to the feeding grounds of the fry. Among migratory fishes which perform catadromous spawning migrations, the larvae of the eel largely migrate passively to their feeding grounds.

Marine fishes also perform passive feeding migrations. The pelagic eggs and larvae of many fishes are transported by currents, sometimes over very great distances. The eggs and larvae of the cod and the larvae of the herring are transported by the Atlantic current from the coast of Norway to their feeding grounds in the Barents Sea. The pelagic eggs of many flatfishes, which are concentrated in a comparatively small area immediately after spawning, are gradually transported away by currents over considerable distances, which ensures that the larvae, on hatching, have the best feeding conditions.

In marine fishes there sometimes occurs a passive vertical migration of eggs and larvae. Thus, the eggs of the oceanic flying fishes, which are spawned in the surface layers of the ocean, gradually sink downward, reaching a depth at which, on hatching, the larvae are well protected from predators, and yet have a sufficient food supply.

The pelagic eggs and larvae of the mullet, *Mullus barbatus* L., in the Black Sea are transported by currents from the coast into the open sea, where there is more food and fewer predators, and they only return to the coastal zone when they have reached a stage in which they feed on benthos.

Passive feeding migrations have also evolved among freshwater fishes. Enormous numbers of pelagic eggs, free embryos, and larvae are transported downstream from the spawning grounds, particularly in the rivers of eastern Asia. The eggs of many fishes, including the grass-carp (*Ctenopharyngodon idella* Val.), the black Chinese roach (*Mylopharyngodon piceus* Rich.), the bigheads (*Hypophthalmichthys molitrix* Val., *Aristichthys nobilis* Rich.), the gudgeons (*Saurogobio, Rostrogobio*, etc.), and the razor-fish (*Pelecus cultratus* L.) are adapted to developing in the floating state. If in the rivers of Eastern Asia the spawning and descent of the eggs and larvae coincide, as they usually do, with the period of rising water-level in the rivers, the eggs and larvae are carried by the currents in masses into flood lakes, creeks, and channels with quiet currents, on to their feeding grounds. If the descent takes place during the period of falling water level, the larvae migrate actively to their feeding grounds after absorbing the yolk-sac.

When they finish spawning (if they do not then die, of course) the adult fishes start an active migration to their feeding grounds, usually in a some-what exhausted condition. Many species of both marine and freshwater fishes start to feed immediately after the end of spawning, their feeding migration taking place while they are actually feeding. A number of migratory fishes either do not feed at all or else feed very little while making the return journey downstream to the sea. On entering the sea, migratory fishes con-tinue to move, and their feeding grounds are often at very great distances from the mouths of the rivers in which they spawned. Thus, for example, the Caspian sturgeon, *Acipenser stellatus* Pall., which enters the Kura to spawn, feeds mainly at the east coast of the Caspian.

Active feeding migrations are also very well marked among marine fishes. Some perform regular journeys, going from one good feeding ground to another. Thus, for example, the cod, after spawning at the Norwegian coast, feeds heavily while moving eastward. When spawning is finished, the cod is extremely thin, and its liver contains negligible amounts of fat, but as it moves eastward the condition of the cod improves. Toward the end of its feeding season it attains its peak condition of nourishment and then practically ceases to feed (Fig. 114). The Norwegian herring, *Clupea harengus* L., also performs a considerable feeding migration after spawning, going from its spawning grounds into the open sea and moving north and east to regions where the plankton is richer, keeping to places where there are concentra-tions of the planktonic organisms on which it feeds (Fig. 115). The migra-tions of many marine predatory fishes are to a considerable extent related to those of other fishes, their prey. Thus the movements of the herring shark *Lamna cornubica* (Gm.) are to a great extent related to the distribution and movements of the herring. When the herrings approach the coast, large numbers of sharks usually appear immediately.

Besides horizontal feeding migrations, many marine fishes perform regular vertical movements, which are related to the search for food. The mackerel rises into the surface waters when there is a rich development of plankton there. When the plankton sinks downward, so does the mackerel. The sword-fish, when its food species (mainly the sardine and *Coryphaena*) move down-ward, itself moves down to great depths, where it feeds on the scopelids which live there. It is interesting to note that the swordfish, in contrast to many other fishes, is capable of moving very rapidly from a great depth to the surface.

Many pelagic larvae of marine fishes perform diurnal vertical feeding migrations, in which they follow the vertical movements of their prey, the

planktonic invertebrates which move down to great depths by day, and rise
to the surface by night.

However, the diurnal vertical migrations of marine and freshwater organisms, including fishes, are not only for feeding. In many cases, as Kozhov

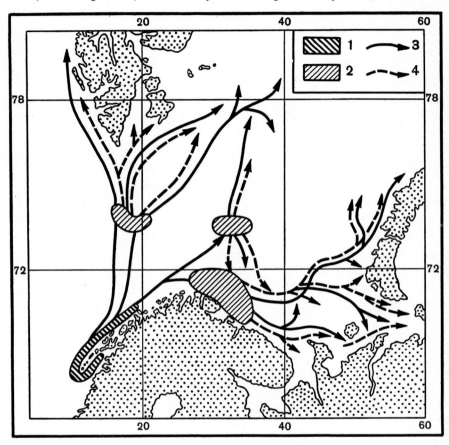

FIG. 114. The migrations of the Norwegian cod. 1, Spawning grounds; 2, wintering
grounds of immature cod; 3, course of migrations of mature cod; 4, course of migrations
of immature cod.

(1954) showed, for the vertical migrations of aquatic organisms in Lake
Baikal, and Manteufel (1959) for marine organisms, they have a protective
significance against predators.

Feeding migrations are also often clearly expressed in fishes of inland
waters. Thus, in the Aral Sea the bream and the white-eyed bream after

spawning move into great depths, where they remain until the end of the feeding season. As they move away from the shore and feed more intensively, the condition of these fishes continuously improves, until it reaches a peak (Fig. 116). The bream and white-eyed bream then cease feeding and commence their return journey to the shore. The movement of the whitefish, in

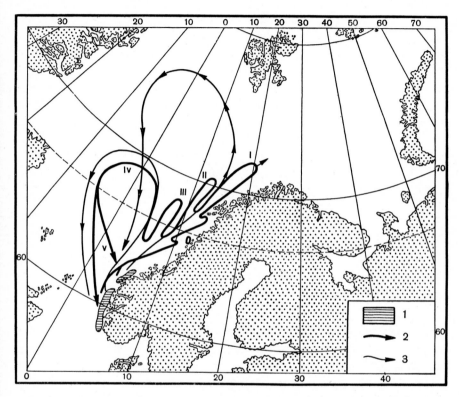

Fig. 115. The migrations of the Norwegian herring. 1, Spawning grounds; 2, course of migrations of the herring before its first spawning; 3, course of the migrations of the herring after spawning. O, littoral stage (stage of metamorphosis); I, "small" herring; II and III, "fatty" herring; IV, "oceanic" stage; V, spawning stock.

Lake Baikal, after spawning, into the open part of the lake, and its vertical movements after food organisms (Fig. 117), may serve as an example of this (Kozhov, 1954). In many rivers, after overwintering or spawning the fishes go to the flood plains to feed. This occurs, for example, in the lower reaches of the Ob, where it even has a special name. A feeding migration from the river Ob to the flood plain is performed by the cyprinoids and whitefishes (subfamily Coregoninae). In the Amur the feeding migration of many fishes, both adults and young, takes the form of a movement from the river to the lakes.

Diurnal feeding migrations are very clearly marked in many freshwater fishes. Thus, many fishes which live in midstream by day enter creeks at night

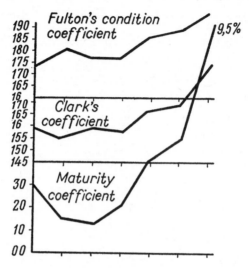

Fig. 116. Dynamics of the condition factor and the maturity of the white-eyed bream *Abramis sapa aralensis* Tjapkin from May to November in the Aral Sea (from Nikolsky, 1940).

where there is usually a rich invertebrate fauna on which they feed. Similar migrations are also made by the dace, gudgeon, and other fishes. Such predatory fishes as the sheat-fish, aspe, etc. follow the passive fishes into the creeks. In freshwater as in marine fishes, there are clearly marked vertical feeding migrations, which can be both seasonal and diurnal.

Fig. 117. Vertical migrations of the planktonic food organisms of the whitefish *Coregonus autumnalis migratorius* Georgi in Lake Baikal (from Kozhov, 1954). I, January–February (temperature indicated is that of open water on February 1st); II, April–May (temperature that of open water at end of April); III, June–first half of July (temperature that of open water at end of June; temperature in shallow water at 0 m, 9°; at 25 m, 4°); IV, second half of July–September (temperature that of open water in second half of August; temperature in shallow water at 0 m, 16°; at 25 m, 11°); V, November–December (temperature that of open water in second half of November; temperature near surface about 2–1°). 1, Shoals of whitefish; 2, the sculpin *Cottocomephorus*; 3, small fish (golomianky) (Comephoridae); 4, 10 kg/hektare biomass of planktonic crustaceans in the layers indicated; 5, predominating direction of vertical movements of zooplankton.

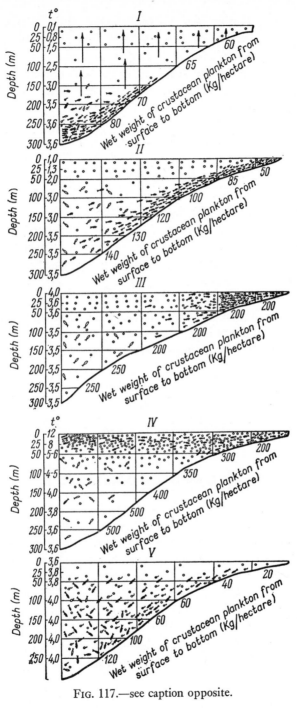

FIG. 117.—see caption opposite.

The razor-fish, *Pelecus cultratus* (L.), in the Aral Sea, moves from the bottom at night in pursuit of the rising dipterous larvae and amphipods, on which it feeds. The Aral bleak in spring and the roach in autumn also perform similar migrations in the Aral Sea. In the lakes of East Africa the sheat-fish *Synodontis*, which lives on the bottom, also rises to the surface by night in pursuit of dipterous larvae.

The cause of the feeding migrations, as already stated, is connected with the shortage of food in the spawning and overwintering grounds. The feeding migrations represent a movement away from the grounds which are poor in food to grounds with a rich food supply. The immediate stimulus for the start of the feeding migration is the demand for food after the exhausting effects of spawning and overwintering. The nearer the concentrations of the food organisms which are essential for the restoration of the energetic resources to the spawning or overwintering rounds, the shorter the feeding migration of the fish. As they consume their food organisms, the fish reduce the concentration of the food to a level at which the energy expended in obtaining the food cannot ensure the necessary rate of accumulation of the energy resources. When they have reduced the concentration of the food organisms below a certain level (which varies from species to species of both food and fish), the fish must move away and seek further concentrations of food organisms.

Knowing the minimal feeding concentration of the food organisms and the rate at which the fishes are consuming them, we may determine approximately how long the concentrations of fishes will remain on a "food patch" (Novikova, 1956), which has a considerable practical significance.

Overwintering Migrations

The overwintering migration is a movement away from the feeding to the wintering grounds (see page 258). It only occurs in those fishes which have a wintering ground. Often adult fishes, as for example the bream in the Aral Sea, make an overwintering migration and winter in holes in the rivers, while the immature individuals continue to feed in the sea in the winter and do not enter the rivers.

The overwintering migration is performed by migratory and semi-migratory, as well as marine and freshwater fishes. In migratory fishes it is usually the start of the spawning migration. The winter form of the migratory fishes move from the feeding grounds in the sea to the wintering grounds in the rivers, where they concentrate in deep pits and overwinter in a somewhat inactive state, and usually not feeding. Among migratory fishes which perform overwintering migrations are the sturgeons, Atlantic salmon, Aral Sea barbel, and certain others. Many semi-migratory fishes also perform well-marked overwintering migrations. At the end of their feeding seasons in the North Caspian and Aral Seas and the Sea of Azov, the adult roach, sea-roach, bream, pike-perch, and certain other semi-migratory fishes move to the lower reaches of the rivers where they overwinter.

Some marine fishes also perform an overwintering migration. Many flat-fishes move off after the end of their feeding period into deeper water and concentrate there in a relatively small area, in which the conditions are favourable for overwintering (Moiseev, 1946). The anchovy *Engraulis en-crasicholus* (L.) moves from its feeding grounds in the Sea of Azov to winter in the Black Sea, where it concentrates at a depth of 70–150 m in a compara-tively inactive state.

The overwintering migration is also expressed in many freshwater fishes. Many, like the grass-carp *Ctenopharyngodon idella* Val., leave the lakes when they finish feeding in the autumn, and concentrate in pits in the lower reaches of rivers such as the Amur.

The reason for the overwintering migrations of fishes is the need to move away from the feeding grounds into such regions as provide favourable abiotic conditions and some protection against predators for these fishes, which are in a state of relative inactivity and reduced metabolic rate.

The overwintering migration is only started by those fishes which are "prepared" for it, i.e. which have attained a certain condition and fat content, which is essential for the successful completion of the overwintering and to ensure the development of the gonads. The fish, on reaching this state, begins to sense definite changes in the environmental factors as a natural migrating stimulus. Fishes which are not prepared for the migration do not migrate. To forecast the time when the overwintering migration will start, it is neces-sary, as stated above, to know the feeding rate and to have hydrometeor-ological forecasts.

All the types of migrations—spawning, feeding, and overwintering—are links in a single migration cycle, which during the life of various species of fishes may be repeated from once to ten or more times. The change over to migration depends on the attainment of a particular biological condition by the fish—well-nourished, high fat content, development of gonads, etc. However, fishes often make movements which are not connected with a particular condition. These movements are made in various biological conditions of the fish, and usually have a protective significance. Thus, for example, the movement of many fishes away from the surface waters into greater depths by day is a protective adaptation, which ensures a lower rate of consumption by predators. This has been observed for the anchovy in the Black Sea, where it keeps to great depths and is relatively unavailable to fish-eating birds by day, and by night, when the birds have ceased to feed, it rises to the surface. The signal for this species to start its vertical migration is a change in the light intensity.

Many fishes leave the shallow parts before the water-level in the rivers falls, otherwise they would be left behind to die; the signal for the start of this movement is the start of the fall in level (see page 256). Such movements are observed in very many rivers and numerous species of fish. Oxyphil fishes usually react more sensitively to a change in the water level than fishes which are better able to withstand some oxygen deficit which develops in the pools left as the water recedes.

A fall in the sea-level also acts as the signal for fishes which feed in the littoral zone during high water and leave the tidal zone at low water.

Protective movements may take place during the spawning, feeding, or overwintering migrations, and also during spawning and feeding.

The Overwintering and Hibernation of Fishes

Overwintering and hibernation are a part of the life cycle of a fish which is characterized by a reduced activity, complete cessation or sharp reduction of the consumption of food, and a fall in the level of metabolism and its maintenance at the expense of energy resources accumulated in the organism, particularly fat deposits.

Overwintering and hibernation are an adaptation which ensure the survival in the population through a period of the year which is unfavourable for an active mode of life (poor oxygen conditions, lack of food, low temperatures, drought, etc.). They do not occur in all fishes, and are much less often observed in marine fishes than in freshwater ones.

Among marine fishes, typical overwintering is expressed in many flatfishes, as for example *Limanda aspera* Pall., species of the genus *Pseudopleuronectes*, and others. The flatfish move out from the coasts into water of 150–300 m or more in depth to overwinter, forming considerable concentrations there. A lowering of activity and overwintering in deep water are mainly characteristic of boreal species among the Far Eastern flatfishes. These species accumulate fat during their feeding period to enable them to continue their metabolism during the overwintering period.

Flatfishes of arctic origin in Far Eastern waters, such as *Liopsetta glacialis* (Pall.) and *L. obscura* (Hertz), do not go into deep water but continue to feed in the coastal zone in the winter. In connection with this, they do not accumulate any substantial fat deposits in their body, and their fat content varies but little throughout the year.

The Azov and Black Sea anchovies pass the winter in a relatively inactive state and scarcely feeding, at a depth of 100–150 m in the southern part of the Black Sea. To ensure successful overwintering, considerable amounts of fat are deposited in the body.

Overwintering also takes place in many migratory fishes. The winter forms of the sturgeons—beluga (white sturgeon), Russian sturgeon, sevruga —enter the rivers and spend the winter lying in pits in the stream-bed. In certain migratory fishes, such as *Acipenser nudiventris* Lov. in the Aral Sea, those individuals which are not prepared for the migration into the river, and will not spawn in the following year, remain in the sea but lower their activity substantially and aggregate in pits in the northern part of the Aral Sea.

Overwintering is more widely distributed among freshwater fishes, especially those of temperate latitudes. The phenomenon is not equally distributed among all the various ecological groups of freshwater fish. Most of the species which have this property are limnophil or stagnophil fishes [crucian carp, black fish (*Dallia pectoralis* Bean), etc.].

Overwintering is less common among fishes which live in rivers. Various phytophagous fishes, like the grass-carp, bighead, and others, winter in the Amur. These fishes spend the winter aggregated in the stream-bed, and their bodies become covered over with a thick layer of slime.

In the Arctic zone the majority of fishes feed round the year, and not only do they not lower their activity during the winter, but in many, such as various species of whitefish, the activity actually increases during the winter. Examples of fishes in the Arctic zone in which overwintering occurs include the common crucian carp and the blackfish, *Dallia pectoralis* Bean, in the Chukotsk peninsula. These fishes which live in lakes, in which an active mode of life is impossible during the winter, dig themselves into the mud and fall into a state of torpor. Their metabolism almost completely ceases. The blackfish and crucian carp may even be frozen into the mud and yet remain alive, even in a lump of ice. Death only ensues if the body fluids freeze (Kalabuchov, 1956).

The number of fishes which overwinter increases substantially in temperate latitudes. In the majority of pond and lake species of temperate latitudes the activity decreases considerably during the winter, and movement ceases completely; they concentrate in the deep parts, where they pass the winter in an inactive state. Some species pass out into the stream-beds to overwinter. In temperate latitudes, in the majority of cases, overwintering is an adaptation to an unfavourable oxygen regime in stagnant water when it has an ice cover. By reducing its activity during the winter and existing on the reserves which it accumulated during the summer, the fish can live at a low oxygen concentration (Borutsky, Kliuchareva, and Nikolsky, 1952).

For herbivorous fishes in temperate latitudes the overwintering is an adaptation to the absence of vegetating plants during the winter. In the vegetating period the fish accumulates in its body the necessary amounts of reserve materials, at the expense of which it lives during the winter when there is no food for it. Very often the same species in the southern part of its range scarcely reduces its activity during the winter and continues to feed (for example, the carp, grass-carp, etc.), while in the northern part of its range, where the water is covered by ice and there are no vegetating plants during the winter these fishes sharply reduce their activity and their rate of metabolism.

In certain species of fishes, for example the Aral Sea bream, the adult individuals reduce their metabolic rate and cease to feed, but the young immature ones continue feeding (Konstaninova, 1958). This peculiarity is connected with the fact that in the young individuals all the food resources are used for making linear growth, an adaptation which removes them from the influence of predators. The food resources are insufficient for the accumulation of these reserves during the vegetative period, and the young fishes continue to feed during the winter, though usually admittedly at a somewhat lower intensity. In fishes which have reached maturity, less of the food material goes into protein growth, and part of it is deposited in the form of fats and used during the overwintering.

In tropical and equatorial fresh waters a reduction in the activity of fishes is connected, not with falling temperatures, but usually with the period of drought. The peculiar summer aestivation is most clearly expressed in the dipneusts—African species of the genus *Protopterus* and the American *Lepidosiren paradoxa* Fitz. These fishes burrow into the ground during periods of drought and spend the whole of the unfavourable period in an inactive state, carrying on their metabolism at the expense of the reserves that they accumulated in their bodies during the feeding period, which usually coincides with the wet season in the equatorial zone. The dipneusts may not aestivate in certain waters, if the conditions remain favourable for an active life during the dry season, or in years of heavy precipitation, when the waters inhabited by these fishes do not dry up. For successful overwintering the fish must accumulate in its body the necessary amounts of reserve material, mainly fats of a particular quality.

As the figures below show (Poliakov, 1950, 1958), the length of time a starving carp can survive even in a relatively inactive state is closely related to its condition and fat content:

Average coefficient of condition	Average fat content	Average time of survival when starved
2·56	2·15%	141 days
2·81	4·25%	191 days

The same was also observed by Kirpichnikov (1958) for Amur carp fingerlings kept at a temperature of 0°:

Average coefficient of condition	Time of survival at 0°
1·92	6 days
2·29	10 days
2·33	15 days
2·40–2·50	Over 40 days

These data show that when the coefficient of condition is more than 2·40 the winter resistance of the Amur carp increases sharply.

The winter resistance of the different forms of carp varies for the same value of the coefficient of condition. Thus, according to the data of Kirpichnikov and Berg (1952), the minimal value of this coefficient at which successful overwintering is assured for yearling Amur carp is 2·4, for the common carp 2·9, and their hybrid 2·7.

For the successful overwintering of young carp which have attained various sizes, the minimal values of the coefficient should be as follows:

Weight of fish	Coefficient of condition
Over 25 g	2·5–2·6
15–25 g	2·7
Under 15 g	2·9

Many examples are known in fish-rearing practice, in which a planting for overwintering of quite large but thin young carp has given very high losses. In this connection definite instructions are published for the planting for overwintering of fish with a certain value of the coefficient of condition.

Both the quantity and the quality of the accumulated food materials are important. In particular, successful overwintering requires the deposition of fats with saturated fatty acids. The conditions under which the overwintering takes place are also of considerable importance. If the carp is disturbed during the winter it becomes more active, its reserve materials are used up more quickly, and exhaustion sets in more rapidly (Sigov, 1947; Judin, 1948).

Thus, the successful overwintering largely depends upon the extent to which the fish has prepared for it—how successful its feeding season was.

The signal for the start of overwintering in temperate and high latitudes is a drop in the temperature to below a certain value. However, if the fish has not attained the necessary state of preparedness, it usually continues to feed and does not enter the state of overwintering. During the overwintering period the fishes usually aggregate. The formation of overwintering concentrations has an adaptive significance. The metabolism is less intensive in aggregated fishes than in isolated ones. The mucus secretion, which forms an isolating factor, is usually used more rationally in aggregations, and so on.

A knowledge of the factors which govern overwintering is of great practical importance, especially in pond cultivation.

As stated above, the success of the fishes' preparation for overwintering largely determines the success of the overwintering. Attention must be paid both to the quality of the fish being planted for overwintering, and to the provision of favourable conditions for this period.

Feeding and the Feeding Relationships Among Fishes

Feeding is one of the most important functions of an organism. The basic functions of an organism—its growth, development, reproduction—all take place at the expense of the energy which enters the organism in the form of its food. All the other energy processes within the organism of the fish also proceed at the expense of the food. The first stage in the life cycle of a fish is completed at the expense of the food reserves which it receives from the maternal organism (the yolk in the egg). However, the fish can only live on its yolk for a comparatively short time, and after a short period of mixed feeding it goes over completely to the consumption of external food. Fishes differ greatly in the character of the food they consume. Both the size and the systematic position of the food organisms are extremely variable; the range of types of food consumed by fishes is greater than that for other groups of vertebrates.

Adult fishes may be divided into the following groups according to the character of the food they consume: (1) herbivorous and detritophagic, such as the Trans-Caspian barbel, *Varicorhinus heratensis* Keys., the Amur nase, *Xenocypris macrolepis* Bl.; (2) carnivores, which feed on invertebrates, like the bream, sheat-fish,etc.; (3) predators, which feed on fish, such as the herring-shark, pike, sheat-fish, etc. This division is very subjective, because the majority of fishes feed on a mixed diet, and carnivorous fishes can often feed as predators and vice versa. There are also fishes which lead a parasitic mode of life (see above).

As already stated (see page 26), some nutrient salts (phosphorus, calcium, etc.) can enter the body of the fish directly in aqueous solution through the gills, oral surface, and skin.

Every species of fish is adapted to feeding on a particular food, its sensory organs are adapted to seeking out this food, its buccal cavity to seizing it, its intestine to digesting it. However, the adaptation to feeding on a particular diet does not remain constant throughout the life of the fish; it changes as the fish grows. During the process of development of the fish, changes take place in its food, which are connected with changes in its structure. Thus, for example, the roach, *Rutilus rutilus caspicus* Jak., in its first stages of ontogeny, feeds on small slow-moving plankton, i.e. algae and rotifers; it then starts to feed on planktonic crustaceans; in its next stage it feeds mostly on benthic insect larvae; and, finally, the basic food of the adults consists of molluscs (Fig. 84). Corresponding to the changes in the composition of the food, onto-genetic changes also take place in the structure of the feeding and digestive organs.

Sometimes the food of the different sexes also differs. The female bream in the Sea of Azov feeds mainly on *Hypaniola kovalevskii* Annenk., while the male feeds mainly on *Nereis succinea* Leuckart. Sometimes the differences between the foods eaten by males and females are very substantial, as for example in the deep-water anglers, in which the females lead a predatory life while the males are parasitic on them, and feed on the females' body fluids.

Very great changes also take place in the food of fishes throughout the year. This is primarily due to the great changes in the composition of the food organisms and their availability. Thus, for example, the haddock, *Gadus aeglefinus* (L.), consumes large amounts of herring spawn in the spring, while in the summer it feeds on benthos. The giant shark, *Cetorhinus maximus* (Günn), feeds on plankton in the spring and summer, and in the winter it feeds on bottom organisms in deep water. It is interesting that certain seasonal structural changes in this shark are associated with the change in diet. For example, the long gill-rakers which enable it to feed on plankton during the summer disappear in the winter (Parker and Boeseman, 1954). There are also very great differences in the food of a single species in different regions. Thus, the pidschian whitefish, *Coregonus lavaretus pidschian* (Gmel.), feeds mostly on molluscs in the river Pechora, on crustaceans in the Gida, and chironomid larvae in the Kara.

Fishes may be classified as follows, according to the amount of variation in the types of food consumed by them: (1) euryphagic, feeding on a variety of foods; (2) stenophagic, feeding on a few different types of food; and (3) monophagic, feeding on only a single type of food.

The feeding behaviour is a species characteristic, which becomes formulated during its evolution. The more stable the feeding conditions of the species, the smaller the range of foods to which it is adapted, and, conversely, the more variable the food supply, the greater the variety of foods eaten by the species.

Fishes have also evolved organs by means of which they seek out their food, according to the characteristics of their feeding behaviour. In the pike, a predator which captures its prey, partly lying in wait for it, and partly chasing it, the main organs by means of which it orientates toward its prey are the lateral line and the eyes. The first orientation toward its moving prey occurs through the lateral line, while the eyes provide a correction when the pike darts at the prey. If the eyes are extirpated the pike can still feed, orientating itself toward its prey by means of the lateral line alone. In the sea-scorpion *Scorpaena*, a different type of predator which ambushes its prey, the main organs by means of which it discovers its prey are also the eyes and lateral line, while in the American sheat-fishes of the genus *Amiurus* the olfactory and taste organs are used. In the benthophagic carp, *Cyprinus carpio* L., the tactile and taste organs are used in searching for prey.

Changes take place in the role of the various sense organs during the ontogenetic development of a single species. In the majority of fishes in their earliest stages of development, when they feed on plankton, the eyes and the organs of the lateral line play the major part in orientation toward food, while in the adult fishes, as for example the roach or bream, when they change over to feeding on bottom organisms they orientate toward their food by means of their tactile and taste organs.

For tasting their food fishes usually possess large numbers of sense cells on the lips surrounding the mouth, and these are sometimes situated on special

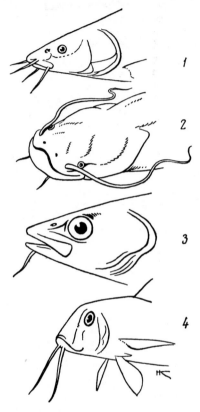

FIG. 118. Various types of barbels of fishes. 1, The barbel *Barbus barbus* (L.); 2, The sheat-fish *Siluris glanis* L.; 3, the cod *Gadus morhua* L.; 4, the red mullet *Mullus barbatus* L.

outgrowths, or barbels (Fig. 118). The number of barbels and their size vary considerably. In the cod family, Gadidae, there is often one unpaired barbel, set on the lower jaw. This barbel is longer in the various species of gadoids which feed mainly on bottom invertebrates, than in the predatory species. In some sheat-fishes there may be as many as sixteen barbels, and some of these may be longer than the body, as in the Indo-Malayan sheat-fish,

Siluroides eugeneiatus Vaill. In the Mormyridae there is an outgrowth at the end of the snout which is sometimes of considerable length, and which is rich in sensory nerve endings. Burrowing about in the silt by means of this long snout, the mormyrid easily feels the buried invertebrates on which it feeds.

FIG. 119. Elongated fin-rays serving as tactile organs. 1, The gourami *Osphronemus* (Perciformes); 2, *Benthosaurus* (Scopeliformes).

In some species, particularly of deep-water fishes, the rays of the paired or dorsal fins are greatly elongated and modified to form tactile organs. In the deep-water genus *Bathypterois*, the rays of the pectoral fins are drawn out into long threads, which are one and a half times as long as the fish. These threads are rich in sensory endings. In many representatives of the labyrinthici Anabantoidei the long threadlike pelvic fins serve as tactile organs (Fig. 119). The organs of taste are developed in fishes in the buccal cavity, on barbels (the burbot), and on the fin-rays (gurnards). In general, in predators and planktophages the leading role in searching for food is usually played by the visual organs, and in benthophages by the tactile and taste organs.

The diurnal rhythm of feeding is also to a considerable extent related to the method by which the fish orientates itself toward its food. Thus, in the white aspe, *Leucaspius delineatus* (Heck.) and the cod, *Gadus morhua* L., the food consumption falls sharply when the light intensity decreases (Fig. 120). A change in the light intensity does not greatly affect the rate of feeding

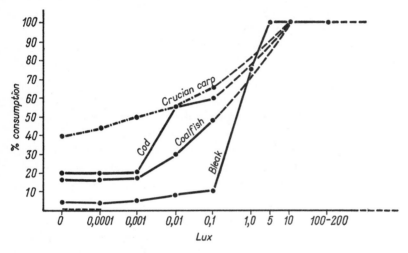

FIG. 120. Rate of consumption of amphipods by the cod and coalfish, and also of *Daphnia* by the common crucian carp and bleak with varying amounts of illumination (100 %=the rate at 100 lux) (from Girsa, 1960).

of the common crucian carp, *Carassius carassius* L. (Girsa, 1960). The light intensity is significant as a factor which, on the one hand, assists a predator that orientates itself visually in finding its prey, and on the other hand, enables the prey to observe the predator better. Thus, the white aspe easily escapes from the burbot by day, and only becomes its prey by night. But the burbot catches as many of the relatively inactive bloodworms by day as by night (Pavlov, 1960), although it is unable to catch the white aspe by day.

Regarding the group of fishes as a whole, probably hearing is the only sense which plays a subsidiary role in the search for food.

The development of the sense organs for the purpose of orientation toward food is related to the development in the prey of a corresponding protective adaptation. This applies in particular to those fishes which form the prey of other fishes (see above).

Closely related to the variety of foods consumed by fishes is the function of the organs for seizing and assimilating the food. The buccal apparatus which serves for seizing, comminuting, and swallowing the food varies in fishes and cyclostomes from a funnel in the lamprey to a beak in the Ostraceidae. With all the variety of structure and function of the mouth, fishes can be classified in a number of types (Fig. 121):

(a) Grasping mouth—large, with sharp teeth both on the jaw bones and often on the vomerines and the palatine bones. Gill rakers short, few, and serving only to protect the gill plates from harm by the food, but not for straining off food organisms; intestine usually short, stomach usually differentiated; this group includes the predators: **pike-perch**, sheat-fish, pike, and many others.

(b) Mouth forming a sucker—no jaws, teeth in the form of horny tubercles; a "tooth" also present on the tongue, which is the basic boring organ; this group includes the semiparasitic lampreys and hagfish.

(c) Imbibing mouth—in the form of a tube of variable length, sometimes extensible, usually toothless; usually feeding on bottom invertebrates, less commonly on invertebrates in the water; this group includes, for example, the Mormyridae, bream, pipefish, and a number of others.

(d) Crushing mouth—sometimes in the form of a beak (trunkfish), with powerful teeth, sometimes plate-like (skates, devil-fish) or spines (catfish); usually serves for crushing the hard armature of invertebrates such as molluscs, echinoderms, corals.

(e) Planktophagic mouth—usually large or of medium size and immobile; teeth small or completely lacking; gill-rakers long, acting as a net (Fig. 122). This group includes the herring, whitefish, some cyprinoids, etc.

(f) Periphyton-eating mouth—feeding on water weeds; placed on the lower side of the head, shaped like a transverse crack, lower lip usually has a sharp cutting edge, sometimes with a horny covering; teeth usually lacking; this group includes the nase, species of *Varicorhinus*, *Schizothorax*, etc.

These basic types of mouth structure are related to each other by a number of transitional types. As an exception, the oral aperture is reduced in some fishes, in relation to their parasitic mode of feeding, thus, the males of many Ceratiidae, such as the deep-water *Edriolychnus schmidtii* Regan, fuse the skin of the oral aperture and tongue on to the female's body and feed on the fluids transported in the blood vessels of the female. The intestine

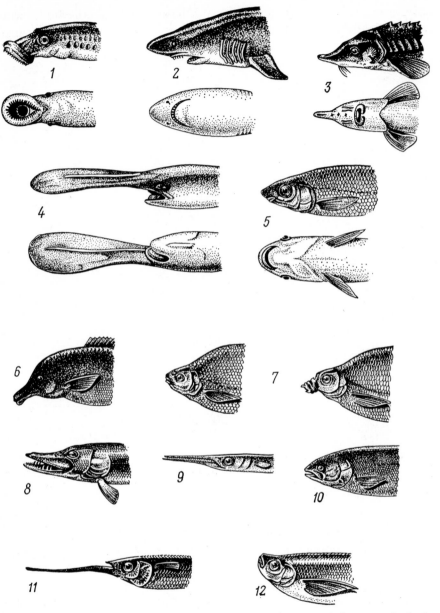

FIG. 121. Various types of mouths in fishes and cyclostomes. 1, lamprey; 2, shark; 3, sturgeon; 4, paddlenose; 5, nase (*Chondrostoma nasus* L.); 6, *Mormyrus;* 7, bream; 8, pike; 9, saury pike; 10, salmon; 11, *Hyporhamphus sajori* (Temm. et Schl.); 12, *Pelecus cultratus* (L.).

degenerates in these fishes. The females feed normally, like other fishes, and their digestive organs do not undergo any changes.

In connection with the mode of feeding, not only the structure of the mouth but its position also varies (Fig. 123). The mouth may be dorsal, i.e. lying above the body axis [*Pelecus cultratus* (L.)]; terminal, placed on the body axis (dace, herrings, and many other fishes); ventral, lying on the underside of the body (skates, sturgeons, and many others).

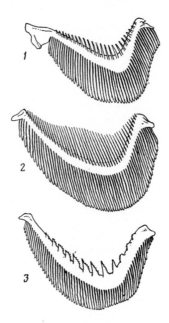

FIG. 122. Gill-rakers of planktophagic and predatory fishes. 1, The Neva whitefish *Coregonus lavaretus* L.; 2, *Coregonus muksun* (Pall.); 3, pike-perch *Lucioperca lucioperca* L. The first two species feed on planktonic crustacea. For purposes of comparison, the gill-arch of a predator, the pike-perch, is shown.

The method of capture of food by fishes is extremely variable. The majority of predators seize their prey whole, sometimes across the body, squeeze it slightly, and then eject it, so that they can again seize it by the head. Some predators, for example, the African lungfish *Protopterus* or the pirhana *Rooseveltiella*, bite pieces of flesh out of their prey. Very many bentho-phagic and planktophagic fishes suck their food into the buccal cavity together with a current of water. Finally, fishes which feed on water-weeds scrape them with their lower lips, which are usually sharpened. Certain trunkfishes and skates which feed on sessile organisms bite them off the substrate.

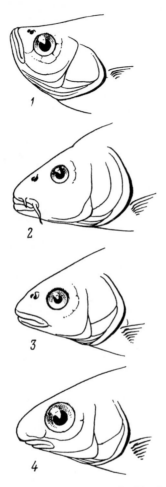

FIG. 123. Various positions of the mouth in cyprinoids, from top to bottom. 1, Dorsal mouth, *Pelecus cultratus* L.; 2, terminal mouth, *Cyprinus carpio* L.; 3, semiventral mouth, *Rutilus rutilus caspicus* Jak.; 4, ventral mouth, *Capoetobrama kuschakewitschi* (Kessl.).

The structure of the pharynx is also closely related to the feeding behaviour of the fish. As already stated, the number and structure of the gill-rakers can vary considerably, from a few small hard tubercles in predatory fishes to a complex network of numerous rakers in fishes such as *Hypophthalmichthys molitrix* Val., which feeds on planktonic algae. In the mullets, Mugilidae, the pharyngeal muscles are adapted to compressing the food bolus, which consists of detritus and weeds. A number of fishes possess teeth on the pharyngeal bones. The teeth may occur on both the dorsal and the ventral bones of the pharynx, as, for example, in the Labridae, or else only on the lower ones, as in the cyprinoids.

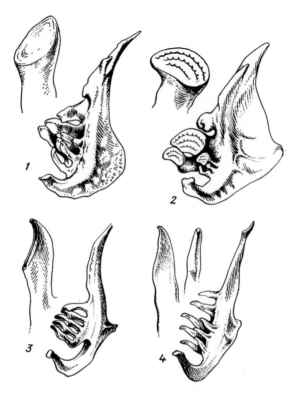

FIG. 124. Pharyngeal teeth of cyprinoid fishes. 1, The Aral Sea barbel, *Barbus brachycephalus* Kessl.; 2, the carp, *Cyprinus carpio* L.; 3, the bream, *Abramis brama* L.; 4, the aspe, *Aspius aspius* L.

Haeckel (1843) (Vasnetsov, 1953) divides the lower pharyngeal teeth of the cyprinoids according to their structure, in relation to their function, into four types: (1) hollowed out—*excavati*, the barbel type; (2) masticatory—*masticatori*, the carp type; (3) hook-shaped with a masticatory platform—*uncinato submolares*, the bream type; (4) hook-shaped without a masticatory platform —*uncinato conici*, the chub and aspe type (Fig. 124). These types are, in turn, subdivided in greater detail. Cyprinoid fishes have a small callosity formed of horny epithelium, above the lower pharyngeal teeth on the under side of the skull. The lower pharyngeal teeth work against this callosity.

The pharyngeal teeth change during the ontogeny of the fish in relation to changes in the food of the fish. In larval bream and carp they are conical; in the adult bream they are hook-shaped with a masticatory platform, in the adult carp they are masticatory.

The structure of the intestine is closely related to the peculiarities of the buccal and pharyngeal apparatus. Predators have a large mouth, short and few gill-rakers, a large stomach, usually a large number of pyloric caecae, and a short intestinal tract. The connection between the gill-rakers and the pyloric caecae is well shown in the example of the Caspian shads (Table 24).

TABLE 24

Relation between the Feeding Behaviour and the Number of Gill-Rakers and Pyloric Caecae in Caspian Shads (from Svetovidov, 1953)

Species of shad	Average number of gill-rakers	Average number of pyloric caecae	Food
Dolginka, *Caspialosa brashnikovi*	34·2	51·2	Fish
Large-eyed shad, *Caspialosa saposhnikovi*	30·4	45·9	Fish
Kessler's shad, *Caspialosa kessleri*	72·4	48·2	Fish and plankton
Volga shad, *Caspialosa volgensis*	125	44·3	Fish and plankton
Caspian shad, *Caspialosa caspia*	116	40·8	Planktonic crustaceans

The size of the stomach in fishes is closely related to the feeding behaviour and, particularly, to the size of prey. In fishes which swallow large prey, or else consume large amounts of food at the same time, the stomach is usually large. In predatory fishes, not only is the food bolus broken up and partially digested in the stomach, but the prey is sometimes also killed there, a process in which hydrochloric acid plays an important part. The function of the sometimes numerous pyloric caecae in predators is apparently primarily connected with the neutralization of the food, on its passage from the stomach into the intestine, because, as is well known, the reaction in the stomach is acid, and that in the intestine alkaline.

Absorption takes place in the pyloric caecae, which also have an enzymatic function. The number of pyloric caecae varies even within a single species in relation to the type of food consumed. Thus, the white Baikal grayling, which feeds mostly on fish, has an average of 19·1 caecae, while the black grayling, which feeds mostly on amphipods and caddis larvae, has 15·3 (Svetovidov, 1953).

The length of the digestive tract is also closely related to the type of food. Among fishes which have no stomach (cyprinoids), the intestine comprises less than 100 % of the length of the body in carnivores, and more than 100 % in herbivores. In adult cyprinoids the relative length of the intestines varies from 60 % of the body length in the Indian *Chela bacaila* Ham. to 1500 % in

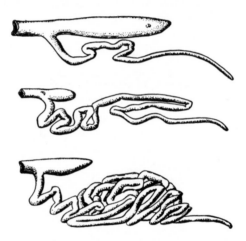

FIG. 125. Intestines of various representatives of the fam. Cichlidae (Perciformes). Top to bottom, a predator, *Cichla temensis* Gumboldt; a carnivore, *Geophagus brasiliensis* Quoyi et Gaimard; a herbivore, *Tilapia heudeloti* Dumeril (from Pellegrin, 1921).

the Amur bighead *Hypophthalmichthys molitrix* Val. (Das and Moitra, 1958). A similar picture is also seen in fishes which possess a stomach. As Fig. 125 shows, in different members of the Cichlidae the predator *Cichla temensis* Gumb. has a large stomach and short intestine, while the herbivore *Tilapia heudeloti* Dumeril has a small stomach and a long intestine.

An increase in the absorbing surface of the intestine is obtained not only through its elongation. In ancient fishes (sharks, sturgeons, ganoids), the absorbing surface of the intestine is increased by means of a spiral valve; in certain other fishes, as, for example, the Amur nase, *Xenocypris macrolepis* Blkr., which in the adult stage feeds on detritus, it is increased by the development of longitudinal folds in the intestine.

Substantial changes take place in the structure and function of the intestine as the fish grows. Thus, in the larvae of *Hypophthalmichthys*, which feed on zooplankton, the intestine is short, comprising less than 100 % of the body length (Fig. 126), while in the adult, as stated above, it is fifteen times as long as the body (Verigin, 1950). Naturally, the mode of action of the enzymes in passive and predatory fishes also differs (Table 25).

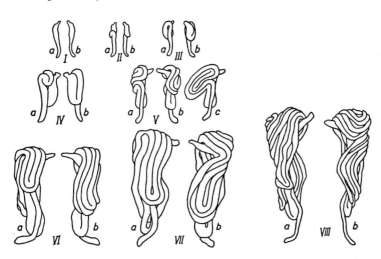

FIG. 126. Growth changes in the intestinal tract of the white bighead, *Hypophthalmichthys molitrix* (Val.) (from Verigin, 1950). a, Viewed from the left; b, viewed from the right; I, Intestine of a larva 8 mm in length (stage III); II, intestine of a larva 9 mm in length (stage IV); III, intestine of a larva 11 mm in length (end of stage IV); intestine of a larva 14·5 mm in length (end of stage V); V, intestine of a young fish 15·5 mm in length (start of stage VI); c, viewed from the left with the loops of the right side turned out to the left; VI, intestine of a young fish of length 48 mm (end of stage VI); VII, intestine of a young fish of length 52 mm (start of stage VII); VIII, intestine of a fish 243 mm in length.

The enzymes of passive and predatory fishes differ not only in their distribution, but in the strength of their action as well. Thus, the amylase which digests carbohydrates is 150 times as strong in its action in the carp as in the pike.

The activity of the enzymes also varies in the same fish. In predatory fishes the acidity of the stomach juices increases greatly when the prey has been swallowed. Thus, in the sea-scorpion, *Myoxocephalus scorpius* L., the pH is 4·0–7·4 in the empty stomach, and falls to 2·8–2·2 when the stomach is full of food, i.e. the acidity increases sharply.

Certain other properties of the enzymes are also variable: thus, in closely related species in arctic and temperate latitudes the cold-resistance of some of the enzymes varies, usually being greater in the cold-water fishes than in those which live in warmer waters (Koshtoyants and Korzhuev, 1934). There are also changes in the enzymatic activity in the ontogeny of the fish. Thus in the intestines of larval carp there are special cells which secrete an enzyme which digests crustaceans (*Cyclops* and *Daphnia*) even before the development of the subgastric glands, which secrete the necessary enzymes in the adult fish.

TABLE 25

Enzymes of the Intestinal Tract in Passive and Predatory Fishes (Wunder, 1936)

| Feeding behaviour | Organ | Enzymes which digest | | |
		Carbohydrates	Fats	Proteins
Predatory fish (with stomach)	Stomach	—	—	Pepsin, hydrochloric acid
	Digestive glands	Amylase	Lipase	Tripsin
	Intestine	—	—	Enterokinase, erypsin
Passive fish (without stomach)	Digestive glands	Amylase, maltase	Lipase	Tripsin
	Intestine	—	—	Enterokinase, erypsin

Not only does the chemistry of the digestive processes differ in passive and predatory fishes, but there are also differences in the mechanics of the destruction of the food bolus. While in predatory fish the bolus is broken up only in the stomach (cod, Cottidae), in passive fishes, even those which possess a stomach, such as the flounder *Pleuronectes flesus* L., the food bolus is also broken up in the intestine (Karpevich and Bokova, 1936–37).

The size of the food particles ingested by various species of predatory fishes also varies considerably. Sometimes, particularly in deep-water fishes, such as *Chiasmodus*, the prey may be two or more times as large as the predator. The relation between the size of the prey and that of the predator is subject to very strong variation even among individuals of the same species. In the majority of predators, the number of food objects found together in the stomach usually decreases as the fish grows, while the relative size of the separate food objects swallowed increases.

Thus, the young pike in the first stages of active feeding uses planktonic crustaceans as food and develops satisfactorily on these. But very soon the amount of energy expended on the capture of the crustaceans starts to exceed their calorific value, and the pike then starts to feed on young fish. If the pike is retained on a diet of planktonic crustaceans, it gradually ceases to grow, and eventually dies. In the adult pike the size of the prey increases as the fish grows (Fig. 127).

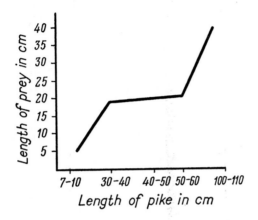

FIG. 127. Changes in the relative sizes of prey eaten by the pike in relation to its growth.

In certain other fishes, however, the relative size of the food objects decreases as the fish grows. We have already said that the larval bighead feeds on planktonic crustaceans, while the adult feeds on planktonic algae, particularly diatoms.

The linear size of the food is also closely related to its shape. Predatory fishes consume cylindrical-shaped fishes of larger size than the high-bodied fish which they also eat.

The size of the food used by a fish depends on a number of factors, the main ones being the calorific value of the food and the energy which has to be expended by the fish in capturing it. The value of a given type of food for a given fish is assessed on the basis of its nutritional coefficient.

The nutritional coefficient of the food is the ratio of the weight of the food consumed by the fish to the growth in weight. In the adult pike-perch, *Lucioperca lucioperca* L., feeding on fishes, an increase in weight of one unit is obtained from the consumption of seven units of food. The roach, *Rutilus rutilus caspicus* Jak., feeding on molluscs, gives an increase in weight of one unit for the consumption of 40–43 units of food, and feeding on a mixed diet of crustaceans plus molluscs requires 20–26 units of food.

The nutritional coefficient varies considerably according to the concentration of the food organisms. The nutritional coefficient for young sturgeons feeding at a concentration of 1030 *Diaptomus* per litre is 8·8, while at a concentration of 5134 of these crustaceans per litre it is 4·1 (Karzinkin, 1952). The nutritional coefficient also changes as the fish grows. The ratio between the maintenance and the growth parts of the food changes in favour of maintenance as the fish grows. Growth food is used for increasing the mass of the body. The maintenance food is that part which supports the metabolism but not growth.

In the young sturgeon, *Acipenser güldenstädtii* Brandt, feeding on crustaceans, the nutritional coefficient changes in the following way as the fish grows (Karzinkin, 1952):

Age of fish from start of external feeding (days)	3–11	21	31	36	74–81
Nutritional coefficient	2·1	2·7	2·8	4·0	5·1
Coefficient of the production effect	2·5	2·3	2·4	3·0	2·5

However, a more correct assessment of the actual value of foods and their assimilation is given by the coefficient of the production effect, which represents the amount of nutritional material which is required to produce one unit increase in weight of the same substance. This coefficient is usually expressed as the ratio of the dry weight of the food consumed to the increase in dry weight of the fish.

The nutritional coefficient and the production effect depend upon what percentage of the food consumed is assimilated. A lower fraction of the food is usually assimilated when the food is abundant than when it is scarce.

The state of nourishment of the fish is usually expressed in terms of the index of fullness of the gut, which is the ratio of the dry weight of the contents of the digestive tract to the body weight of the fish. Some authors express this ratio as a percentage (Nikitinsky, 1929, etc.) while others represent it in decimilles ($^\circ/_{ooo}$) (Zenkevich, 1933; Shorygin, 1952, etc.).

For the representation of the feeding intensity of the fish it is necessary to know not only the value of the index of fullness, but also the diurnal rhythm of feeding and the rate of passage of the food through the gut (Novikova, 1949).

The diurnal rhythm of feeding depends, as stated above, on the method by which the fish orientates toward its food, and it is also very closely connected to the behaviour of the food organisms, as also is the diurnal dynamics of the composition of the food. In the Aral Sea the bream feeds at night very intensively on the chironomid larvae which come to the sea-bed surface then, and which go down to a deeper level in the deposit by day; by day the bream feeds mainly on amphipods which rise at night into the upper levels of the water. A rhythm of feeding is found in fishes whether they consume large or small prey.

The periodicity in food consumption is not the same for all fishes. Thus, in the Caspian roach, food consumption takes place approximately every 4 hours (Bokova, 1940), while in predatory fishes that eat large prey, the intervals in the consumption of food may be more than a day.

The amount of food consumed daily depends, as does the annual amount consumed, on the quality of the food. Thus, the yearling pike consumes daily an amount of Cyclops equivalent to 160–175 % of its body weight, of enchytraeids 150–330 %, bloodworms 150–250 %, amphipods 110–120 %, fish 30–50 % (Scholtz, 1932). The adult Caspian roach at a temperature of 20°C consumes molluscs (*Dreissena*) up to 28–43 % of its body weight, and crustaceans (Mysidacea) 17 % (Bokova, 1938).

The rate of consumption of food is also closely connected with the condition of the fish itself. Many fishes cease to feed at their spawning times. A well-fed, satiated fish usually feeds less intensively than a thin, underfed one. In the Aral Sea in the autumn, the bream, with a condition coefficient of 2·3, has an index of fullness averaging 197 %, while a bream with a condition coefficient of 2·5 has an index of fullness averaging 86 %, i.e. it is feeding at half the intensity. Many migratory fishes cease to feed during their migration up-river (see above).

The seasonal rhythm in food consumption has been evolved as an adaptation to changes in the abiotic conditions. As was stated above (see page 260), a worsening of the oxygen conditions in the period of ice-cover causes benthophagic fishes to cease feeding. The feeding intensity also changes in relation to variations in the food-supply. Thus, for example, in the Volga delta the adult common sheat-fish, *Silurus glanis* L., eats from 62–68 % of its annual ration during one spring month. This concentration in the intensity of feeding is related to the arrival of the Caspian roach to spawn in the lower reaches of the Volga. In the immature sheat-fish, in contrast to the adults, the most intensive feeding takes place in the summer months, the food consisting mostly of the young of other species of fish (Fig. 128) (Fortunatova,

1955). The fishes' supply of food thus changes through the year, and the seasonal rhythm of feeding is connected with this to a significant extent.

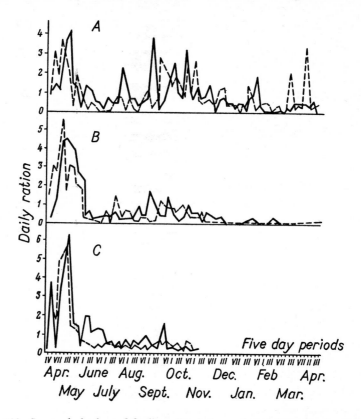

Fig. 128. Seasonal rhythm of feeding of certain predatory fishes in the Volga delta (from Fortunatova, 1955). A, Pike; B, pike-perch; C, sheat-fish. Solid line indicates the food ration in 1949–1950, broken line 1948–1949.

The term food supply* must be understood to include not only the presence of food organisms available for consumption by the fish, but also the existence of such conditions as ensure that the fish can assimilate the food and construct new tissues out of it.

If the species evolved under the conditions of a stable and plentiful food

*I consider the term "competition for food" to be an unsuitable anthropomorphism, which does not reflect the reality of the biological phenomenon. In the human sphere, competition arises over the surplus production of something, while in the animal kingdom an increase in the force of feeding relationships arises when food is scarce.

supply, then it is a stenophage, i.e. it is adapted to feeding on a narrow range of foods. Stenophagism ensures that the species expends less of its energy in searching for, seizing, and assimilating its food. But at the same time stenophagism is related to a restriction in the food supply of the species, because a stenophage, which is adapted to a narrow range of foods, is at the same time least capable of feeding on other types of food. Euryphagism has evolved as an adaptation to an unstable food supply. The euryphagic species can feed on a wider range of foods, but it expends more energy than the stenophage in obtaining each species of food. Euryphagism and stenophagism are two ways of ensuring the food supply of the species.

Changes in the food-spectrum are observed in the same population throughout the year. Usually the period of most intensive feeding occurs at the time of appearance of some mass form of food, which forms the basis of its food. Thus, for example, in the whitefish *Coregonus muksun* (Pall.), the food spectrum consists of seven basic components, with an index of fullness of 58·5 in the summer; in the winter, which is the main feeding period, the food comprises three components altogether, while the index of fullness rises to 112·0 (Pirozhnikov, 1950). A similar pattern is observed in the feeding of the sheat-fish in the delta of the Volga (see above).

In the Aral Sea in spring and autumn, the bream remains close to the coast and mostly consumes the molluscs which it finds there, while in the summer it feeds on amphipods at a distance from the coast. In the Aral Sea far from the coast, in summer, the roach scarcely eats any aerial insects, because the occurrence of a vertical temperature stratification reduces its ability to rise to the water surface; in the autumn and spring, when the surface and bottom temperatures are the same, the roach rises to the surface at night, and feeds upon the aerial insects, mostly chironomid midges, which fall into the water.

Seasonal Changes in the Relative Weight of Aerial Insects in the Food of the Roach in the Aral Sea

May	June	July	August	September
33·08 %	0·08 %	1·64 %	8·3 %	53·0 %

When there is an abundant food supply, all the fishes in a feeding shoal feed alike; when these conditions become impoverished, those fishes which differ in the structure of those organs which are connected with the capture of food start to consume different foods. Thus, for example, in conditions of good food supply all the individuals of the common gudgeon, *Gobio gobio* L.,

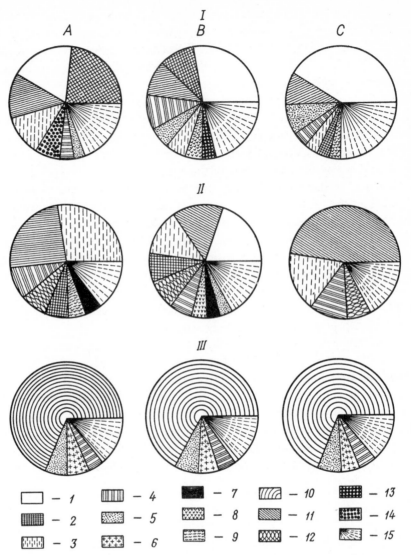

FIG. 129. Food spectra of the gudgeon in the river Moskva (from Nikolsky and Pikulev, 1958). I, Spectrum of females at the start of June; II, spectrum of males at the start of June; III, spectrum of females at the end of June. A, "Short-barbelled" gudgeon; B, "medium-barbelled" gudgeon; C, "long-barbelled" gudgeon; chironomid larvae—1, *Chironomus;* 2, *Cricotopus;* 3, *Ablabesmyia;* 4, *Tanytarsus;* 5, *Polypedilum;* 6, *Crypto-chironomus;* 7, *Tienemanniella;* 8, *Orthocladius;* 9, chironomid pupae; 10, *Limnodrilus* (Oligochaeta); 11, ephemerid nymphs, *Ordella;* 12, other ephemerid nymphs; 13, Hemiptera nymphs; 14, Ostracoda; 15, other organisms.

eat the same type of food (Fig. 129), but when these conditions become impoverished the short-barbelled individuals start to feed on one type of food, while the long-barbelled individuals feed on another type (Nikolsky and Pikuleva, 1958).

The change in the composition of the food with age is a substantial adaptation toward increasing the range of the food supply of a population, by enabling the species as a whole to assimilate a variety of foods. The ontogenetic changes in feeding are not only an adaptation toward increasing the supply of food, they are also determined by the need for the food of the organism to correspond to its structure.

As will be seen from the data given below, in the goby, *Neogobius fluviatilis pallasi* (Berg), the amounts of the various crustaceans in the food change very greatly with the age of the fish: the quantity of amphipods increases with age, while the proportion of mysids decreases (Kinalev, 1937).

Changes in the Percentage of Various Components of the Food with the Growth of *Neogobius fluviatilis pallasi* (Berg)

Size of fish (cm)	5–7	7–9	9–11	11–13	13–15
Amphipods	16·8 %	32·0 %	35·1 %	67·1 %	74·4 %
Mysids	24·3 %	11·8 %	3·0 %	4·0 %	0·0 %

In the majority of fishes there is a widening of the food spectrum and an increase in the numbers of components in the food, as they grow and change from one stage of development to the next. This is equally characteristic for both planktophages and benthophages. An example in illustration is the increase in the variety of food of the Amur ide, *Leuciscus waleckii* Dyb., as it grows:

Length of fish (mm)	5–10—20—30—40	adults
Number of components in food	2 7 8 8	12

A different pattern is observed only for those herbivorous fishes in which there is a changeover in ontogeny from animal to plant food, because, in contrast to the previous group of fish, the food supply is greater for older fish. As an example of this, we have the change in the food spectrum of a detritophage, *Xenocypris macrolepis* Blkr., in which, during its stage of feeding on animals and mixed food, the variety of its food is much greater than when it is feeding on detritus:

Size of fish (cm)	1·0–2·5	3·5	4·5	5·5	8·0	9·0	10	adult
Number of components in its food	6	4	4	4	–	3	2	2

A decrease in the food supply is often accompanied by an increase in the variability of growth and the size composition, as a result of which the food spectrum of the species as a whole is broadened, because the smaller fishes consume one type of food and the larger ones another (Poliakov, 1958). This enables the population as a whole to assimilate a wider range of foods.

The divergence in the composition of the food of males and females is a substantial adaptation to an increase in the food supply. Often this divergence is connceted with a difference in the structure of the digestive organs, as, for example, in the numbers of pyloric caecae, as in certain salmon.

The males of *Pseudorasbora parva* Schl. consume larger quantities of midge larvae of the genera *Glyptotendipes* and *Cricotopus*, while the females consume more of *Limnochironomus*; the males of the Azov Sea bream, as already stated, consume larger quantities of *Hypaniola kovalevsky* Annenk., and the females more *Nereis succinea* and chironomid larvae.

Many fishes, especially planktophages, feed in shoals (see page 90); these fish locate their food and feed more intensively in shoals. Benthophages and many predators, in contrast, feed less intensively in shoals than when isolated. For the bream it was noted (Vorobiev, 1937) that its young feed more intensively when greatly concentrated than in smaller concentrations, while the adult fish, in contrast, lowers its intensity of feeding when substantially concentrated (Fig. 130). As in the bream, so in the cod—as the concentration of the adult fishes increases, the intensity of food consumption decreases (Zenkevich, 1931).

The goldfish feeds less intensively in shoals than in isolation, but the converse holds for the American sheat-fish, *Amiurus nebulosus* Le Sueur (Nikolsky and Kukushkin, 1943).

The fish eats those types of food which it can capture most easily, i.e., on which it is adapted to feeding.

The food of fishes may be divided into several categories according to the relationship between the fishes and their food, though this is to some extent subjective: (1) basic food—that which the fish usually consumes, comprising the main part of the gut contents; (2) secondary food—frequently found in the guts of fishes, but in smaller amounts; (3) incidental food—only rarely enters the guts of fish. It is also necessary to distinguish the category obligatory food, which the fish consumes in the absence of the basic food.

In defining the selectivity of the fish in respect to any particular type of food the selection coefficient is used, which is obtained by dividing the percentage of each type of food in the gut of the fish by the percentage of the same type of food in the association on which the fish is feeding (for planktophagic fishes, in the catch of the plankton net; for benthophages, in samples taken with a grab; for predators, in the trawl catch). If the selection coefficient is greater than unity, this means that the food is being selected by the fish; if it is less than unity, the food is being avoided (Shorygin, 1939; Zheltenkova, 1939, etc.). But the use of this coefficient must not be approached mechanically; it is essential to take into account a number of factors which

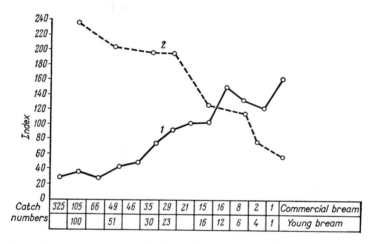

Catch numbers	325	105	66	49	46	35	29	21	15	16	8	2	1	Commercial bream
		100		51		30	23		16	12	6	4	1	Young bream

Fig. 130. Changes in the rate of feeding of the bream in relation to its density on the feeding grounds. 1, Adults; 2, young fish (from Vorobiev, 1937).

obscure the natural pattern. First of all, it is necessary to consider the type of gear which is used to make the collection. For example, a slowly towed trawl allows the faster fishes to escape from it, which affects the proportions of the prey species in the association, and thereby the selection coefficient. The grab very often scares bottom organisms away by a current of water when it is lowered to the bottom, which also affects the actual proportions of the food species. All the same, it is often possible to obtain very interesting data. Thus, for example, the basic food of the pike-perch in the open parts of the Aral Sea is *Pelecus cultratus* (L.), for which the selection coefficient has an enormous value—24·2; while the selection coefficient for the bream in the food of the pike-perch is 0·37, i.e. the bream is clearly avoided as an object of food by the pike-perch. The preferred foods of the Caspian roach are the mollusc *Dreissena* (coefficient 13·5), *Adacna* (7·3), and Corophiidae (39·3).

Naturally, the coefficient depends both on the behaviour of the food species and the abiotic conditions in which the fish feeds, as well as on the state of the fish itself. The different fishes which feed on benthos penetrate to different depths into the bottom. Among fresh water fishes the deepest penetrating is the carp (Fig. 131) (Suetov, 1939). Naturally, the availability of the food also depends on the firmness of the deposit. The fish can penetrate deeper into softer deposit (Fig. 132).

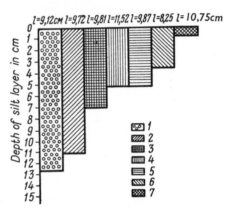

Fig. 131. Depth of penetration into the ground by various species of benthophagic fishes (from Suetov, 1939). 1, Carp; 2, ruffe; 3, tench; 4, bream; 5, roach; 6, crucian carp; 7, perch.

The food obtained by the fish, and also the size of the fish stocks, are to a significant extent related to the size of the food supply. Some authors have even attempted, by using the value of the biomass of the fish-food, to calculate the fish production of a water-mass. In particular, the Swedish investigator Alm (1922, 1924) introduced the coefficient F/B, where F is the fish production and B the biomass of the benthos; this ratio Alm called the "Fischerei Benthos produktion Koefficient." However, later workers have shown that the relationship is considerably more complicated, and it is not possible to relate directly figures concerning the live biomass of a non-fish population to the value for the mass of fish flesh (Karzinkin, 1935, 1952), although, of course, the biomass of food is one of the indices of the fish production of a water-mass.

Problems concerning the feeding of fishes have an enormous significance in fish husbandry. One encounters them in the solution of nearly all the most important problems related to the raw basis of the fishing industry.

Rational pond cultivation of fishes is inconceivable without a knowledge of the basic problems of the nutrition of fishes.

The taxation of water-masses by fisheries cannot be successfully carried on if no account is taken of the distribution and seasonal dynamics, and the consumption by fishes of the food resources in them.

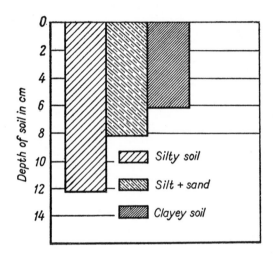

FIG. 132. Depth of penetration by carp into various deposits in search of food (from Suetov, 1939).

Acclimatization projects, concerned with the planting of water-masses with both fishes and their food species, should only be carried out after a detailed study of the feeding interrelationships and food supply of the fishes in the water-mass.

The explorations which are carried out for the study of the distribution of commercial fishes in the sea are at present largely based on a knowledge of the distribution of the food species.

The construction of a rational method of exploiting a stock of commercial fishes would be impossible without a knowledge of the manner in which the fish exploits its food resources, of the nature of the interrelationships between the fish and others which consume the same food, and also of predators.

PART III

THE SIGNIFICANCE OF FISHES IN THE LIFE OF MANKIND AND THE BIOLOGICAL BASIS OF A RATIONAL FISHERY

Part III

THE SIGNIFICANCE OF FISHES IN THE LIFE OF MANKIND AND THE BIOLOGICAL BASIS OF A RATIONAL FISHERY

FISHES HAVE a great significance in the life of mankind, being a most important source of protein and providing certain other useful products. The total present world catch of fish and other aquatic organisms reaches the enormous figure of about 30 million metric tons. In various countries fish forms from 17 to 83 % of the protein intake of mankind. Fish plays a most important role in the economics of many countries. The world catch of fish is still increasing. Between 1949 and 1957 the world catch of fish and other aquatic organisms increased from 22 to 29·96 million metric tons.

Mankind exerts both a direct and an indirect effect upon fishes. The direct effect is expressed in the form of the catch, and the indirect effect through changes in the aquatic environment.

The catch exerts a very large influence on the stock of commercial fishes. By reducing it, the catch changes the feeding conditions for the remaining part of the stock. An excessive catch destroys the reproductive capacity of the stock and leads to overfishing.

Overfishing in a biological sense is a condition of the stock in which, due to excessive catches, the numbers of individuals which are capable of reproducing under the optimal (average) conditions cannot ensure the maintenance of the stock, i.e. when the reproductive capacity of the population cannot compensate for the losses due to fishing.

Overfishing in an economic sense is a condition of the stock of a commercial species in which, as a result of excessive catches, the abundance of the stock is reduced to such a level that the fishery becomes unprofitable, i.e. the effort expended in catching the fish starts to outweigh its value.

There are numerous examples of the reduction of stocks of fishes due to excessive fishing. A characteristic example would be the history of the fishery for the soupfin shark on the Pacific coast of the U.S.A., or of that for the tiger flathead *Neoplatycephalus microdon* Ogilby, on the Australian coast. The indirect influence of mankind on the ichthyofauna is extremely variable. When forests are felled in the area of a watershed the character of the run-off is altered. The spring floods become much higher and shorter, while the river becomes shallower, which first affects the summer and autumn spawning fishes and the overwintering conditions in the rivers. By partitioning off the rivers with dams and creating reservoirs, man on the one hand destroys the conditions for the reproduction of migratory fishes, by barring them from access to their spawning grounds, sometimes actually destroying the spawning grounds, because they are under a head of water and often become silted up. On the other hand, the reservoirs frequently provide more favourable conditions for the life of limnophil fishes than there were in the former streams, and these fishes increase in abundance. At the same time the conditions for rheophil fishes often deteriorate, and these are forced to enter the tributaries. Finally, the formation of a reservoir greatly affects the flow of water in the rivers, which changes the conditions for the reproduction of semi-migratory fishes, as, for example, those of the bream, carp, pike-perch, etc. in the lower reaches of the Volga and the Don. The area of the flood-meadows in which these fish spawn is reduced, the duration of the flood period is changed, and this is naturally reflected in the reproduction of these fishes. The total volume of the flow is also changed, in connection with which there may be a fall in the level of land-locked seas and lakes (such as the Caspian, Aral, etc.), while there may be an increase in the salinity of the estuarine parts of seas and salt-lakes into which regulated waters discharge. The biological stock also changes. A significant part of the biogenic elements accumulates in the reservoirs and is no longer carried out by the rivers into the sea, which causes the food supply of the fishes in these estuarine regions to be greatly reduced. This did, in fact, take place in the Sea of Azov as a result of the construction of the Tsimliansk hydroelectric scheme. Naturally, the reduction of the food supply affects the growth rate, fat content, fecundity, and other properties of the commercial fishes.

The pollution of the water by various substances (see page 31) also has a serious adverse effect on fishes. Pollution destroys the reproductive conditions, and it also disrupts the metabolism of fishes and leads to the mortality of the fishes' food organisms. In a number of cases mechanical pollution may also be caused by refuse, as, for example, the products of timber-rafting. This latter type of pollution has a particularly bad effect on rivers in which the salmon spawn.

There are many other forms of influence of mankind upon the ichthyofauna and the fish resources of waters. By joining different water-masses with canals, man facilitates the spread of aquatic organisms. Thus, for example, twelve species of fish were able to enter the Mediterranean Sea through the Suez Canal from the coast of Eritrea (Ekman, 1935). Other animals also spread along the same route. Not only reservoirs, but numerous other artificial water-masses, such as ponds, irrigation channels, etc., become populated with fish. In this way man facilitates the increase in numbers of fish and in the area of their distribution.

The meaning of a rational fishery is a fishery conducted in such a way as to ensure the maximum production of fish of the highest possible quality with the minimum expenditure of effort and materials. The widespread productivity of the stock of commercial fish and maximum catches are thereby assured. The maximum productivity does not occur just once but is repeated from year to year. It should be borne in mind that a particular level of fishing corresponds to its own particular maximum production. The more perfect the conduct of the fishery, the higher is the productivity of the stock of commercial fish. The rational fishery must be constructed on a scientific basis.

Ichthyology, and particularly the ecology of fishes, should facilitate the solution of the fundamental problems of the biological basis of fisheries. All the links in the industrial exploitation and production of the resources of fisheries should be based on a knowledge of the mode of life of the fishes.

In order to ensure the highest catches, it is essential to take control of the factors which determine both the reduction and the increase of the stocks.

The fundamental causes of the reduction of stocks include consumption by predators, mortality due to diseases and to the activities of mankind, especially by fishing. As stated above, the population of every species is adapted to a certain relative rate of mortality (which fluctuates naturally in relation to the condition of the population), and, therefore, the smaller the effect of predators upon the commercial stocks, the greater the amounts that can be removed in the form of catch. Consequently, it is often possible to increase the outcome of commercial production significantly by restricting the influence of predators on the population.

However, there is no simple approach to the solution of this problem. It cannot be assumed that because a predator consumes a species of commercial fish, the predator should be exterminated. Usually the predators consume not only the commercial fishes, but noncommercial species as well, which compete with the commercial species for their food. Extermination of the predator would therefore remove its influence on both the commercial and the noncommercial species, thereby affecting the food supply of the commercial species. Thus, for example, the char *Salvelinus* feeds on the young of both the sockeye salmon, *Oncorhynchus nerka* Walb., and the stickleback, *Pungitius pungitius* L. Extermination of the char often leads to a sharp deterioration in the feeding conditions for the young sockeye. For this reason it is often necessary to protect the young fish from the predators, rather than to exterminate the predators. There are various methods of protection. In some cases it is possible to provide special cover for the young of commercial fishes, in the form of heaps of stones or brushwood obstructions, as is done in certain lakes in the U.S.A.; in other cases it is necessary to make access to the places where the young fishes concentrate difficult for the predators. For example, a serious predator on young salmon of the genus *Oncorhynchus* in the Amur is the salmonid *Brachymystax lenok* (Pall.), which feeds on the young salmon for a brief period, mainly during their descent from the spawning grounds into the sea. At this time it is important to hinder the access of the predator into the shallow spawning rivers, which it enters in the spring from the deep plains rivers where it overwinters. After the major part of the young migrant salmon have descended, the *Brachymystax* is brought into use as a consumer of the minnow, *Phoxinus*, which feeds to a large extent on the same food as the young salmon in the spawning rivers. And since the *Brachymystax* is itself a valuable commercial fish, its destruction would be wasteful.

In certain cases, especially when the predator is a stenophage, feeding mainly on a commercial species of fish, but with little commercial value itself, it is necessary to limit its abundance. It is particularly important to catch the predator at the time and in the places where it feeds most intensively on the commercial species, for example, in the delta of the Volga and in places where the young of commercial fishes are released from hatcheries, or in the estuary of the Amur outside the mouths of the salmon spawning rivers, at the time of the seaward migration of the young salmon. By regulating the influence of predators (including invertebrate predators) it is possible to increase the productivity of a stock of fishes substantially. However, the methods of restricting the effect of predators can only be worked out on a basis of a knowledge of the ecology of the commercial fish, especially its biotic relationships, and the ecology of the predators which consume the commercial species whose productivity it is desired to increase.

In certain cases a reduction in the amount of mortality due to diseases could play a substantial part in the system of measures taken to increase the productivity of a stock of commercial fishes. Admittedly, the mass mortality of fishes due to diseases does not usually bear a regular character, but is expressed in the form of an epizootic, and is episodic in its character, but sometimes an epizootic outbreak can cause very substantial injury to a stock of commercial fishes. Mass mortalities of fish due to disease usually occur when some biotic or abiotic relationship of the fish is altered. For this reason the control against the possibility of an epizootic outbreak and its prophylaxis should be strengthened, particularly at those times when the environmental conditions are changing.

Parasitic and other diseases of fish affect the productivity of the stock far more in an indirect way, through changes in the growth rate and reproductive capacity of the individuals. This form of influence probably has far greater significance than the direct mortality of fishes due to disease. Hatcheries and pond fish-farms are, of course, exceptions to this.

The proper organization of the fishery is a very important method of increasing the productivity of the stocks of commercial fishes. Methods of capture in which the spawned eggs and hatching larvae are killed, and also those which lead to the mass mortality of fishes, as, for example, the use of explosives or poisons, cause great injury to the fishery and substantially reduce the productivity of the stocks. In the majority of countries which have well-developed fisheries special fisheries legislation exists, which forbids the use of harmful methods and gear. The first fishery laws were initiated long ago. In India the fishery legislation was initiated even before our era. In Russia the first laws concerning the conservation of fishes were made in the time of Peter I.

The proper organization of fisheries, which would ensure high productivity of the commercial fish stocks, should include not only the prohibition of capture by methods which lead to a mass mortality and which kill the brood, but a number of other measures as well. A very important measure, which would increase the productivity of the fishery, would be the capture of the fish at the size and age that are the most profitable for the catch.

In order to obtain the maximum and perennially most stable productivity from the stock of a commercial species, it is essential to determine the size and age composition of the stock where the fish exploits its food supply most rationally, and at which the greatest productivity is obtained. For the majority of species of fish the maximum catches should by no means occur in the first age group which attains to maturity. For instance, when the main fishing on the Aral Sea bream is transferred from the 4-year olds to the 6- and 7-year olds, and the capture of the 3-year olds completely ceases, it is possible to obtain an increase in the catch of more than 30 % by weight. But before such a reconstruction of the fishery for bream can be proposed, it is necessary to study certain problems, such as:

(1) The value of the natural mortality from 4 to 7 years of age, and whether such a shift in the average age of the bream in the commercial catches would not lead to large losses due to natural mortality. For the Aral Sea bream the answer to this is in the negative.

(2) What differences are there between the offspring obtained from bream of different ages? Would such a change in the age composition of the stock lead to a deterioration in the quality of the offspring? For the final answer to this problem, naturally, a special investigation is necessary, but, to judge from the size of the eggs of bream of various ages, it is possible to say now that up to an age of 12 years the Aral Sea bream apparently gives viable sexual products, and an increase in the legal size of bream for capture does not cause any deterioration in the quality of the offspring.

(3) What sex ratio in the stock is essential in order to ensure the full viability of the offspring? It is known, for example, that if there is a shortage of males on the spawning grounds, the number of eggs fertilized decreases, and in certain cases (perch) the sex ratio in the offspring also apparently changes. Since the males and females are of different sizes in the majority of fishes, a displacement of the average size of the fish in the commercial catches in either direction will also alter the sex composition of the stock. It is essential to take account of this factor.

The problem for biologists, therefore, is the forecasting of the desirable size and age composition of the catches. This is particularly essential for fishes with a long life cycle. For fishes with a short life cycle, and usually a single spawning (anchovy, sprat, gobies, Far Eastern salmons, migratory Caspian shads), it is usually impossible to obtain any significant increase, or even any increase at all, in the productivity, by means of a reconstruction of the age-composition of the catches of the mature stock.

The realization by the fishery of the projected desirable size composition of the stock is obtained through the choice of the corresponding type of gear (Fig. 133) with a particular size of meshes; or by organizing the fishery in particular places in which there are fish of the desirable sizes, and so on. The fishery laws should also contain corresponding minimal sizes of fish which may be captured—the "commercial size." For the majority of commercial fishes with a long life cycle (longer than 6–7 years) the present-day commercial length should be raised. A minimum mesh size, corresponding to the commercial size of the fish, should also be established, whether the gear used is of the filtering type (seine, trawl, purse seine, etc.), or net traps (stake nets, fyke nets, etc.), or of the enmeshing type (stake or floating gill nets). In certain cases, for example in the sea-fishery for salmon, it may be necessary to establish a minimum size of hooks to be used on lines. As a first approximation for the determination of the minimum permissible mesh size the nomogram of Baranov (1933) (Fig. 134) may be used. However, the size of the fish caught depends on a number of other factors besides the height of the body. The size of the fish caught by the same mesh varies in relation to the condition of the fish, i.e. there is a seasonal variation. For filtering gear the selective action of the meshes varies according to the cut and make-up of the net. Therefore, the investigation of the nature of the selective action (selectivity) of fishing gear is one of the most important problems in fishery research.

The most important method of increasing the productivity of a stock of commercial fishes is the capture of the fish when they are in the commercially most valuable condition. In the majority of fishes the fat content and state of nourishment show very strong seasonal variations. This is particularly clearly expressed in migratory species, which perform great migrations without taking any food, and also in fishes which cease to feed during their over-wintering period.

Thus, for example, the fat content of the autumn chum salmon in the mouths of the Amur is 11 %, while at the spawning grounds it is only 3 %, and the quality of the eggs obtained in the estuary is much higher than in the middle reaches of the Amur. In the large cod at the beginning of the summer following spawning, the fat content of the liver is only 3·5 % of the body weight; in the well-nourished cod in the winter it increases to 5·6 %. In the Aral Sea bream (Bervald, 1956) it is only when the basic fishery is transferred from the spring to the autumn that an increase of 15–20 % in the catches is obtained. To this must be added a great difference in the fat content. The Aral Sea bream has a considerably greater fat content in the autumn and early winter than in the spring and summer.

Thus, the fishing industry and the ichthyologist are confronted with the problem of working out a seasonal graph of the catch, and a dislocation of the fishery in space, so that the maximum catches might consist of fishes of the highest quality. For the salmon this is related to the concentration of the fishery at the mouths of rivers and along the course of approach to the mouths of rivers in the sea. For the bream it is necessary, for this purpose, to transfer the basic fishery from the second and third quarters of the year to

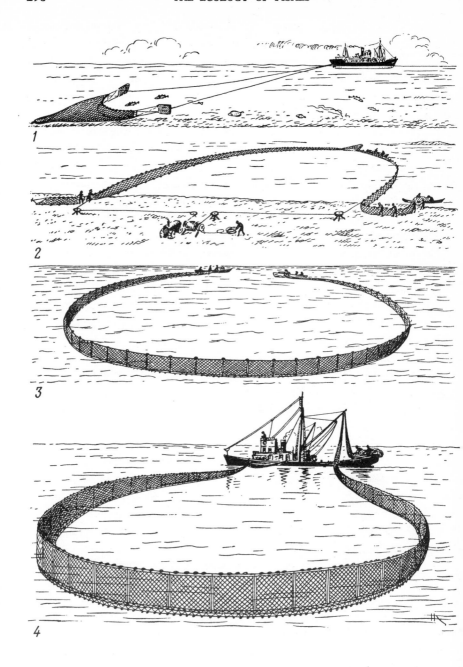

1

2

3

4

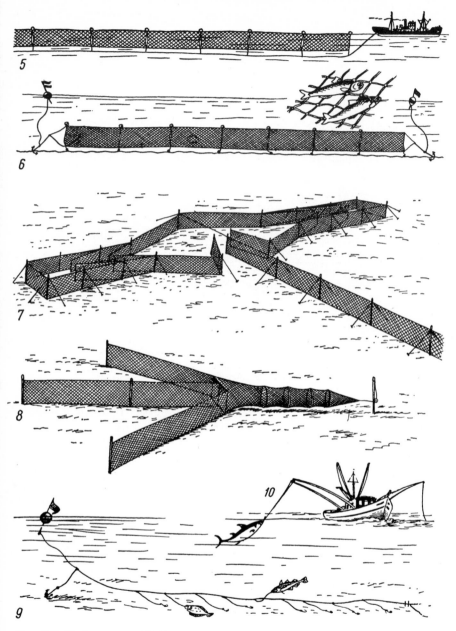

FIG. 133. Various types of fishing gear. Filtering gear—1, trawl; 2, beach seine; 3, ring seine; 4, purse seine. Enmeshing gear—5, drift net; 6, stake net. Traps—7, staked seine; 8, bag-net. Hooks—9, long-lining; 10, trolling.

the fourth and first. The working out of the seasonal course of the catch and the dislocation of the fishery would require the carrying out of a wide range of ecological investigations.

In the organization of a rational fishery it is essential to ensure not only the removal of the highest quality fishes in the greatest possible amounts, but also the necessary replacement of the stock. It is important to ensure the quality of the replacement, which must not consist of undernourished fishes. The problem boils down to the fact that all the spawning areas should be occupied by spawners, which must be able to reach them freely. The spawners which

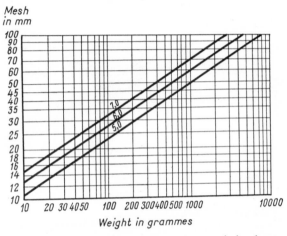

Fig. 134. Baranov's nomogram for determining the correlation between the mesh size and the sizes of fishes with various shapes of body.

are allowed access to the spawning grounds must be of high quality. It is well known that the composition of a stock of fish on the move changes with its progress. Changes occur not only in the sex ratio (males often predominate at first, and females at the end), but also in the age composition, even in morphological characteristics (in Far Eastern salmon, for example, the number of vertebrae changes). It is absolutely essential to take this into account in organizing a stratified restriction on spawning rivers, by allowing only a particular part of the stock to have access to the spawning grounds. It is very important to ensure that spawners of high quality reach the spawning grounds.

It is also essential in this respect to study the selectiveness of the fishery in relation to the quality of the spawners, and to work out measures to ensure the access of the required maternal stock to the spawning grounds. Since the composition of the spawning stock might be altered, and in some cases the quality of the brood might deteriorate, through selection by fishing gear or through allowing only a selected part of the stock to have access to the spawning grounds, serious attention should naturally be paid to this factor both in investigations and in practice.

The protection of the spawning grounds, with the aim of promoting normal reproduction, and the incubation of the eggs and development of the larvae while they remain on the spawning grounds is of considerable significance for the reproduction of commercial fishes. Successful reproduction of commercial fishes should be attained not only through restrictions on fishing at certain times on the spawning grounds, but also, for certain species of fish, by reducing the total catch during the reproductive period, with the aim of increasing the catch at other times.

A most important means of ensuring the required replacement is by the protection of the young and immature individuals from fishing. The use of young, immature individuals by industry is irrational in the majority of cases. This includes, particularly, fishing on the feeding grounds, but also fishing on the overwintering grounds.

An important problem in the construction of a rational fishery is the organization of the fishery in such a way that the population of commercial fishes is fished after it has mostly completed its feeding period and used its food supplies. If the major part of the stock is fished before the start of the feeding period, the food supplies are not fully utilized by the commercial species, and this may cause less valuable species to increase at the expense of the unused food. A number of examples of this are known from both the sea and fresh waters. For example, as a result of the intensive fishery in Peter the Great Bay the proportions of the species of flatfishes have changed, the more valuable species having been replaced by the less valuable ones. The fall in the catches of the winter flounder, *Pseudopleuronectes americanus* Walb., the basic object of the trawling industry off New England, was paralleled by an increase in the relative catches of the small skate, *Raja erinacea* Mitchill. Both these species feed on the same food. The main food of both is the amphipod *Leptocheirus*. The food supplies released by the decline of the winter flounder were consumed by the small skate (see Nikolsky, 1958). In order to avoid the replacement of a more valuable by a less valuable species in the event of an intensification of the fishery for one of the species, it is essential also to intensify the fishery for the other, less valuable ones, which consume the same food.

Thus, in organizing a rational fishery, which would ensure a high productivity of the stock of commercial fishes, besides establishing annually the permissible size of the catch, it is essential to institute the following measures:

1. The capture of fish of a size and age at which the highest production of high quality fish is ensured, and where the food supply is used most rationally

2. Ensuring the necessary replacement of the stock, in sufficient quantity and high quality, which would be obtained by allowing for the access to the spawning grounds of the necessary numbers of high-quality spawners, preserving the normal course of reproduction and of the development of larvae.

3. Capturing the fish in those places and at those times of the year when they have reached a high quality and where there are the best nourished and fattest individuals.

4. Capturing the fishes at a time when they have mostly finished their feeding period and exploited their food supplies.

These measures should be reflected in the fishery legislation, the basic aim of which is to ensure that a large production of high-quality fish is obtained from the fisheries. In those cases in which a fishery is common to a number of countries, it is essential to organize the proper exploitation of the stocks on an international scale, by means of agreements. Such agreements do exist between various countries.

However, in constructing a rational fishery one must not be restricted only to the proper organization of the reduction of the stocks through a regulated fishery and reducing the influence of predators and diseases on the population of commercial fishes. The management of the stock through reproduction and growth is also of great importance.

The management of the reproduction of commercial fishes is of particular importance when the flow of rivers is regulated, dams are constructed, and reservoirs created, but it is also important in regions in which there are no such schemes. When the conditions for reproduction are improved, the replacement is greater, and this makes larger catches possible. Work on the improvement of the production of the stocks of commercial fishes should proceed in two main directions: through improvement of the natural conditions for reproduction, and through artificial rearing of fishes in fish-farms (Cherfas, 1956).

Nearly all marine fishes and a substantial part of freshwater ones reproduce through natural spawning, and will continue to do so for very many years. In many places, however, the conditions for natural spawning have been greatly spoiled by man: the natural spawning grounds have been polluted (as, for example, those of certain herrings in the coastal zone of the sea or those of a number of freshwater fishes), or the necessary hydrological conditions have been destroyed and the food impoverished. Sometimes the access to the natural spawning grounds has been hindered, and this can take place not only where hydroelectric schemes are constructed, but also when rivers dry up, or as a result of the construction of locks, weirs, etc.

Improvement of the natural spawning grounds is not only important when these have deteriorated. It is well known that the natural spawning grounds are subjected to considerable changes, which lead to fluctuations in the yield in various years. Thus, for example, in several parts of the Far East a mass freezing up of the spawning redds and mortality of the salmon spawn occurs in dry winters when there is little snow, which causes a significant reduction in the size of the replacement. Raising the water level in the rivers during the winter by the construction of temporary dams, which are closed after the spawning is over, snow-retention on the ice of spawning rivers, and a number of other measures can reduce the harmful influence of the dry, snowless winter. Considerable harm is caused to many fish by the destruction of the spawning substrate. Shortages of spawning substrate may also occur without human interference, as for example in years of low rainfall, when the coastal weeds, which form the spawning substrate of phytophil fishes (carp), are not flooded. This phenomenon occurs, for example, in the Amur, Dunai, and other rivers.

The commercial exploitation of marine plants such as *Zostera* may destroy the spawning conditions for certain forms of oceanic herring. A shortage of spawning substrates may arise in reservoirs due to fluctuations in their level. It may also take place for lithophil fishes (salmon, Black Sea bream, *Vimba vimba*, sturgeons) when their spawning grounds become silted up or polluted.

To compensate for the destruction of natural spawning grounds several types of artificial ones may be provided. For phytophil fishes the spawning grounds may be either fixed or floating (Fig. 135). Floating spawning grounds are particularly important under the conditions of large fluctuations of water-level, when the fixed type are rather unsuitable. Woven baskets may be used as spawning substrate for fishes which construct a nest.

Artificial spawning grounds for lithophil fishes are particularly important under the conditions of a hydroelectric scheme. They may consist either of special canals, or artificial stony beds in the streams, or baskets containing stones. For lithophil fishes which bury their eggs in the ground, it is particularly important to provide the necessary conditions of a flow of water. Apart from the provision of artificial spawning grounds, an important method of increasing the effectiveness of natural reproduction is the provision of more favourable biotic and abiotic conditions on the spawning grounds.

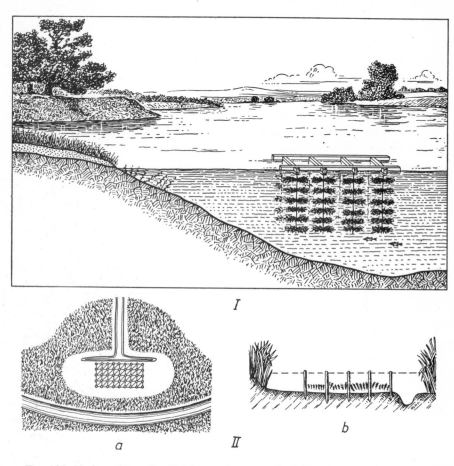

Fig. 135. Various types of artificial spawning grounds. I, Floating spawning ground for phytophil fishes; II, stationary spawning ground (for the tench): (a) plan view, (b) section.

The abiotic improvements should ensure the access of the necessary numbers of spawners to the spawning grounds by clearing obstructions and clearing channels. Abiotic improvements would provide favourable conditions for the development of the eggs and larvae (sufficient oxygen saturation, flow of water, etc.). Finally, the problem of abiotic improvement includes ensuring that the growing young fish can leave the spawning grounds and reach their feeding grounds. This would be attained by clearing obstructed channels leading from the spawning grounds, by lowering the young fishes from the separated water-bodies to the main stream, and by various other means.

The effectiveness of natural reproduction may also be raised by biotic improvements. An important link in biotic improvements is the protection of the eggs and larvae against consumption by predators and diseases, which was discussed above. An equally important, though less well-developed, method is the improvement of the food supplies on the spawning grounds. This is achieved primarily by fertilizing the water-body, thereby ensuring the most favourable conditions for the existence of the organisms on which the larvae feed. The use of green manure holds great promise at present (Karzinkin, G. S. and Karzinkin, S. G., 1955).

Naturally the biotic and abiotic improvements should be carried out not in isolation, but in the form of a unified complex. In those cases when the natural reproduction is disrupted and the various improvements do not bring about a large enough replacement of the stock of commercial fishes, it is necessary to resort to artificial rearing.

The simplest, yet often the most effective method, is to catch the larvae in a natural water-body and to rear them to a more resistant stage. This method achieves a higher survival of the larvae by comparison with the natural conditions, particularly in respect of predatory activities. However, this method can only be of any significance when the natural conditions for reproduction have not been disrupted. This method is sometimes undertaken for the rearing of fishes for sale as "domestic fishes" (Chinese roach, grass-carp, two species of bighead) in China, or for the fry of carp caught in natural waters in a number of countries.

Another widely used method is to allow commercial fishes to spawn in artificial water-bodies, the larvae being reared up to the stage when they are ready to make their descent of the river, and then being released into the natural waters. This method is in use for the artificial rearing of semi-migratory fishes, such as the bream, carp, etc., in fish-farms in the Volga delta and the lower reaches of the Don, Kuban, and other rivers. An equally important form of fish-rearing is the one in which man takes charge of the whole process from the moment of obtaining the ripe eggs and milt from the fishes, fertilizing the eggs, and incubating them until the resistant larvae are released from the hatchery into the natural water-body. This method is used primarily for rearing migratory fishes, such as sturgeons on the Kura, salmon in the north and the Far East, whitefishes, and certain others (Cherfas, 1956). In this method of rearing it is frequently necessary to keep the spawning fishes until their gonads mature, and sometimes to stimulate the release of the gametes by means of injections of the hypophyseal hormones. The eggs are incubated in special apparatus, either placed in a special location, or else set out in the stream-bed. The larvae are usually reared in special basins or ponds up to the state of migration. They are fed with artificial or natural diets. In many fish-farms there are special techniques for the cultivation of live foods—crustaceans, oligochaete worms, caterpillars. The efficiency of the work of a fish-farm is determined by the viability of the larvae which are released from it, i.e. by the size of the commercial returns. Naturally, the better the techniques employed in fish-rearing, the higher its efficiency.

An important method of raising the productivity of a water-body is by raising the supply of fish-food, and by increasing the rate of consumption of the food supplies by the fishes. Besides fertilization of the water, raising the supply of fish-food is also obtained, for example, by attracting insects to the water-body, and by providing wind-breaking plantations on the shores of the water-body, hindering the blowing away of insects, particularly chironomid midges, from the water, etc.

The nearer the useful end product (in this case, fishes) stands to the first link in the food chain, the higher the yield from the water-mass. In the link of the food chain "herbivorous fish → predatory fish" there is a loss in weight of five to ten times. An increase in the productivity of the water by reducing the number of links in the food chain can only be obtained if there is a fairly complete utilization of all the food resources in the preceding links of the food chain. Of course, in nature it is only rarely that the maximum productivity may be obtained only from the second link of the food chain, i.e. from herbivorous and detritophagic fishes. Usually part of the plants and detritus cannot be consumed by commercial fishes and serves as the food of invertebrates and noncommercial fishes, which in their turn form the food of planktophagic, benthophagic, and predatory fishes. A substantial part of the organic matter produced by plants is missed by fishes, forming muddy deposits and being partially used as food by invertebrates and even by animals which are harmful to fishes. Thus the highest productivity of a water-mass is usually obtained by means of polyculture, when the business is based on fishes which require various foods. The Chinese "domestic fishes" are an example of a very successful selection of fishes for polyculture (Fig. 136). In this combination the white bighead consumes phytoplankton, the striped

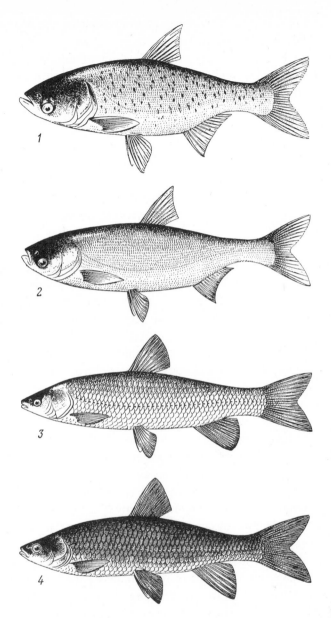

Fig. 136. Chinese "domestic" fishes. 1, Striped bighead *Aristichthys nobilis* Richardson; 2, white bighead *Hypophthalmichthys molitrix* (Val.); 3, grass-carp *Ctenopharyngodon idella* (Val.); 4, black Chinese roach *Mylopharyngodon piceus* Richardson.

bighead mainly eats zooplankton, the grass-carp higher bottom plants, and the Chinese black roach invertebrates.

In some cases it is necessary to base fish cultivation on a predator, i.e. on the final link in the food chain. Thus, for example, in many of the lake fish-farms of the Baltic states, Poland, and Germany the main product is the pike. This is inevitable when the only fishes which feed on the benthos and plankton are of little value, like small roach and perch, which give a very low-quality product.

In many cases it is possible to raise the productivity of a water-mass by introducing and acclimatizing new commercial fishes, and even food organisms for the fish. Acclimatization may be carried out by means of "supplanting," when a more valuable commercial species is introduced into the water, and uses the same foods as the less valuable or valueless members of the local fauna. In other cases the species introduced is a commercial one which feeds on types of food which are not eaten by the local fauna. This leads to the establishment of new feeding relationships, and the formation of new food niches. In the U.S.S.R. a number of acclimatizations of commercial fishes have been successfully carried out: the Aral sturgeon was introduced into Balkhash, the Sevang trout into Issik-Kul, the whitefish into the lakes of the Urals and into Lake Sevang, the mullet into the Caspian, etc.

These are the fundamental methods of raising the productivity of a water-mass. Naturally, for their implementation, as also for the organization of the proper exploitation of a stock of commercial fishes, a great deal of research is essential. Biological fishery investigations, like any others, produce the greater effect when based on the most correct theory.

The contemporary theory of the biological productivity of water-masses stems from the concept of productivity as the result of the interaction between organisms, their environment, and the form of economy including the fishing industry. The problem of productivity of water-masses should be regarded as a problem in bioeconomics. The most important element which determines the productivity is the type of economy. Of course, the natural properties of the water-mass and of the fishes which inhabit it are also of great significance in ensuring the value of the products obtained from the water, but the type of economy is the determining factor in the majority of cases.

One of the most important features which determines a rational fishery is obtaining the production for the least expenditure of effort and means. This should be attained through the use of perfect fishing gear, rapid location of concentrations of commercial fishes, and the reduction of time spent on unproductive work. The first method of orientation of the fishing fleet is through the fishing chart, on which are shown the concentrations of fishes, and also the abiotic (temperature, salinity) and biotic elements of the environment (food patches, etc.) with which the commercial fishes are associated (Figs. 137, 138, 139).

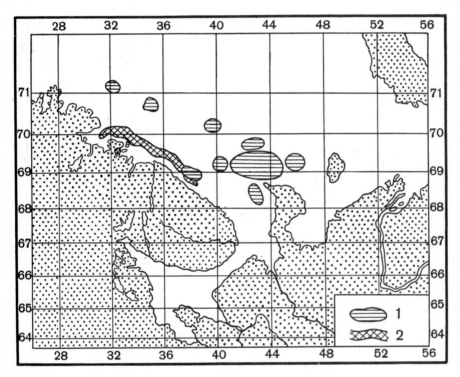

FIG. 137. Kopytov's chart. 1, Fishing banks; 2, long-lining areas.

Since the fish leads a mobile form of life, the direction of the fleet into a fishing area should be preceded by a survey for the concentrations of fish. In every large fishery region of the U.S.S.R. there is a special service of fishing survey, one of whose tasks is the exploration for concentrations of commercial fishes and leading the fishing fleet to them (Marty, 1948) (see p. 241). Various methods are used in the search for fish: trial tows with various kinds of gear, searching for the fish by means of hydroacoustic instruments, searching for concentrations of pelagic fishes from the air, and a number of other methods. Naturally the search for fish is based on a knowledge of the principles of distribution and movements of fishes, and on the experience accumulated by the industry. The perfection of the search is related to the carrying out of much research on the migrations and shoaling behaviour of fishes.

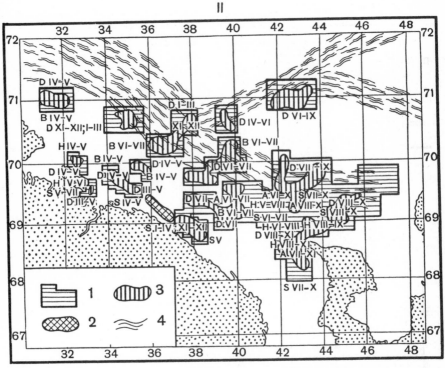

Fig. 138. Averintsev's chart. 1, Fishing banks; 2, long-lining areas; 3, areas with most abundant fish; 4, warm current streams. A, Haddock; B, redfish; D, cod; H, halibut; S, plaice. The roman figures indicate the months in which fish appear in the stated areas.

However, it is not enough to discover the concentrations of fishes; they must be caught with the least expenditure of effort and means. The concentration, perfection, and application of fishing gear is impossible without a knowledge of a number of aspects of the mode of life of the fish, and, particularly, its shoaling behaviour and the peculiarities of its sense organs, by means of which the fish orientates itself to the fishing gear.

The structure, size, colour, material, and a number of other properties of the fishing gear, and also of the region in which they are applied, are related to the mode of life which the fish leads.

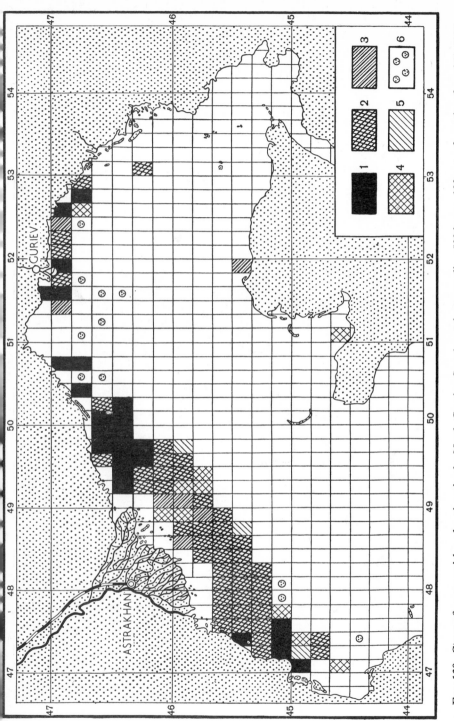

Fig. 139. Chart of commercial explorations in the North Caspian Sea. 1, catches exceeding 500 kg per 100 nets; 2, catches from 251–500 kg; 3, catches 151–250 kg; 4, catches 51–150 kg; 5, catches 1–50 kg; 6, no catches.

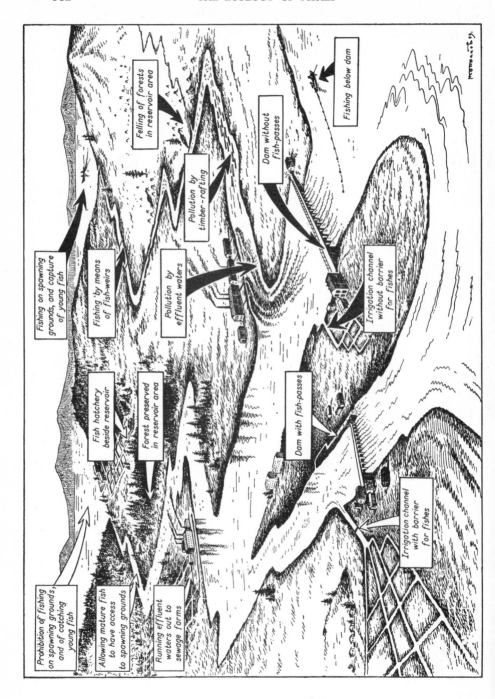

Felling of forests
in reservoir area

Fishing below dam

Dam without
fish-passes

Pollution by
timber-rafting

Fishing on spawning
grounds, and capture
of young fish

Fishing by means
of fish-weirs

Pollution by
effluent waters

Irrigation channel
without barrier
for fishes

Fish hatchery
beside reservoir

Forest preserved
in reservoir area

Dam with fish-passes

Prohibition of fishing
on spawning grounds,
and of catching
young fish

Allowing mature fish
to have access
to spawning grounds

Running effluent
waters out to
sewage farms

Irrigation channel
with barrier
for fishes

To increase the catching power of the modern types of fishing gear, to develop new gears and methods of capture, there must be a great deal of cooperative investigation by technicians and biologists. Technology alone without biology cannot lead to this improvement. In the development of the biological basis of a rational fishery, biological fisheries science and, particularly, ichthyology, have a number of important problems to solve. The leading problem at present is that of the population dynamics of fish stocks, i.e. the reproduction, growth, and mortality of the populations. The scientist's problem is to find the factors which govern this process, and to develop methods of controlling them with the aim of increasing the productivity of the stocks of commercial organisms. This can only be achieved, however, if other branches of industry take the interests of the fishing industry into account (Fig. 140).

Another most important problem which scientists are tackling is the behaviour and distribution of fishes, i.e. the adaptive significance of fish-shoals, the reactions of fishes to various stimuli, including the study of the behaviour of fishes within the zone of influence of the fishing gear.

The development of this problem presents material for the perfection of surveying methods for fishes, the concentration and employment of fishing gear, etc.

Success in the development of investigations along these lines can only be guaranteed as long as they are based on a progressive theory, as long as the general problems are investigated together with the more specific ones. In other words, the successful solution of the problems which confront the ichthyologist is possible only if it is based on the unity of theory and practice.

Bibliography

Aliavdina, L. A. (1929). Free-living nematodes as food for fishes in the Volga. *Russk. gidrobiol. Zh.* 8, no. 4, 5.

Aliavdina, L. A. (1951). The condition and distribution of the sturgeon spawning grounds in the section of the Volga between Saratov and Kamyshin. *Trans. Saratov section of Casp. Branch Inst. Fish. U.S.S.R.* 1.

Allee, W. and Bowen, E. (1932). Studies in animal aggregations: mass protection against colloidal silver among goldfishes. *J. exp. Zool.* 61.

Allen, K. (1938). Some observations on the biology of the trout (*Salmo trutta*) in Windermere. *J. Anim. Ecol.* 7, 2.

Alm, G. (1924). Die quantitative Untersuchungen der Bodenfauna und flora in ihrer Bedeutung für die theor. und angew. Limnologie. I. *Verh. int. Ver. Limnol.*

Andriashev, A. P. (1939). "Essay on the Zoogeography and Origins of the Fish Fauna of the Bering Sea and Adjacent Waters" (Ocherk zoogeography i proiskhozhdenie fauna ryb Beringova Moria i sopredelnykh vod). Leningrad University Press.

Andriashev, A. P. (1944). Determination of the natural specific gravity of fishes. *C.R. Acad. Sci. U.R.S.S.* 43, no. 2.

Andriashev, A. P. (1953). Ancient and secondary deep-water forms of fishes and their significance for zoogeographical analysis. "Essays on General Problems in Ichthyology" (Ocherki po obschem voprosam ikhtyologi).

Andriashev, A. P. (1954). "Fishes of Northern Soviet Seas" (Ryby Severnykh morei S.S.S.R.). U.S.S.R. Academy of Sciences Press.

Annandale, N. (1919). Notes on fishes of the genus *Discognathus* from India and Persia. *Rec. Indian Mus.* 18, no. 1.

Assman, A. V. (1957). Microorganisms as donors of vitamins in the nourishment of young fishes. *Vop. Ikht.* no. 9.

Azevedo, Dias et Veiera, (1938). Biologia do saguiru (Characidae, Curimatinae). *Mem. Inst. Oswaldo Cruz*, 33, no. 4.

Baburina, E. A. (1955). Structural and functional features of the eyes of fishes. *Trans. Conf. Fish Behaviour and Exploration.*

Baer, K. M. (1854). Data on the history of the fishing industry in Russia and its seas. *Uchenye zapisky AN*, 4.

Barach, G. P. (1952). The significance of the brook trout in the reproduction of the stocks of Black Sea salmon. *Zool. Zh.* 31, no. 6.

Baranov, F. I. (1960), "The Technique of Industrial Fishing."

Beak, T. (1958). Toleration of fish to toxic pollution. *J. Fish. Res. Bd. Can.* 15, no. 4.

Beebe, W. (1936). On the world's greatest fishing ground. *Bull. N.Y. sci. Soc.* 39.

Beebe and Tee Van (1928). The fishes of Port-au-Prince Bay, Haiti. *Zoologica*, 10.

Beliavskaia, L. I. and Konstantinov, A. S. (1956). The feeding of larval *Procladius choreus* Meig. (Chironomidae, Diptera) and the harm they cause to the food of fishes. *Vop. Ikht.* no. 7.

Belling, D. E. (1912). Der Bau der vorderen paarigen Extremitaten und des Schultergurtels der *Trigla* im Zusammenhang mit dem Bau entsprechender Organe bei anderen Teleostei. *Bull. Soc. Nat., Moscou*, 1911 (1912).

Belopolsky, L. O. (1957). The Ecology of the Colonial Sea-birds of the Barents Sea (Ekologia morskikh kolonialnykh ptits Barentseva moria). U.S.S.R. Academy of Sciences Press.

Berg, L. S. (1935). The salmon, its biology and fishery. *Bull. Inst. freshw. Fish, Leningr.* 20.

Berg, L. S. (1937). New data on the biology of the salmon *Salmo salar* L. *Adv. mod. Biol.*, *Moscow*, 6, no. 1.

Berg, L. S. (1948–1949). "Freshwater Fishes of the Soviet Union and Adjacent Countries," vols. I–III (Ryby presnykh vod SSSR i sopredelnykh stran). U.S.S.R. Academy of Sciences Press.

Berg, L. S. (1953). Spring and winter races in migratory fishes. "Essays on General Problems in Ichthyology" (Ocherki po obschem voprosam ikhtyologi).

Berg, L. S. (1955). Classification of recent and fossil fishes and fish-like animals. *Trudy zool. Inst.* 20.

Berg, L. S., Bogdanov A. S., Khozhin N. I. and Rass T. S. (ed.) (1949). "Commercial Fishes of the Soviet Union" (Promyslovye ryby SSSR). Food Industries Press.

Bervald, E. A. (1956). The influence of fishing on the yield of the stocks of Aral Sea bream. *Vop. Ikht.* 7.

"Biochemistry of Fishes" (1953) (Collected papers) (Biokhimia Ryb [Sbornik statei]).

Birman, I. B. (1951). On the biological productivity of water-masses and its significance for the assessment of the biological basis of the fishing industry. *Zool. Zh.* 30, no. 6.

Black, E. (1958). Energy stores and metabolism in relation to muscular activity in fishes. "The Investigation of Fish-power Problems."

Bodrova, N. V. and Kraiukhin, B. V. (1958). On the reactions of fishes to the action of an electric current. *Trans. Conf. Physiol. Fishes.*

Bogoslovsky, A. S. (1955). Rotifers may cause the death of carp and other fish. *Fish. Ind.*, *Moscow* (*Rybnoe Khoz.*).

Bokova, E. N. (1940). The consumption and assimilation of food by the roach. *Trans. Inst. Fish. USSR*, 11.

Bokova, E. N. (1955). The feeding of the Azov Sea anchovy in various stages of development. *Trans. Inst. Fish. USSR*, 31.

Borisov P. G. (1955). The behaviour of fishes under the influence of artificial light. *Trans. Conf. Fish Behaviour and Exploration.*

Borisov, P. G. and Bogdanov, A. S. (1955). "The Bases of the Soviet Fishing Industry." Food Industries Press.

Borisov, P. G. and Ovsianikov, N. S. (1958). Key to the commercial fishes of the U.S.S.R. Food Industries Press.

Borodulina, T. L. (1953). The biology and commercial significance of the tern. *Trud. Inst. Morf. Zhiv.* no. 9.

Borutsky, E. V. (1950). Data on the feeding of *Xenocypris macrolepis* Bleeker. *Trans. ichthyol. Exped. to the Amur* (*Trudy Amurskoi ikhtiologicheskoi expeditsie*), 1.

Borutsky, E. V. (1960). On the food resources. *Trud. Inst. Morf. Zhiv.* no. 13.

Borutsky, E. V., Kliuchareva, O. A. and Nikolsky, G. V. (1952). Bottom invertebrates, and their role in the nourishment of fishes in the Amur. *Trans. ichthyol. Exped. to the Amur*, 3.

Brauer A. (1906–1908). Die Tiefseefische. *Wiss. Erg. Valdivia Exped.*

Breder C. (1942). On the behaviour of young *Oligoplites saurus* (Bl. Schn.). *Copeia*, no. 4.

Brem, A. (1939). "The Lives of Animals. Fishes, Amphibians, Reptiles" (Zhizne zhivotnykh. Ryby, zemnevodnye, presmykaiushchiesia). Biomed. Press.

Bridge, T. and Boulenger, G. (1922). Fishes *in* "The Cambridge Natural History." Macmillan, London.

Brown, M. (ed.) (1957). "The Physiology of Fishes." Vol. 1, Metabolism, Vol. 2, Behavior. Academic Press, New York.

Brown, C. (1938). Observations on the life-history and breeding habits of the Montana grayling. *Copeia.* no. 3.

Bruun, A. (1935). Flying fishes (Exocoetidae) of the Atlantic. *Dana Report,* no. 6.

Bull. H. O. (1936). Studies on conditioned responses in fishes, Part VII. Temperature discrimination in Teleosts. *J. Mar. biol. Ass. U.K.,* **21,** no. 1.

Carpenter, K. (1930). The lethal action of soluble metallic salts on fishes. *J. exp. Zool.* 56, 4.

Cheprakova, Ju. I. (1960). Some data on the effect of concentrations of iron salts on the development and survival of fish eggs. *Vop. Ikht.,* no. 14.

Cherfas, B. I. (1956). "Fish Culture in Natural Water-masses" (Rybovodstvo v estestvennykh vodoemakh). Food Industries Press.

Chugunova, N. I. (1931). The biology of the pike-perch in the Sea of Azov. *Trans. Azov-Black Sea Exped.* no. 9.

Chugunova, N. I. (1940). The method of estimating the age of the Caspian roach from its scales. *Trans. Inst. Fish. U.S.S.R.* 11.

Chugunova, N. I. (1959). "Handbook on the Determination of the Age and Growth of Fishes" (Rukovodstvo po metodike opredelenie vosrasta i rosta ryb). U.S.S.R. Academy of Sciences Press.

Clark, F. (1928). The weight-length relationship of the Californian sardine (*Sardina coerulea*) at San Pedro. *Fish. Bull., U.S.* no. 12.

Cunningham, J. and Reid, D. (1932). Experimental researches on the emission of oxygen by the pelvic filaments of the male *Lepidosiren* with some experiments on *Symbranchus marmoratus. Proc roy. Soc.* B, 110.

Danilchenko, O. P. (1958). The penetration of radio-active strontium-90 from the water into the body of the fish. *Fish. Ind., Moscow,* no. 2 (*Ryb. Khoz.*).

Das, S. N. and Moitra, S. K. (1958). On variations in the digestive tract of freshwater fishes of India in relation to their food. *Vop. Ikht.* no. 10.

Derzhavin, A. N. (1922). The sturgeon (*Acipenser stellatus*). An essay. *Bull. Ichthyol. Lab. Baku,* 1.

Detlaph, T. A. and Ginsbŭrg, A. S. (1954). The embryonic development of sturgeons (Zarodyshevoe razvitie osetrovykh ryb). U.S.S.R. Academy of Sciences Press.

Disler, N. N. (1953). Ecological-morphological features in the development of the autumn chum salmon in the Amur. *Trans. Conf. Fishing Indust. Problems.*

Disler, N. N. (1955). Structural features of the sensory lateral line organs and their role in the behaviour of fishes. *Trans. Conf. Fish Behaviour and Exploration.*

Disler, N. N. (1960). The lateral line sense organ and its role in the behaviour of fishes. U.S.S.R. Academy of Sciences Press.

Dogel, V. A. (1932). Parasitic Diseases of Fishes.

Dolgopolskaia, M. A. (1946). The harmful influence of barnacles to the fishing industry. *Priroda,* no. 3.

Dziuban, N. A. (1946). New data on the feeding of certain Cyclopidae. *Trans. Moscow Fish. Inst. 2.*

Ekman, S. (1935). "Tiergeography des Meeres."

Ellis, M. (1937). Detection and measurement of stream pollution. *Bull. U.S. Bur. Fish.* 48, no. 22.

Elton, C. (1934). "Animal Ecology."

Essays on the General Problems of Ichthyology (1953). U.S.S.R. Academy of Sciences Press.

Fauvel, P. (1923). Polychètes errantes. *Faune de France*, 5.

Fish, M. (1954). The character and significance of sound production among fishes of the western North Atlantic. *Bull. Bingham oceanogr. Coll.* 14, no. 3.

Fortunatova, K. R. (1955). Methods of studying the feeding of predatory fishes. *Trans. Conf. on Methods of Studying food-resources and feeding of fishes.*

Fowler, H. (1936). "Marine Fishes of West Africa," Vols. I and II.

Fulton, T. (1902). Rate of growth of sea-fishes. *Sci. Invest., Fish. Div. Scot. Rept.* 20.

Galkin, G. G. (1958). An atlas of the scales of fresh-water bony fishes. *Bull. Inst. freshwater Fish., Leningr.* 46.

Gerbilsky, N. L. (1953). Intraspecific biological groups among the sturgeons and the importance of recognising them for the development of the sturgeon fishery in relation to hydro-electrical undertakings. *Trans. Conf. Fishing Indust. Problems.*

Girsa, I. I. (1960). The influence of illumination on the availability of food organisms for certain fishes. *Trud. Inst. Morf. Zhiv.* no. 13.

Giulbadamov, S. B. (1958). "The Use of Electrical Currents in Fishing" (Primenenie elektricheskovo toka v rybolovtsve). Publ. by VNIRO.

Golovinskaia, K. A. and Romashov, D. D. (with the help of Musselius, V. A.) (1947). Investigations on gynogenesis in the silver crucian carp. *Trud. Inst. Prud. Ryb. Khoz., 4, Voronezh.*

Golovinskaia, K. A. and Romashov, D. D. (1958). The effect of ionizing radiation upon the development and reproduction of fishes. *Vop. Ikht.* 11.

Goodrich, E. (1930). "Studies on the Structure and Development of Vertebrates."

la Gorce, J. O. (ed.) (1958). "The Book of Fishes." Washington.

Graham, M. (1929). "Victoria Nyanza and Its Fisheries." Crown Agents for the Colonies.

Gray, J. (1933). Directional control of fish movement. *Proc. roy. Soc.* B, 113.

Grbachek, Ja. (1953). Chemical substances as the stimulants for the flight reactions in toad tadpoles and in the roach. *Zool. Zh.,* 32, no. 2.

Greene, C. (1904). Physiological studies of the Chinook salmon. *Bull. U.S. Bur. Fish.* 24.

Griffin, D. (1950). Underwater sounds and the orientation of marine animals, a preliminary survey. *ONR Techn. Rept. 3, Cornell Univ.* (non vidi).

Hansen, H. and Nansen (1909). The Norwegian Sea. *Rep. Norweg. Fish. Invest.* 2, no. 1.

Hardy, A. (1924). The herring in relation to its animate environment. *Fish. Invest., London,* ser. 2, 7, no. 3.

Hardy, Sir A. (1959). "Fish and Fisheries. The Open Sea, Part 2."

Herre, A. (1936). Some habits of *Amphipryon* in relation to sea anemones. *Copeia,* 3.

Hesse, R. (1924). "Tiergeographie auf Okologischer Grundlage."

Hjort, J. (1914). Fluctuations in the great fisheries of northern Europe. *Rapp. Cons. Explor. Mer,* 20.

Hora, S. (1930). Ecology, bionomics and evolution of the torrential fauna with special reference to the organs of attachment. *Phil. Trans.* B, 218.

Hora, S. (1933). Respiration in fishes. *J. Bombay nat. Hist. Soc.* 36, no. 3.

Hora, S. (1934). A note on the precipitating action of the mucus of the boro fish *Phisodonophis boro* (Ham. Buch.). *J. Asiat. Soc. Bengal,* 29, no. 4.

Hora, S. (1934a). Wanderings of the Bombay duck—*Harpodon nehereus* (Ham. Buch.) in Indian waters. *J. Bombay nat. Hist. Soc.* 37, no. 3.

Hora, S. (1945). Analysis of the factors influencing the spawning of carps. *Proc. nat. Inst. Sci. India.* 11, no. 3.

Hora, S. and Misra, K. (1936). Sexual dimorphism in the carp *Labeo dero* (Ham.). *Rec. Indian Mus.* 38.

Hubbs, C. (1922). Variation in the number of vertebrae and other meristic characters of fishes correlated with the temperature of the water during development. *American Naturalist*, 56.

Idelson, M. S. and Vonokov, I. K. (1938). The feeding of the lake frog in the flood zone of the Volga delta and its significance in the destruction of fish fry. *Trans. Volga-Caspian fishery st.* 8, no. 1.

Ivlev, V. S. (1938). The influence of temperature on the respiration of fishes. *Zool. Zh.* 17, no. 4.

Jogansen, B. G. (1955). The study of the fecundity of fishes. *Trans. Univ. Tomsk.* 131.

Jordan, D. (1925). "Fishes."

Judin, A. G. (1948). The practical significance of the determination of the condition of first-winter carp. *Fish. Indust., Moscow*, no. 1.

Kaganovsky, A. G. (1939). "The Far-Eastern Sardine."

Kalabuchov, N. I. (1956). "The Hibernation of Animals." "Sov. Sci." Press.

Kamshilov, M. M. (1955). The feeding of the ctenophore *Beroe cucumis* Fab. *C. R. Acad. Sci. U.R.S.S.* 102, no. 2.

Karavaev, G. A. (1958). "Instructions on marking fishes." Publ. by VNIRO.

Karpevich, A. F. (1958). The present and the future of the Sea of Azov. *Priroda*, (1).

Karpevich, A. F. and Bokova, E. A. (1936–1937). The rate of digestion in marine fishes. *Zool. Zh.* 15, 1; 16, 1.

Karzinkin, G. S. (1952). "The Bases of Biological Productivity in Water-masses." Food Industries Press.

Karzinkin, G. S. (1958). The physiology of fishes and fishery problems related to it. *Trans. Conf. Physiol. Fish.* U.S.S.R. Academy of Sciences Press.

Karzinkin, G. S. and Karzinkin, S. G. (1955). "The Fertilization of Ponds with Green Vegetation." Food Industries Press.

Karzinkin, G. S. and Shekhanova, I. A. (1957). Some essentially new proposals in the fertilization of water-masses. *Trans. Conf. on Fish-cultivation.*

Kholodov, Ju. A. (1958). The formation of conditioned reflexes to a magnetic field in fishes. *Trans. Conf. Physiol. Fish.* U.S.S.R. Academy of Sciences Press.

Kinalev, N. M. (1937). The feeding of gobies (Gobiidae) in the North Caspian. *Zool. Zh.* 16, no. 4.

Kirpichnikov, V. S. (1935). A biological and systematic essay on the Asian smelt (*Osmerus eperlanus* L.) in the White Sea, Cheshsk Bay and the River Pechora. *Trans. Inst. Fish. Moscow*, 2.

Kirpichnikov, V. S. (1958). Cold-resistance and winter-resistance of the carp and its hybrids. *Trans. Conf. Physiol. Fish.*

Kirpichnikov, V. S. and Berg, R. L. (1952). On the problem of raising the winter-resistance of the carp and its hybrids. *Zool. Zh.* 31, no. 4.

Kirshenblat, Ja. D. (1952). The effect of steroid hormones on the female loach. *C.R. Acad. Sci. U.R.S.S.* 83, no. 4.

Kleerekoper, H. and Sibakin, A. (1956–1957). An investigation of the electrical "spike" potential produced by the sea-lamprey (*Petromyzon marinus*) in the water surrounding the head region. *J. Fish. Res. Bd. Can.* 13, no. 3; 14, no. 2.

Kleinenberg, C. E. (1956). "The Mammals of the Black and Azov Seas." (Mlekopitaiu-shchie Chernovo i Azovskovo Morei). U.S.S.R. Academy of Sciences Press.

Kliuchareva, O. A. (1956). Some problems of intraspecific relationships among fishes. *Zool. Zh.* 35, no. 2.

Knipovich, N. M. (1939). "The Hydrology of the Seas and Brackish Waters." (Gidrologia morei i solonovatykh vod). Food Industries Press.

Konstantinov, A. S. and Konstantinova, N. S. (1957). The organization of cultivation of live foods (enchytraeids and chironomids) on fish-farms. *Trans. Conf. on Fish-cultivation.*

Konstantinova, N. S. (1958). The dynamics of the basic biological properties of the bream in the north Aral Sea. *Vop. Ikht.* no. 10.

Korzhuev, P. A. (1938). Osmoregulation in aquatic animals. *Adv. mod. Biol., Moscow,* 9, 3.

Koshtoyants, Kh. S. (1940, 1957). "The Fundamentals of Comparative Physiology." Vols. I and II. U.S.S.R. Academy of Sciences Press.

Koshtoyants, Kh. S. and Korzhuev, P. A. (1934). The trypsin of cold-blooded and warm-blooded animals. *Zool. Zh.* 13, no. 1.

Kostin, I. A. (1953). The toxicity of *Schizothorax. Vop. Ikht.* no. 1.

Kozhov, M. M. (1954). The vertical distribution of plankton and the planktophagic fishes of Lake Baikal. *Vop. Ikht.* no. 2.

Krokhin, E. M. (1954). Investigations on the numbers of saprophtyic bacteria in Lake Dalnye. *Microbiology, Moscow,* 23, no. 1.

Krykhtin, M. L. (1951). Some data on the effects of the parasitic crustacean *Livoneca amurensis* Gersfeldt on the stocks of the Amur ide (*Leuciscus waleckii* Dyb.). *Trans. Ichthyol. Exped. to the Amur,* 2.

Kryzhanovsky, S. G. (1948). Ecological groupings of fishes and regular features in their formation. *Trans. Pacific Inst. Fish. U.S.S.R.* 27.

Kryzhanovsky, S. G. (1949). Ecological-morphological principles in the development of Cyprinid, Cobitid and Silurid fishes. *Trans. Inst. Morf. Zhiv.* 1.

Kryzhanovsky, S. G. (1953). Characteristics of the ripe eggs of teleosts. *Vop. Ikht.* no. 1.

Kryzhanovsky, S. G. (1956). Data on the development of clupeoid fishes. *Trud. Inst. Morf. Zhiv.* no. 17.

Kryzhanovsky, S. G., Disler, N. N. and Smirnova, E. I. (1953). Ecological and morphological principles in the development of percomorph fishes. *Trud. Inst. Morf. Zhiv.* no. 10.

Kryzhanovsky, S. G., Smirnov, A. I. and Soin, S. G. (1951). Data on the development of fishes of the Amur. *Trans. Ichthyol. Exped. to the Amur,* 2.

Kulkarni, C. (1940). On the systematic position, structural modifications, bionomics and development of a remarkable new family of Cyprinodont fishes from the Province of Bombay. *Rec. Indian Mus.* 42, (2).

Kulkarni, C. (1943). Breeding habits and early stages of the gourami (*Osphronemus gourami* Lac.). *J. Bombay nat. Hist. Soc.* 44, no. 2.

Kuznetsov, I. I. (1928). Some observations on the reproduction of the Amur and Kamchatkan salmons. *Bull. Pac. Fish.-res. St.* 2.

Kyle, H. (1926). "The Biology of Fishes." London.

Kyle, H. und Ehrenbaum, E. (1926–1929). *Tierwelt der Nord und Ostsees. Pisces.*

Lange, N. O. (1950). The structure and development of the intestine of the loaches. *Trans. Inst. Morf. Zhiv.* no. 3.

Lea, E. (1910). On the methods used in herring investigations. *Publ. Circ. Cons. Explor. Mer,* no. 33.

Lebedev, N. V. (1940). The possibility of forecasting the period of migration of the Azov anchovy. *Zool. Zh.* 19, no. 4.

Lebedev, N. V. (1946). Elementary populations of fishes. *Zool. Zh.* 25, no. 2.

Lebedev, V. D. (1959). The neogenic fauna of freshwater fishes of the Zaisansk depression and the West Siberian lowlands. *Vop. Ikht.* no. 12.

Lebedev, V. D. (1959a). On the causes of origin of the migrations of the European river eel in Atlantic waters. *Sci. Papers for Higher Schools, ser. Biol. Sci.* no. 3.

Lebour, M. (1918–1920). The food of post-larval fishes. *J. Mar. biol. Ass. U.K.* 11, no. 4; 12, no. 1; 12, no. 2.

Levanidov, V. Ja. (1951). On the feeding of *Brachymystax lenok* Pall, in the foothill tributaries of the Amur. *Zool. Zh.* 30, no. 1.

Levestad, H., Andersen, P. and Scholander, P. (1957). Physiological response to air exposure in codfish. *Science*, 126, no. 3272.

Liaiman, E. M. (1939). "Diseases of Fish (Bolezni ryb)." Food Industries Press.

Liao Hsiang Hua and Shih Leu Chang (1956). Contribution to the biology and control of *Bothriocephalus gowkongensis* Jeh., a tapeworm parasitic in the young grass-carp *Ctenopharyngodon idellus* C. Val. *Acta hydrobiologica Sinica*, 2.

Lindberg, G. U. (1934). On the systematics of the gambusias. *Parazitol. sb.* 4.

Lipin, A. N. (1950). "Life in Fresh Waters" (Presnye vody i ikh zhizn).

Lishev, M. N. (1950). The feeding and feeding inter-relationships of the predatory fishes of the Amur river basin. *Trans. Ichthyol. Exped. to the Amur*, 1.

Loeb, J. (1926). "The Organism as a Whole from a Physiological Point of View."

Makeeva, A. P. (1956). One reason for the pre-spawning mortality of the humpback salmon in rivers. *Zool. Zh.* 35, no. 11.

Maksunov, V. A. (1956). The morphology and biology of the pike in the Farkhadsk Reservoir. *Izv. otd. est. nauk AN Tadzhikistan SSR*, no. 15.

Manteufel, B. P. (1959). The adaptive significance of the periodical migrations of aquatic organisms. *Vop. Ikht.* no. 13.

Margetts, A. R. and Holt, S. J. (1948). The effect of the 1939–1945 war on the English North Sea trawl fisheries. *Rapp. Cons. Explor. Mer.* 123.

Markevich, A. P. (1951). The parasitic fauna of freshwater fishes of the Ukraine (Parazitofauna presnovodnykh ryb Ukrainskoi SSR.) Ukrainian S.S.R. Acad. Sci. Press.

Markevich, A. P. (1956). Parasitic Copepods of Soviet fishes (Paraziticheskie veslonogie ryb SSSR). Ukrainian S.S.R. Acad. Sci. Press.

Marty, Ju. Ju. (1948). "Commercial Exploration for Fish" (Promyslovaia razvedka ryby). Food Industries Press.

Martyshev, F. G. (1958). "Pond Cultivation of Fishes" (Prudovye rybovodstvo). "Sov. Sci." Press.

Matsubara, K. (1955). "Fish Morphology and Hierarchy."

Mazilkin, I. A. (1957). A biological method of combating *Saprolegnia*. *Trans. Conf. on Fish-cultivation*.

Mazokhin-Porshniakov, G. A. (1957). The use of ultraviolet light in combating harmful insects at fish farms. *Trans. Conf. on Fish-cultivation*.

Meek, A. (1916). "The Migrations of Fishes." London.

Milinsky, G. I. (1938). The biology and fishery of the plaice (*Pleuronectes platessa* L.) in the Barents Sea. *Trans. Polar Inst.* 2.

Miller, R. (1943). The status of *Cyprinodon macularius* and *Cyprinodon nevadensis*, two desert fishes of western North America. *Occ. Papers Mus. Zool.* no. 473.

Miller, R. (1945). Effect of *Triaenophorus* on the growth of two fishes. *J. Fish. Res. Bd. Can.* 6, no. 4.

Minkina, A. L. (1946). On the effect of iron and aluminium on fishes. *Trudy Mosk. Zooparka*, 3.

Minkina, A. L. (1949). The influence of various concentrations of iron on the growth and metabolism of fishes. *Trud. Mosk. Zooparka*, 4.

Mironov, A. T. (1948). Electrical currents in the sea and their effects upon fishes. *Trudy Morsk. gidrofiz. in-ta AN SSSR.* 1.

Moisev, P. A. (1946). "Commercial Flatfishes of the Far East" (Promyslovye kambaly Dalnevo Vostoka).

Moisev, P. A. (1958). New data on the effects of thermonuclear explosions on fisheries. *Fish. Indust., Moscow*, no. 7.

Moisev, P. A. (1960). Some data on the behaviour of the Pacific cod in various zoogeographical regions. *Zool. Zh.* 39, no. 4.

Monastyrsky, G. N. (1924). A modification of Einar Lea's board. *Trudy Nauchn. in-ta rybn. khoz.* 1.

Monastyrsky, G. N. (1926). On the method of determining the growth rate of fishes from measurements of the scales. *Coll. pap. methods of invest. age and growth of fish.*

Monastyrsky, G. N. (1940). The stocks of roach in the north Caspian and methods for assessing them. *Trans. Inst. Fish. U.S.S.R.* 11.

Monastyrsky, G. N. (1952). The population dynamics of commercial fishes. *Trans. Inst. Fish. U.S.S.R.* 21.

Monastyrsky, G. N. (1953). On types of spawning populations in fishes. "Essays on General Problems in Ichthyology" ("Ocherki po obshchem voprosam ikhtyologi").

Morawa, I. (1956). Die regionale Verteilung des Fettes bei verschiedenen Susswasser fischarten. *Z. Fisch.* 5, no. 1, 2.

Mosevich, N. A. (1947). Winter freezing phenomena in the rivers of the Ob-Irtysh basin *Bull. Inst. freshw. Fish., Leningr.* 25, 1.

Mosevich, N. A., Dragulin, M. G., Kushnareva, V. S. and Mosevich, M. V. (1952). Sulphuric acid factory effluents, their effect on aquatic organisms and standardisation of their discharge. *Bull. Inst. freshw. Fish., Leningr.* 31.

Movchan, V. A. (1948). "The Ecological Basis of Increasing the Growth-rate of the Carp (Ekologicheskie osnovy intensificatsii rosta karpa). Ukrainian S.S.R. Acad. Sci. Press.

Naumov, N. P. (1955). "Animal Ecology" (Ekologia zhivotnykh). "Sov. Sci." Press.

Neave, F. (1953). Factors affecting the size of pink and chum salmon populations in British Columbia. *J. Fish. Res. Bd. Can.* 9, no. 9.

Nikitinsky, V. Ja. (1929). The feeding of certain lake fishes during their spawning period. *Russk. gidrobiol. Zh.* 8, no. 6, 7.

Nikolsky, A. M. (1902). "Reptiles and Fishes" (Gady i ryby).

Nikolsky, G. V. (1934). The Aral carp: data on its systematics, biology and fishery. *Trudy Aralsk. rybkhoz. St.* 3.

Nikolsky, G. V. (1938). "The Fishes of Tadzhikistan" (Ryby Tadzhikistana). U.S.S.R. Acad. Sci. Press.

Nikolsky, G. V. (1940). "The Fishes of the Aral Sea" (Ryby Aralskovo Moria). Moscow Natural History Society.

Nikolsky, G. V. (1943). On the history of the ichthyofauna of the White Sea basin. *Zool. Zh.* 22, no. 1.

Nikolsky, G. V. (1947). On the biological specificity of faunistic complexes and its significance for zoogeography. *Zool. Zh.* 26, no. 3.

Nikolsky, G. V. (1950). On the dynamics of fish populations and the problem of the productivity of water-masses. *Zool. Zh.* 29, no. 6.

Nikolsky, G. V. (1953). On the principles of feeding inter-relationships among freshwater Fishes. "Essays on General Problems in Ichthyology" (Ocherki po obshchem voprosam ikhtiologi). U.S.S.R. Academy of Sciences.

Nicolsky, G. V. (1953a). The fundamental principles in the formation and development of a fluvial ichthyofauna. "Essays on General Problems in Ichthyology" (Ocherki po obshchem voprosam ikhtiologi). U.S.S.R. Academy of Sciences.

Nikolsky, G. V. (1953b). On the theoretical bases of work on the dynamics of fish populations. *Trans. Conf. on Problems of the Fishing Industry.*

Nikolsky, G. V. (1954). "Special Ichthyology" (Chastnaia ikhtiologia). "Sov. Sci." Press.

Nikolsky, G. V. (1955). On the biological significance of the fish shoal. *Trans. Conf. on Fish Behaviour and Exploration.*

Nikolsky, G. V. (1956). "Fishes of the Amur Basin" (Ryby baseina Amura). U.S.S.R. Academy of Sciences Press.

Nikolsky, G. V. (1956a). References to animal ecology in the Indian epics of "Mahabharata" and "Ramajana." *Vop. istorii estestvoznani i tekhn.* no. 2.

Nikolsky, G. V. (1958). On the biological basis of fishery regulations. *Vop. Ikht.* no. 11.

Nikolsky, G. V. and Belianina, T. N. (1959). On the characteristics of the population dynamics of certain forms of the Atlantic herring. *Zhurn. Obshch. Biol.* no. 3.

Nikolsky, G. V. and Kukushkin, A. A. (1943). The influence of the density of plantings on the rate of consumption of food by fishes. *Zool. Zh.* 22, no. 2.

Nikolsky, G. V. and Pikuleva, V. A. (1958). On the adaptive significance of the variability of the specific characters and properties of organisms. *Zool. Zh.* 37, no. 7.

Nikolsky, G. V. and Soin, S. G. (1954). On the biological basis of the salmon fishery in the basin of the Amur. *Priroda*, no. 4.

Norman, J. (1958). "A History of Fishes." London.

Novikova, N. S. (1949). On the possibility of determining the daily ration of fishes under natural conditions. *Bull. Moscow Univ.* no. 9.

Novikova, N. S. (1956). The behaviour of the North Caspian roach on its feeding grounds. *Vop. Ikht.* no. 7.

Nusenbaum, L. M. (1958). The behaviour of fishes in an electrical field in relation to their conservation in hydroelectric schemes. *Trans. Conf. Physiol. Fish.*

Paraketsov, I. A. (1958). The protective significance of spines and thorns in fishes. *Zh. Obshch. Biol.* 19, no. 6.

Parker, H. and Boeseman, M. (1954). The basking shark *Cetorhinus maximus* in winter. *Proc. zool. Soc. Lond.* 124.

Pavlov, D. S. (1959). Experiments on the feeding of the burbot *Lota lota* L. *Papers for Higher School, ser. Biol. Sci.* no. 4.

Pavlovskaia, R. M. (1955). The survival of the early stages of the Black Sea anchovy. *Trans. Azov-Black Sea Inst. Fish.* (16).

Pavlovsky, E. N. (1931). Poisonous animals of the U.S.S.R. (Iadovitye zhivotnye S.S.S.R.). Med. Press.

Pellegrin, J. (1921). Les poissons des eaux douces de l'Afrique du Nord Francaise etc. *Mem. Soc. Sci. Nat. Maroc.* 1, no. 2.

Perminov, G. N. (1936). A review of the species of *Eumicrotremus* (Obzor vid r. Eumicrotremus). *Bull. Far-Eastern Branch Acad. Sci.* no. 18.

Petrov, V. V. and Petrushevsky, G. K. (1929). Data on the structure of the scales of the carp (*Cyprinus carpio*). *Bull. Dept. Applied Ichthyol. and Sci. Invest.* 9, no. 3.

Petrovich, P. (1939). Insects harmful to fish-farms, and methods for combating them. *Zool. Zh.* 18, no. 5.

Pirozhnikov, P. L. (1950). On the feeding of whitefishes in estuarine regions. *Zool. Zh.* 29, no. 2.

Poliakov, G. D. (1950). "Grants for Hydro-chemistry for Fish-rearers." Food Industries Press.

Poliakov, G. D. (1958). Exhaustion as one of the causes of the mortality of yearling carp during winter. *Trans. Conf. Physiol. Fish.*

Poliakov, G. D. (1958a). The adaptive significance of the variability of the weight of yearling carp. *Zool. Zh.* 37, no. 3.

Protasov, V. P. and Golubtsov, K. V. (1960). Certain functional characteristics of the eye of the cod *Gadus morrhua* and the sea-scorpion *Myoxocephalus scorpius*. *Trans. Inst. Morf. Zhiv.* no. 13.

Prozorovskaia, M. L. (1952). On the method of determining the fat-content of the roach from the quantity of fat on the intestines. *Bull. Inst. Fish. U.S.S.R.* no. 1.

Puchkov, N. V. (1954). "The Physiology of Fishes." Food Industries Press.

Radakov, D. V. (1956). Studies on the behaviour of fishes at the time of capture. *Vop. Ikht.* no. 6.

Radakov, D. V. (1958). On the adaptive significance of the shoaling behaviour of young coalfish (*Pollachius virens* L.). *Vop. Ikhtiol.* no. 11.

Rass, T. S. (1948). "The World Fishery for Aquatic Organisms." "Sov. Sci." Press.

Rass, T. S. (1950). A remarkable instance of a connection between a fish and a crab. *Priroda*, no. 7.

Rass, T. S. (1953). The significance of the structure of the eggs and larvae for the systematics of fishes. "Essays on General Problems in Ichthyology" (Ocherki po obshchem voprosam ikhtiologi).

Reibisch, J. (1902). Eizahl bei *Pl. platessa* und Alterbestimmung dieser Form aus den Ueberden Einfluss der Temperatur auf die Entwicklung von Fische-Eirn. *Wiss. Meeresuntersuch.* 6.

Rodionova, L. A. (1959). The feeding of the bladderwort on animals. *Papers for Higher Schools, ser. Biol. Sci.* no. 3.

Rounsefell, G. (1930). Contribution to the biology of the Pacific herring *Clupea pallasii* and the condition of the fishery in Alaska. *Bull. U.S. Bur. Fish,* no. 45.

Rounsefell, G. and Dahlgren, E. (1935). Races of herring *Clupea pallasii* in South-eastern Alaska. *Bull. U.S. Bur. Fish.* no. 47.

Rounsefell, G. and Everhart, W. (1953). "Fishery Science." New York.

Rupp, R. (1955). Beaver-trout relationships in the headwaters of the Sunkhaze Stream, Maine. *Trans. Amer. Fish. Soc.* 84.

Salnikov, N. E. (1957). The overwintering of the Mediterranean shearwater *Puffinus puffinus yelkonan* (Acerbi.) in the Black Sea in relation to the distribution of the anchovy. *Vop. Ikht.* no. 8.

Samokhvalova, G. V. (1935). The effect of X-rays on the gonads and secondary sexual characters of *Lebistes reticulatus. Trudy dinamike razvitie,* 10.

Samokhvalova, G. V. (1938). The effects of X-rays on fishes (*Lebistes,* swordtail and crucian carp). *Biolog. Zh.* 7, no. 5, 6.

Savchenko, P. (1886). "An Atlas of Poisonous Fishes."

Schaperclaus, W. (1954). Fischkrankheiten. *Akad. Verl. Berlin.*

Scheuring, L. (1929–1930). Die Wanderung der Fische. *Ergebn. der Biologie,* 5–6.

Schmalhausen, I. I. (1935). Definition of the basic concepts and methods of studying growth. *Coll. papers "Growth of animals" (Sb. "Rost zhivotnykh").*

Schmidt, P. Ju. (1947). "The Migrations of Fishes" (Migratsii ryb). U.S.S.R. Academy of Sciences Press.

Scholtz, C. (1932). Experimentale Untersuchungen uber die Nahrungswertung des ein- und zweisommerigen Hechtes. *Z. Fisch.* 30.

Schultz, L. (1948). "The Ways of Fishes." New York.

Severtsov, S. A. (1941). "Population Dynamics and the Adaptive Evolution of Animals." (Dinamika naselenie i prisposobitelnaia evoliutsia zhivotnykh). U.S.S.R. Academy of Sciences Press.

Shamardina, I. P. (1957). The developmental stages of the pike. *Trud. Inst. Morf. Zhiv.* no. 16.

Shekhanova, I. A. (1958). A method of mass marking for young sturgeons using radioactive phosphorus.

Shorygin, A. A. (1939). The feeding, selective adaptations and feeding inter-relationships of certain Caspian Sea gobies (Gobiidae). *Zool. Zh.* 18, no. 1.

Shorygin, A. A. (1952). "The Feeding and Feeding Inter-relationships of Caspian Sea Fishes" (Pitanie i pishchevye vzaimootnoshenia ryb Kaspiiskovo moria). Food Industries Press.

Shuleikin, V. V. (1953). "Physics of the Sea" (Fizica moria). U.S.S.R. Academy of Sciences Press.

Sigov, V. A. (1947). Biometrical criteria for the life-adaptation of first-time wintering carp. *Trud. Inst. prud. ryb. Khoz.* 4, Voronezh.

Skadovsky, S. N. (1955). "The Ecological Physiology of Aquatic Organisms." (Ekologicheskaia fiziologia vodnykh organizmov). "Sov. Sci." Press.

Skokova, N. N. (1955). The feeding of the greater cormorant in the Volga delta. *Vop. Ikht.* no. 5.

Smirnov, A. I. (1954). The influence of mechanical action on the developing eggs of the humpback salmon. *C.R. Acad. Sci. U.R.S.S.* 97, no. 2.

Smirnov, A. I. (1954a). Problems arising in the rationalization of the biological techniques of salmon rearing in Sakhalin. *Trans. Conf. Salmon Fishery Problems in the Far East.* U.S.S.R. Academy of Sciences Press.

Smirnov, A. I. (1959). Functional significance of the pre-spawning changes in the integument of the salmon (with particular reference to the genus *Oncorhynchus*). *Zool. Zh.* no. 5.

Soin, S. G. (1953). The development of unfertilized salmon eggs. *Fish. Indust., Moscow,* no. 5.

Soin, S. G. (1959). The embryonal-larval period in the development of *Erythroculter erythropterus* (Bas.). *Vop. Ikht.* no. 13.

Snyder, I. (1931). Salmon of the Klamath River, California. *Fish. Bull., U.S.* no. 34.

Soldatov, V. K. (1928). "Fish and Fisheries" (Ryby i rybnyi promysel).

Soldatov, V. K. (1934, 1938). "Fisheries Ichthyology" (Promyslovaia ikhtiologia), vols. I and II.

Squires, H. (1957). The squid *Illex illecibrosus* (Le Sueur) in the Newfoundland fishing area. *J. Fish. Res. Bd. Can.* 14, no. 5.

Stensio, E. (1927). The Downtonian and Devonian vertebrates of Spitzbergen. pt. 1. Fam. Cephalaspidae. *Skrift. of Svalbard.* no. 12.

Sterba, G. (1959). "Susswasserfische aus Aller Welt." Leipzig.

Stroganov, N. S. (1938). The survival of sperm of the Volga shad under various environmental conditions. *Zool. Zh.* 17, no. 2.

Suetov, S. V. (1939). The significance of the silt layer in the consumption of food by fishes. *Arb. Limnol. Sta. Kossino,* no. 22.

Sumner, F. (1933). The differing effects of different parts of the visual field upon the chromatophore responses of fishes. *Biol. Bull., Wood's Hole.* 65.

Sushkina, A. P. (1932). Some data on the biology of the cormorant with reference to the harm it inflicts on fisheries.

Sushkina, A. P. (1940). The feeding of the larvae of the migratory shads in the River Volga. *Trans. Inst. Fish. U.S.S.R.* 14.

Suvorov, E. K. (1948). Foundations of ichthyology (Osnovy ikhtiologi). "Sov. Sci." Press.

Suvorov, E. K. (1948a). The commercial water-masses of the U.S.S.R. (Promyslovye vodoemy S.S.S.R.). Moscow University Press.

Svetovidov, A. N. (1950). Structural features of the clupeioid swimbladder. *C.R. Acad. Sci. U.R.S.S.* 74, no. 3.

Svetovidov, A. N. (1953). On the correlation between the numbers of pyloric caecae and the feeding behaviour of fishes. "Essays on General Problems in Ichthyology" (Ocherki po obshchem voprosam ikhtiologi). U.S.S.R. Academy of Sciences Press.

Svetovidov, A. N. (1953a). On certain factors which determine the abundance of clupeoids. *Trans. Conf. on Problems of the Fishing Industry.*

Tåning, A. V. (1944). Experiments on meristic and other characters in fishes. *Medd. Kom. Havundersφg., Kbh., Fiskeri,* 2, no. 3.

Tarasov, N. I. (1956). "The Sea Lives" (Moria Zhivet). Moscow University Press.

Templeman, W. and Hodder, V. (1958). Variation with fish length, sex, stage of sexual maturity and season in the appearance and volume of the drumming muscles of the swimbladder in the haddock *Melanogrammus aeglefinus* (L.). *J. Fish. Res. Bd. Can.* 15, no. 3.

Teplova, V. N. and Teplov, V. P. (1953). The feeding of the pike in the upper Pechora basin. *Vop. Ikht.* no. 1.

Tester, A. (1940). A specific gravity method for determining the fatness (condition) in herring (*Clupea pallasi*). *J. Fish. Res. Bd. Can.* 4, no. 5.

Tham Ah, Kow (1950). The food and feeding relationships of the fishes of Singapore Straits. *Fishery Publ. of the Colonial Office,* 1, no. 1.

Thompson, W. (1950). The effects of fishing on the stocks of halibut in the Pacific. *Publ. Fish. Res. Inst. Univ. Washington, Seattle.*

Thorson, G. (1956). Marine level-bottom communities of recent seas, their temperature adaptation and their "balance" between predators and food animals. *Trans. N.Y. Acad. Sci., ser.* 2, 18, no. 8.

Tikhonov, V. N. and Paraketsov, I. A. (1955). Contribution to the life-history of the large horse-mackerel of the Black Sea. *Trans. Azov-Black Sea Inst. Fish.* 16.

Tomilin, A. T. (1957). The mammals of the U.S.S.R. and adjacent countries, IX. Cetacea (Zveri S.S.S.R. i prilezhashchikh stran, T. IX. Kitoobraznye). U.S.S.R. Academy of Sciences Press.

Turdakov, F. A. (1939). The elements of the ecology of fishes in the river Zeravshan. *Zool. Zh.* 18, no. 3.

Vasnetsov, V. V. (1934). An attempt at a comparative analysis of the linear growth in the Cyprinoid family. *Zool. Zh.* 13, no. 3.

Vasnetsov, V. V. (1939). The evolution of the pharyngeal teeth of the cyprinid fishes. "Memorial Volume to Acad. A. N. Severtsov." U.S.S.R. Academy of Sciences Press.

Vasnetsov, V. V. (1941). The function of the fins of teleosts. *C.R. Acad. Sci. U.R.S.S.* 31, no 5.

Vasnetsov, V. V. (ed.) (1948). Morphological characteristics which determine the feeding of the bream, roach and carp in all stages of development. (Morfologicheskie osobennosti, opredeliaishchie pitanie leshchia, vobly i sazana na vsekh stadiakh razvitia). U.S.S.R. Academy of Sciences Press.

Vasnetsov, V. V. (1953). The unity of the ecology of the species in fishes. "Essays on General Problems in Ichthyology" (Ocherki po obshchem voprosam ikhtiologi). U.S.S.R. Academy of Sciences Press.

Vasnetsov, V. V. (1953a). Developmental stages of teleosts. "Essays on General Problems in Ichthyology" (Ocherki po obshchem voprosam ikhtiologi). U.S.S.R. Academy of Sciences Press.

Vasnetsov, V. V. (1953b). Regular features of the growth of fishes. "Essays on General Problems in Ichthyology" (Ocherki po obshchem voprosam ikhtiologi). U.S.S.R. Academy of Sciences Press.

Vasnetsov, V. V. (1953c). The origin of the spawning migrations of migratory fishes. "Essays on General Problems in Ichthyology" (Ocherki po obshchem voprosam ikhtiologi). U.S.S.R. Academy of Sciences Press.

Vasnetsov, V. V. (1953d). Regular features in the development and population dynamics of fishes. *Trans. Conf. on Fish. Indust. Problems.*

Verigin, V. B. (1950). Age changes in the young of the bighead *Hypophthalmichthys molitrix* (Val.) in relation to its biology. *Trans. Ichthyol. Exped. to the Amur.* 1.

Vibert, R. and Legler, K. F. (1961). "Pêches Continentales." Paris.

Vinberg, G. G. (1956). "Metabolic Rate and the Nutritional Requirements of Fishes." Belorussk University Press, Minsk.

Virabandra Rao (1954). Biology and fishery of the squid *Sepioteuthis arctipinnus* Gould. *Indian J. Fisheries,* 1, no. 1, 2.

Vladimirov, V. I. (1953). The biology of the larvae of the Dunai shad and their survival. *Trud. inst. gidrobiol. AN Uk SSR,* no. 28.

Vladimirov, V. I. (1957). On the biological classification of fishes into migratory and fluvial-migratory types. *Zool. Zh.* 36, no. 8.

Vorobief, V. P. (1937). The feeding of the Azov bream. *Zool. Zh.* 16, no. 1.

Voskoboinikov, M. M. (1928). The respiratory apparatus of fishes. *Trans. 3rd Session of zoologists, anatomists and histologists.*

Vovk, F. I. (1955). On the method of reconstructing the growth of a fish from its scales. *Trudy Biol. Sta. "Borok,"* no. 2.

Walford, L. (1958). "Living Resources of the Sea." New York.

Welty, I. (1934). Studies on group behaviour in fishes. *Physiol. Zool.* 7, no. 1.

von Westphallen, F. J. S. (1956). Vergleichendes Wachstum und Nahrungsuntersuchungen an Plötzen holsteinischer Seen. *Z. Fisch.* 5, nos. 1, 2.

Whitley, G. (1943). Poisonous and harmful fishes. *Bull. Coun. sci. industr. Res.* no. 159, Melbourne.

Willer, A. und Schnigenberg, N. (1927). Uber den Einfluss des Raumfaktors auf das Wachstum der Bachforellenbrut. *Z. Fisch.* 25.

Winge, Ö. (1915). On the value of the rings in the scales of the cod as a means of age determination. *Medd. Komm. Havundersog., Kbh., Fiskeri,* 4, no. 8.

Wright, P. (1958). An electrical receptor in fishes. *Nature, Lond.* 181, 4601.

Wunder, W. (1936). "Physiologie der Susswasserfische Mitteleuropas." Stuttgart.

Zaitseva, G. Ja. (1953). The feeding of the Dunai shad. *Trud. in-ta gidriobiol. AN Uk SSR,* no. 28.

Zamakhaev, D. F. (1940). Spawning marks on the scales of the Caspian shad. *Trans. Inst. Fish. U.S.S.R.* 14.

Zatsepin, V. I. (1939). The feeding of the haddock *Melanogrammus aeglefinus* (L.) in the region of Murmansk in respect of the bottom fauna. *Trans. Polar Inst.* no. 3.

Zenkevich, L. A. (ed.) (1931). Data on the feeding of Barents Sea fishes. *Rep. 1st Session Inst. Fish.* no. 4.

Zenkevich, L. A. (1933). Some factors in the zoogeography of the North Polar basin in relation to the problem of its palaeogeographical past. *Zool. Zh.* 12, no. 4.

Zenkevich, L. A. (1947). "The Fauna of the Sea and Its Biological Productivity" (Fauna, i biologicheskaia produktivnosti moria). vol. II. "Sov. Sci." Press.

Zenkevich, L. A. (1955). "The Soviet Seas, Their Fauna and Flora" (Moria S.S.S.R., ikh fauna i flora).

Zernov, S. A. (1949). "General Hydrobiology" (Obshchaia gidrobiologia). U.S.S.R. Academy of Sciences Press.

Zheltenkova, M. V. (1939). The feeding of the roach in the northern part of the Caspian Sea. *Trans. Inst. Fish. U.S.S.R.* **10.**

Zhukova, A. I. (1957). The significance of micro–organisms as a source of food for fishes. *Vop. Ikht.* no. 9.

Zolotnitskii, N. F. (1910–1916). "The Amateur's Aquarium" (Akvarium liubitelia). Vols. I and II.

Zotin, A. I. (1953). Changes in the resistance of the egg-membrane of sturgeon embryos during their development. *C.R. Acad. Sci. U.R.S.S.* **92**, no. 2.

Zotin, A. I. (1954). Characteristics of the secretion of the hatching enzyme in sturgeon and salmon embryos. *C.R. Acad. Sci. U.R.S.S.* **95**, no. 5.

Zotov, A. F. (1958). Investigations on the antibacterial properties of fish-extracts (Communications I and II). *Vop. Ikht.* nos. **10, 11.**

INDEX

Page numbers in italics refer to illustrations

329